Contents

Contents

Strategy Workshop

As you listen to the story "A Mummy Mystery," by Andrew Clements, you will stop from time to time to do some activities on these practice pages. These activities will help you think about different strategies that can help you read better. After completing each activity, you will discuss what you've written with your classmates and talk about how to use these strategies.

Remember, strategies can help you become a better reader. Good readers

- use strategies whenever they read

- use different strategies before, during, and after reading

- think about how strategies will help them

Name _____

Strategy I: Predict/Infer

Use this strategy before and during reading to help make predictions about what happens next or what you're going to learn.

Here's how to use the Predict/Infer Strategy:

1. Think about the title, the illustrations, and what you have read so far.
2. Tell what you think will happen next—or what you will learn.
3. Thinking about what you already know on the topic may help.
4. Try to figure out things the author does not say directly.

Listen as your teacher begins "A Mummy Mystery." When your teacher stops, complete the activity to show that you understand how to predict what the story might be about and what the mystery might be.

Think about the story and respond to the question below.

What do you think the story is about, and what might the mystery be?

_____

_____

_____

_____

_____

As you continue listening to the story, think about whether your prediction was right. You might want to change your prediction or write a new one below.

_____

_____

_____

_____

_____

Name _____

Strategy 2: Phonics/Decoding

Use this strategy during reading when you come across a word you don't know.

Here's how to use the Phonics/Decoding Strategy:

1. Look carefully at the word.
2. Look for word parts you know and think about the sounds for the letters.
3. Blend the sounds to read the words.
4. Ask yourself: is this a word I know? Does it make sense in what I am reading?
5. If not, ask yourself what else can I try? Should I look in a dictionary?

Listen as your teacher continues the story. When your teacher stops, use the Phonics/Decoding Strategy.

Now write down the steps you used to decode the word *Dynasty*.

_____

_____

_____

_____

_____

_____

_____

_____

_____

Remember to use this strategy whenever you are reading and come across a word that you don't know.

Name _____

Strategy 3: Monitor/Clarify

Use this strategy during reading whenever you're confused about what you are reading.

Here's how to use the Monitor/Clarify Strategy:

- Ask yourself if what you're reading makes sense—or if you are learning what you need to learn.
- If you don't understand something, reread, use the illustrations, or read ahead to see if that helps.

Listen as your teacher continues the story. When your teacher stops, complete the activity to show that you understand what's happening in the story.

Think about the mummy and respond below.

1. Describe what happened with the mummy's hand.

_____

_____

_____

_____

2. Can you tell from listening to the story how everyone reacts to the mummy's hand moving? Why or why not?

_____

_____

_____

3. How can you find out what made the mummy's hand move?

_____

_____

_____

_____

Name _____

Strategy 4: Question

Use this strategy during and after reading to ask questions about important ideas in the story.

Here's how to use the Question Strategy:

- Ask yourself questions about important ideas in the story.
- Ask yourself if you can answer these questions.
- If you can't answer the questions, reread and look for answers in the text. Thinking about what you already know and what you've read in the story may help you.

Listen as your teacher continues the story. Then complete the activity to show that you understand how to ask yourself questions about important ideas in the story.

Think about the story and respond below.

Write a question you might ask yourself at this point in the story.

_____

_____

_____

_____

_____

_____

If you can't answer your question now, think about it while you listen to the rest of the story.

Name _____

Strategy 5: Evaluate

Use this strategy during and after reading to help you form an opinion about what you read.

Here's how to use the Evaluate Strategy:

- Tell whether or not you think this story is entertaining and why.
- Is the writing clear and easy to understand?
- This is a mystery story. Did the author make the characters believable and interesting?

Listen as your teacher continues the story. When your teacher stops, complete the activity to show that you are thinking of how you feel about what you are reading and why you feel that way.

Think about the story and respond below.

1. Tell whether or not you think this story is entertaining and why.

_____

_____

_____

_____

2. Is the writing clear and easy to understand?

_____

_____

_____

3. This is a mystery story. Did the author make the characters interesting and believable?

_____

_____

_____

_____

Name _____

Strategy 6: Summarize

Use this strategy after reading to summarize what you read.

Here's how to use the Summarize Strategy:
- Think about the characters.
- Think about where the story takes place.
- Think about the problem in the story and how the characters solve it.
- Think about what happens in the beginning, middle, and end of the story.

Think about the story you just listened to. Complete the activity to show that you understand how to identify important story parts that will help you summarize the story.

Think about the story and respond to the questions below:

1. Who is the main character?

_____

_____

_____

2. Where does the story take place?

_____

_____

_____

3. What is the problem and how is it resolved?

_____

_____

_____

_____

Now use this information to summarize the story for a partner.

Name _____

Courage

The characters in this theme show courage in dangerous or challenging situations. After reading each selection, complete the chart below to show what you learned about the characters.

	Hatchet	**Passage to Freedom**
What challenge does the main character face?	Brian has to survive in the wilderness and build a fire with only a hatchet as a tool. **(2.5 points)**	Mr. Sugihara has to decide whether to obey his superiors or help save the lives of hundreds of refugees. **(2.5)**
Where does the challenge take place?	in the wilderness, in modern times **(2.5)**	in Lithuania, during World War II **(2.5)**
In what ways does the main character show courage?	Brian learns to cope with being alone in the wilderness. He learns to build a fire from sparks. **(2.5)**	Mr. Sugihara disobeys his superiors and puts his own job at risk to help the refugees. **(2.5)**
What do you think the character learns from his or her experience?	Brian learns that he can make a fire from wood scrapings and a spark, and that he can handle difficult situations by himself. **(2.5)**	Mr. Sugihara learns that sometimes one must follow one's conscience instead of obeying orders. **(2.5)**

Theme 1: **Courage**   1
Assessment Tip: Total **10** Points per selection

Name _____

Courage

	Climb or Die	**The True Confessions of Charlotte Doyle**
What challenge does the main character face?	Danielle and Jake must climb a steep, icy mountain without the right climbing tools. **(2.5)**	Charlotte must climb to the top of the royal yard to prove she is fit to be a sailor. **(2.5)**
Where does the challenge take place?	on a snowy mountain in modern times **(2.5)**	on a sailing ship in the 1800s **(2.5)**
In what ways does the main character show courage?	Danielle and Jake bravely complete the climb, using only the tools they have. **(2.5)**	Charlotte completes the climb even though she is terrified. **(2.5)**
What do you think the character learns from his or her experience?	Danielle and Jake learn that they are resourceful and stronger than they thought. **(2.5)**	Charlotte learns that she can climb to the top of the royal yard without falling or getting sick. **(2.5)**

What have you learned about courage in this theme?

Sample answer: Sometimes people surprise themselves with strength they didn't

know they had. **(2)**

Assessment Tip: Total **10** Points per selection and **2** points for the final question

Name _____

Words in the Wild

Answer each of the following questions by writing a vocabulary word.

1. Which word tells what you should seek in a rainstorm so you won't get wet? shelter **(1 point)** _____

2. Which word describes what a snake is doing when it moves across the ground? slithering **(1)** _____

3. Which word names a tool used to chop wood? hatchet **(1)** _____

4. Which word describes small pieces of wood needed to build a fire? kindling **(1)** _____

5. Which word means "very frightened"? terrified **(1)** _____

6. Which word names the sharp spines a porcupine uses to defend itself? quills **(1)** _____

7. Which word means "the process of staying alive"? survival **(1)** _____

8. Which word describes a feeling a person has when he or she keeps trying to do something but cannot do it? frustration **(1)** _____

Write two questions of your own that use vocabulary words from the list above.

9. Accept reasonable answers. **(1)** _____

10. Accept reasonable answers. **(1)** _____

Vocabulary

hatchet
quills
shelter
survival
terrified
frustration
slithering
kindling

Theme 1: **Courage**   3
Assessment Tip: Total **10** Points

Name _____

Details Chart

Page(s)	Brian feels _____.	Details that show how Brian feels
30	terrified	• his nostrils widened and he opened his eyes wider • he thought of every monster he had ever seen • his heart hammered in his throat **(3 points)**
32–33	in pain; hurt **(1)**	• the eight quills in his leg seem like dozens • his pain spreads • catches his breath when he pulls the quills out
33–34	sorry for himself **(1)**	• He thinks, "I can't take this" and "I can't do this." • He cries until he is cried out.
34–35	frustrated	• can't understand what his father and Terry are telling him in his dream • thinks "so what" and "I know" when he thinks about the fire in his dream **(2)**
36–37	motivated; excited; happy **(1)**	• realizes the hatchet can make sparks • recognizes the message about fire from his dreams • begins to make sparks to start a fire
38–41	determined	• doesn't give up when his first attempts fail to start a fire • takes two hours to gather tree bark • finally succeeds in lighting the fire **(3)**
43	satisfied	• smiles and calls the fire a good friend **(1)**

Assessment Tip: Total **12** Points

Name _____

What Really Happened?

These sentences tell about Brian and the things that happen to him in the story. Write T if the sentence is true. Write F if the sentence is false. If the sentence is false, correct it to make it true.

1. <u>F</u> Brian wakes up when he hears a bear growling outside his shelter.

   Brian wakes up when he hears the wind growling outside his shelter. **(1 point)**

2. <u>F</u> Brian's leg gets injured when he kicks out in the darkness and hits the hatchet.

   Brian's leg gets injured when he kicks out in the darkness and hits a porcupine. **(1)**

3. <u>T</u> After crying for a long time, Brian realizes that feeling sorry for yourself changes nothing.

   (1)

4. <u>F</u> Seeing his father and his friend Terry in a dream makes Brian feel happy.

   Seeing his father and his friend Terry in a dream makes Brian feel frustrated. **(1)**

5. <u>F</u> In Brian's dream, his friend Terry shows him a path out of the forest.

   In Brian's dream, his friend Terry shows him a fire in a barbecue pit. **(1)**

6. <u>T</u> Brian thinks that throwing his hatchet to protect himself from wild animals is a bad idea.

   (1)

7. <u>T</u> By hitting the hatchet against a hard black rock, Brian is able to make sparks.

   (1)

Assessment Tip: Total **7** Points

Name _____

Seeing the Solution

Read the story. Then complete the activity on page 7.

The Water Tree

Paul and I had been hiking for six hours. We came upon a dry creekbed that ran through the desert. Paul frowned, and I sighed. "I hope this isn't the creek we've been trying to reach," I said.

"See, Tom, I told you we should have brought more water," said Paul. Between the two of us, we had only about a third of a bottle left. Our clothes were wet with sweat and our throats were dry, but we dared not drink any more water yet. Even if we headed back right away, it was at least a six-hour hike back to our campground.

Paul and I just stared at the dry creekbed. "Check the map," I said to Paul. "Is there any other water within a mile of here?" I thought that even if there was another creek nearby, it might be dry too.

"There's nothing but lava rocks and an occasional cactus for another three miles," he reported grimly as he pulled out his map. Then his eyes lit up. "Wait a second, Tom," he said in a much happier voice. "A cactus!" He grinned and slapped me on the back.

"A cactus what?" I said. I wondered how he could be so excited about desert plants at a time like this.

"Don't you remember what we learned at camp last summer?" Paul asked. Then my own face curled into a smile. At camp they had shown us how to get water from a cactus.

"Do you have a knife?" I asked. "I have a handkerchief we can use to strain the water from the cactus flesh." Within minutes we were squeezing water out of a prickly pear cactus into our water bottles, through a funnel fashioned from a sun visor. We didn't get much water per squeeze, but there were more than enough cacti around. We'd make it back to camp with water to spare.

6   Theme 1: **Courage**

Name _____

Seeing the Solution continued

Answer these questions about the story on page 6.

1. How do Paul and Tom feel when they reach the dry creekbed? Why?

   They feel discouraged because the creek is dry and they are

   almost out of water. **(2 points)**

2. What details in the first paragraph help you figure out how the boys feel?

   Paul frowns. Tom sighs. **(2)**

3. What kind of danger are the boys in? What details help you understand the danger?

   They could run out of water. They are in the hot desert with only a

   third of a bottle of water left, and must hike at least six hours back

   to their campground. **(2)**

4. How does Paul feel when he remembers that they can get water from a cactus? How do you know his feelings change?

   He is suddenly happy. His eyes light up and he says "A cactus!" in

   a happy voice. He then grins and slaps his friend on the back. **(2)**

5. How do the boys make use of what they have to get water?

   They use a handkerchief to strain the water from the cactus pulp.

   They use a visor to funnel the water into their water bottles. **(2)**

6. Do you think that the task of filling the water bottles will be a fast one or a slow one? Why?

   It will probably be slow because they don't get very much water

   per squeeze. **(2)**

Theme 1: **Courage**   7
Assessment Tip: Total **12** Points

Suffixes Aflame

**Circle the words with the suffixes *-ful*, *-less*, and *-ly* in the flames.
Use the circled words to complete the story.**

OXV POWERLESS ABLE
BRIEFLY HMBRQZTEND
CAREFULLY TOAND
FINALLY OAD BEAUTIFUL
SER MEANINGLESS JUS
SKILLFUL BLIYLFRCH
INCREDIBLY XGAN
HANDFUL OZZMEK

Brian's strange dream at first seemed <u>meaningless **(1 point)**</u>, until he
realized that he needed a fire. In one <u>handful **(1)**</u> after another,
he gathered tiny bits of <u>beautiful **(1)**</u> white birch bark. He made
a nest out of the <u>incredibly **(1)**</u> fine bits of bark, but it stayed alight
only <u>briefly **(1)**</u>. He seemed <u>powerless **(1)**</u>
to keep the flame going. <u>Finally **(1)**</u>, he discovered how to fan
the flames with his breath. In time, he would become <u>skillful **(1)**</u>
at building a fire.

Which word has *two* suffixes?

<u>carefully **(2)**</u>

Assessment Tip: Total **10** Points

Name _____

Short Vowels

A short vowel sound is usually spelled *a, e, i, o,* or *u* and is followed by a consonant sound.

/ă/ cr**a**ft   /ĕ/ d**e**pth   /ĭ/ f**i**lm   /ŏ/ b**o**mb   /ŭ/ pl**u**nge

Write each Spelling Word under its short vowel sound.
Order of answers for each category may vary.

1. depth
2. craft
3. plunge
4. wreck
5. sunk
6. film
7. wince
8. bomb
9. switch
10. length
11. prompt
12. pitch
13. else
14. cliff
15. pledge
16. scrub
17. brass
18. grill
19. stung
20. bulk

/ă/ Sound

craft **(1 point)**   brass **(1)**

/ĕ/ Sound

depth **(1)**   else **(1)**

wreck **(1)**   pledge **(1)**

length **(1)**

/ĭ/ Sound

film **(1)**   pitch **(1)**

wince **(1)**   cliff **(1)**

switch **(1)**   grill **(1)**

/ŏ/ Sound

bomb **(1)**   prompt **(1)**

/ŭ/ Sound

plunge **(1)**   stung **(1)**

sunk **(1)**   bulk **(1)**

scrub **(1)**

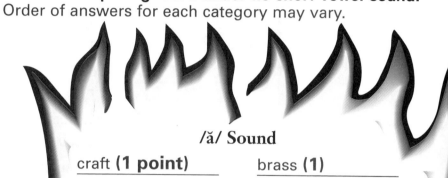

Assessment Tip: Total **20** Points

Name _____

Spelling Spree

Change the Word Write a Spelling Word by adding one letter to each word below.

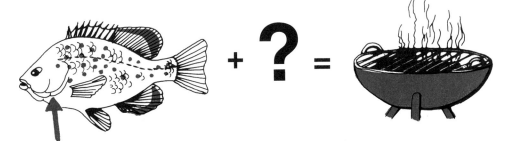

Spelling Words

1. depth
2. craft
3. plunge
4. wreck
5. sunk
6. film
7. wince
8. bomb
9. switch
10. length
11. prompt
12. pitch
13. else
14. cliff
15. pledge
16. scrub
17. brass
18. grill
19. stung
20. bulk

1. ledge   pledge **(1 point)**

2. bass   brass **(1)**

3. sun   sunk **(1)**

4. itch   pitch **(1)**

5. raft   craft **(1)**

6. wine   wince **(1)**

7. lunge   plunge **(1)**

8. gill   grill **(1)**

9. bob   bomb **(1)**

10. sung   stung **(1)**

Word Detective Write a Spelling Word to fit each clue.

11. great size or volume   bulk **(1)**

12. the measure of being long   length **(1)**

13. something used in a camera   film **(1)**

14. an overhanging rock face   cliff **(1)**

15. other or different   else **(1)**

16. what's left after a crash   wreck **(1)**

17. the quality of being deep   depth **(1)**

18. a device used to turn on the power   switch **(1)**

19. to clean very well   scrub **(1)**

20. right on time   prompt **(1)**

Assessment Tip: Total **20** Points

Name _____

Proofreading and Writing

Proofreading Circle the five misspelled Spelling Words in this journal entry. Then write each word correctly.

Spelling Words

I spent all day today starting a fire. Building a fire is a real craft! I began by trying to light pieces of a torn twenty-dollar bill. Then I decided to (swich) to strips of birch bark. I gathered some pieces of the right (lenth) and width and made them into a ball. I lit the ball with the sparks made by striking my hatchet against the rock wall. It was hard work, but I don't know what (els) I could have used to start the fire. I still (winse) when I think about another night without one. My next goal is to figure out how to make a (gril) that I can cook on.

Spelling Words

1. depth
2. craft
3. plunge
4. wreck
5. sunk
6. film
7. wince
8. bomb
9. switch
10. length
11. prompt
12. pitch
13. else
14. cliff
15. pledge
16. scrub
17. brass
18. grill
19. stung
20. bulk

1. switch **(1 point)**
2. length **(1)**
3. else **(1)**
4. wince **(1)**
5. grill **(1)**

✏️➤ **Write an Opinion** What do you think about the way Brian went about building a fire? Was there anything about his behavior that you particularly admired? Is there anything you would have done differently?

On a separate piece of paper, write a paragraph in which you give your opinion of Brian's way of doing things. Use Spelling Words from the list. Responses will vary. **(5)**

Name _____

A Search for Meaning

Your friend doesn't know the meaning of some words in a story she's reading. Use context clues to help her figure out the underlined words, and then fill in the chart. Sample answers shown.

From a safe distance, Marcy squatted low and watched the burning storage barn. The flames were consuming one section after another, as though the building were an enormous meal. The fire left almost nothing behind, so she thought all the building materials must be flammable. She was gratified to hear sirens in the distance. Her 911 call had been heard.

Word	Clues from Context	Meaning
squatted	A person doing this is in a position low to the ground. **(1 point)**	crouched down low in a sitting position **(1)**
consuming	This action is compared to an enormous meal. **(1)**	eating up; destroying totally **(1)**
flammable	Almost nothing of the building is left. **(1)**	capable of burning easily and rapidly **(1)**
gratified	She had placed a 911 call, and help was on the way. **(1)**	pleased; satisfied **(1)**

Assessment Tip: Total **8** Points

Name _____

What Is a Spiny Pig?

Kinds of Sentences A **declarative** sentence makes a statement. It ends with a **period**. An **interrogative** sentence asks a question. It ends with a **question mark**. An **imperative** sentence gives an order or makes a request. It ends with a **period**. An **exclamatory** sentence shows excitement or strong feeling. It ends with an **exclamation point**.

Add the correct end punctuation to each sentence. Then label each sentence *declarative*, *interrogative*, *imperative*, or *exclamatory*.

1. Porcupines are rodents. **(1)** <u>declarative **(1)**</u>

2. They have long, sharp quills. **(1)** <u>declarative **(1)**</u>

3. Treat all animals with respect. **(1)** <u>imperative **(1)**</u>

4. Have you ever seen a porcupine? **(1)** <u>interrogative **(1)**</u>

5. How big the tail is! **(1)** <u>exclamatory **(1)**</u>

6. Do porcupines have fine or coarse fur? **(1)** <u>interrogative **(1)**</u>

7. Please let me see your porcupine quill. **(1)** <u>imperative **(1)**</u>

8. What a sharp tip it has! **(1)** <u>exclamatory **(1)**</u>

9. Did you know the word *porcupine* means "spiny pig" in Latin? **(1)**
<u>interrogative **(1)**</u>

10. *Porcupine* comes from Latin *porcus* (meaning "pig") and *spina* (meaning "spine"). **(1)** <u>declarative **(1)**</u>

Name _____

Campfires Need . . .

Subjects and Predicates The **subject** of a sentence tells whom or what the sentence is about. The **complete subject** includes all the words in the subject. The **simple subject** is the main word or words of the complete subject.

The **predicate** tells what the subject does, is, has, or feels. The **complete predicate** includes all the words in the predicate. The **simple predicate** is the main word or words of the complete predicate.

Draw a line between the complete subject and the complete predicate in each sentence below. Then write the simple subject and the simple predicate on the lines.

1. Brianna| needed kindling for a fire. **(1 point)**

   Simple subject: Brianna **(1)** _____

   Simple predicate: needed **(1)** _____

2. A fire| needs oxygen. **(1)**

   Simple subject: fire **(1)** _____

   Simple predicate: needs **(1)** _____

3. A roaring fire| will keep them warm. **(1)**

   Simple subject: fire **(1)** _____

   Simple predicate: will keep **(1)** _____

4. The first spark| has faded quickly. **(1)**

   Simple subject: spark **(1)** _____

   Simple predicate: has faded **(1)** _____

5. I| am learning about building safe campfires. **(1)**

   Simple subject: I **(1)** _____

   Simple predicate: am learning **(1)** _____

Assessment Tip: Total **15** Points

Name _____

This and That

Combining Sentences A good writer avoids writing too many short, choppy sentences. Combine short sentences by creating **compound subjects** or **compound predicates**.

Moose live in these woods.
Caribou live in these woods too. }
Compound Subject
Moose and caribou live in these woods.

I ate quickly.
I gulped my juice. }
Compound Predicate
I ate quickly and gulped my juice.

Combine subjects or predicates in each group of sentences below.

Example: I sighed. Then I sat down.
I sighed and sat down.

1. Rebecca was prepared for an emergency.
   The other hikers were prepared for an emergency.
   Rebecca and the other hikers were prepared for an emergency. **(1 point)**

2. The scout built the fire.
   The scout stoked the fire.
   The scout built and stoked the fire. **(1)**

3. Hatchets should be used with caution.
   Axes should be used with caution.
   Other sharp tools should be used with caution.
   Hatchets, axes, and other sharp tools should be used with caution. **(1)**

4. The birch trees swayed in the wind.
   The birch trees creaked in the wind.
   The birch trees swayed and creaked in the wind. **(1)**

5. Conrad will gather wood.
   Sam will gather wood.
   Conrad and Sam will gather wood. **(1)**

Assessment Tip: Total **5** Points

Name _____

Writing Instructions

In *Hatchet*, Brian is stranded alone in the Canadian wilderness. The only tool he has is a hatchet. How could Brian explain to someone else how he used the hatchet to start a fire? **Instructions** tell readers how to do or make something. Good written instructions clearly explain the materials needed and the order in which the steps are to be followed.

Use this page to plan and organize your own written instructions. First, choose a process you would like to explain. Then list the materials that are needed. Finally, write each step in the process, giving details that readers will need to know.

How to _____

Materials (2 points)	
Steps	**Details**
Step 1	(2)
Step 2	(2)
Step 3	(2)
Step 4	(2)
Step 5	(2)

Using the information you recorded, write your instructions on a separate sheet of paper. You can either number each step or use sequence words such as *first, next,* and *finally*. Include diagrams or pictures to help readers picture this process. (10)

16   Theme 1: **Courage**
Assessment Tip: Total **22** Points

Name _____

Using Sequence Words and Phrases

Following steps correctly is a matter of life or death for Brian in *Hatchet*. A careful writer gives clear instructions so that a reader can complete the steps in a process. Sequence words and phrases in instructions help readers understand a process and keep track of the order of steps.

The following page is from a first-aid manual. The instructions tell readers how to treat puncture wounds like those Brian suffered from the porcupine quills in his leg. In the blanks provided, add sequence words and phrases from the list to make the connection between steps clearer. Remember to capitalize sequence words as needed.

Sequence Words and Phrases

first	after	by the time
during	prior to	finally
before	then	as soon as possible

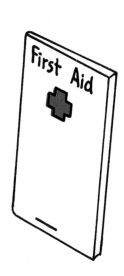

_First **(2 points)**_____, you will need to wash your hands with soap and water. _After **(2)**_____ you have washed your hands, remove the object with a pair of tweezers. _Then **(2)**_____ control any bleeding with direct pressure and elevation. Wash the puncture wound thoroughly with soap and water. _Finally **(2)**_____, cover the wound with a sterile dressing.

Check with a doctor to find out whether a tetanus shot is needed. If you see any signs of infection, such as pus, pain, redness around the wound, or a fever, call the doctor back _as soon as possible **(2)**_____.

Evaluating Your Story

Reread your story. What do you need to make it better? Use this page
to help you decide. Put a checkmark in the box for each sentence
that describes your story.

Loud and Clear!

- [ ] The sequence of events is clear.
- [ ] I vary the sentence types to make my story read smoothly.
- [ ] The narrative is in my own voice and is interesting to read.
- [ ] Details clearly show the setting.
- [ ] My narrative has a satisfying ending that makes sense.
- [ ] There are very few mistakes.

Sounding Stronger

- [ ] The sequence of events is sometimes confusing.
- [ ] The sentence types could be more varied.
- [ ] The point of view is unclear.
- [ ] The setting is described in a general way.
- [ ] The ending isn't resolved well.
- [ ] Errors make parts of the story hard to follow.

Turn Up Volume

- [ ] My plot is a series of disconnected events.
- [ ] The sentence types are all the same.
- [ ] There is no consistent point of view.
- [ ] My story has no clear setting or conflict.
- [ ] Too many mistakes make the story hard to read.

Name _____

Improving Your Writing

Varying Sentences Rewrite the paragraphs in the spaces provided. Each paragraph should include at least one example of each type of sentence: declarative, interrogative, imperative, and exclamatory. (4 points each)

Backstage Pass NO SENTENCE VARIATION I shook hands with Whole New Crew! I was at their concert! I went backstage! I met Jeff! I met Pinky! I met Wanda! I met Therese! At first, I was so excited I could hardly breathe! And guess what — they ignored me! After a while it got boring! So we went home!	**Backstage Pass** SENTENCE VARIATION _____ _____ _____ _____
Jalapeño Biscuits NO SENTENCE VARIATION Do I know how to make biscuits? Sort of. Did I put in the flour, butter, and baking powder? I did. Did I add jalapeño peppers? Accidentally. What did it taste like? It was sort of good. Then why did I end up running to get a drink of water? Because it was so HOT.	**Jalapeño Biscuits** SENTENCE VARIATION _____ _____ _____ _____
Early Start NO SENTENCE VARIATION The coach said to meet at 6 A.M. for Saturday's game. Anyone late would not play, the coach said. On Friday, I set my alarm for 5. I went to the field. Everyone was there — except the coach. We finally found her. Her car had broken down. She said, "I guess I don't get to play."	**Early Start** SENTENCE VARIATION _____ _____ _____ _____

Name _____

Spelling Words

Most of the Spelling Words on this list are often misspelled because they are **homophones,** words that sound alike but have different meanings and spellings. Look for familiar spelling patterns to help you remember how to spell the words on this page. Think carefully about the parts that you find hard to spell in each word.

Write the missing letters and apostrophes in the Spelling Words below.

Spelling Words

1. your
2. you're
3. their
4. there
5. they're
6. its
7. it's
8. wouldn't
9. we're
10. to
11. too
12. that's
13. knew
14. know

1. y <u>o</u> <u>u</u> <u>r</u> **(1 point)**

2. you <u>'</u> <u>r</u> <u>e</u> **(1)**

3. th <u>e</u> <u>i</u> r **(1)**

4. th <u>e</u> r <u>e</u> **(1)**

5. th <u>e</u> <u>y</u> <u>'</u> re **(1)**

6. it <u>s</u> **(1)**

7. it <u>'</u> <u>s</u> **(1)**

8. w <u>o</u> <u>u</u> <u>l</u> dn't **(1)**

9. we <u>'</u> <u>r</u> <u>e</u> **(1)**

10. t <u>o</u> **(1)**

11. t <u>o</u> <u>o</u> **(1)**

12. tha <u>t</u> <u>'</u> <u>s</u> **(1)**

13. k <u>n</u> ew **(1)**

14. <u>k</u> <u>n</u> ow **(1)**

Study List **On a separate piece of paper, write each Spelling Word. Check your spelling against the words on the list.**
Order of words may vary. **(2)**

Assessment Tip: Total **16** Points

Name _____

Spelling Spree

Spelling Words

1. your
2. you're
3. their
4. there
5. they're
6. its
7. it's
8. wouldn't
9. we're
10. to
11. too
12. that's
13. knew
14. know

Homophone Blanks The blanks in each of the following sentences can be filled with homophones from the Spelling Word list. Write the words in the correct order.

1-3. I think that _____ sitting over _____ on _____ blanket.

4-5. If you don't hurry, _____ going to miss _____ bus.

6-7. The pizza's still _____ hot _____ eat.

8-9. Since _____ so hot today, the school is letting _____ students go home early.

1-3. they're, there, their **(3)**

4-5. you're, your **(2)**

6-7. too, to **(2)**

8-9. it's, its **(2)**

Word Addition Write a Spelling Word by adding the beginning of the first word to the end of the second word.

10. than + it's

11. we'll + score

12. knack + flew

13. work + shouldn't

14. knight + grow

10. that's **(1)**

11. we're **(1)**

12. knew **(1)**

13. wouldn't **(1)**

14. know **(1)**

Name _____

Proofreading and Writing

Proofreading Circle the five misspelled Spelling Words in this poster. Then write each word correctly.

1. your
2. you're
3. their
4. there
5. they're
6. its
7. it's
8. wouldn't
9. we're
10. to
11. too
12. that's
13. knew
14. know

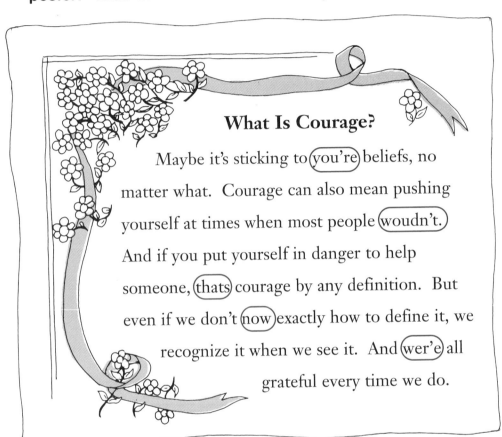

What Is Courage?

Maybe it's sticking to (you're) beliefs, no matter what. Courage can also mean pushing yourself at times when most people (woudn't.) And if you put yourself in danger to help someone, (thats) courage by any definition. But even if we don't (now) exactly how to define it, we recognize it when we see it. And (wer'e) all grateful every time we do.

1. your **(2 points)**
2. wouldn't **(2)**
3. that's **(2)**
4. know **(2)**
5. we're **(2)**

Writing Headlines Suppose that a newspaper were going to write articles covering the events that take place in each of the selections in this theme. What would some good headlines be?

On a separate piece of paper, write a headline for each selection in the theme. Use Spelling Words from the list. Responses will vary. **(5)**

22   Theme 1: **Courage**
Assessment Tip: Total **15** Points

Name _____

The Official Word

**Read the word in each box below from *Passage to Freedom*.
Then write a word from the list that is related in meaning.
Use a dictionary if necessary.**

Vocabulary

bosses
documents
envoy
organization
choice
approval
victims

superiors	government	visas
bosses **(2 points)**	organization **(2)**	documents **(2)**

refugees	diplomat	decision
victims **(2)**	envoy **(2)**	choice **(2)**

permission
approval **(2)**

**Choose *three* words from the list above. Write a short paragraph
about what Hiroki Sugihara's father did in *Passage to Freedom*.**

Accept reasonable answers. **(4)**

_____

_____

_____

_____

Name _____

Judgments Chart

	Facts from the Selection	Own Values and Experiences	Judgment
What kind of person is Mr. Sugihara?	He sees a sad, needy child in a store who doesn't have enough money to buy what he wants, and he gives the child some money. **(2 points)**	I think people should do what they can to help those in need. **(2)**	Mr. Sugihara has done a good thing and has shown himself to be a compassionate person. **(2)**
Is Mr. Sugihara's decision right or wrong?	First Mr. Sugihara says he will only write a few visas. After talking with the refugees, although his goverment refuses permission, he says he will issue visas to everyone. When his wife offers to help, he writes the visas alone for safety's sake. **(2)**	I think a person should do what he or she knows to be right, but not involve others in the process. **(2)**	Mr. Sugihara's values are excellent. He decides to give the refugees visas and not to listen to his government. **(2)**
What kind of a person is Hiroki's mother?	Hiroki's mother says they must think about the people outside before themselves. She massages her husband's arm; she encourages him when he is too tired to write. **(2)**	I think that to be unselfish, you have to think of others in big and small ways. **(2)**	Hiroki's mother is a good person because she puts the well-being of others ahead of her own. **(2)**

Assessment Tip: Total **18** Points

Name _____

Award for a Hero

Complete the fact sheet below about Chiune Sugihara. Then on a separate sheet of paper design an award that honors Mr. Sugihara.

FACT SHEET

Who Chiune Sugihara was:	the Japanese consul to Lithuania **(1 point)**
Where he was from:	Japan **(1)**
Where he was working at the beginning of World War II:	in a small town in Lithuania **(1)**
What his job was:	to represent the Japanese government in Lithuania **(1)**
Why people needed his help:	to give the refugees visas—written permission to travel east through another country **(1)**
What conflict he faced:	The Japanese government refused to allow Sugihara to issue visas to the refugees, but Sugihara knew the refugees would probably die if they didn't escape to the east. **(1)**
What decision he made:	to write visas for as many refugees as he could, and to go against the wishes of his government **(1)**
Why he is remembered:	He saved thousands of lives by writing the visas and had the courage to do the right thing. **(1)**

Assessment Tip: Total **8** Points

Name _____

Judge for Yourself

Read the passage. Then answer the questions on page 27.

A South African Hero

In 1918, Nelson Mandela was born into a royal African family in South Africa. He was raised to be a chief, but instead chose to become a lawyer. He hoped to help blacks win equal rights in South Africa. At the time, the country was ruled by a white minority that discriminated against blacks. This policy was later called *apartheid*.

In the 1940s, Mandela earned his law degree. He helped set up the first black law firm in South Africa. He also joined the African National Congress (ANC), a group that worked to end apartheid. Mandela soon became a top official in the ANC and a leader of nonviolent protests.

The government cracked down on the ANC, however, and responded to peaceful protests with violence. In 1960, Mandela decided to abandon nonviolence and support armed struggle against apartheid. "The government left us no other choice," he said. Arrested several times for his work, he was tried for treason in 1963. At his trial, Mandela declared, "I have cherished the ideal of a democratic and free society. . . . It is an ideal which I hope to live for and to achieve. But if needs be, it is an ideal for which I am prepared to die."

Mandela was sentenced to life in prison and spent the next twenty-seven years behind bars. The struggle for equal rights in South Africa continued, however, and people around the world called for an end to apartheid. The government offered to free Mandela in exchange for his cooperation, but he refused. Finally, in 1990, the government released him from prison. He later won the Nobel Peace Prize and became South Africa's first black president. As president, Mandela called for peace and harmony in South Africa and tried to ensure equal rights for all South Africans.

Judge for Yourself continued

Answer these questions about the passage on page 26.

1. What was important to Nelson Mandela as a young man?

    He valued equal rights for blacks in South Africa. **(2 points)**

    _____

2. What facts from the passage reveal his values as a young man?

    He chose to become a lawyer to help blacks win equal rights. He

    became a top official in the ANC and worked to end apartheid. **(2)**

3. Circle three words you would use to describe Nelson Mandela. Sample answers

    (selfless)   (compassionate)   nonviolent   shown.

    powerless   alienated   (determined)

4. Write each word you circled below. Then tell why you made that
   judgment about Mandela's character. Use facts from the passage to
   support your judgment.

Word	Reasons for Judgment
selfless **(1)**	He was willing to go to prison
	and even to die for equal rights.
	(2)
compassionate **(1)**	He believed that every person
	should have equal rights and that
	apartheid should end. **(2)**
determined **(1)**	Even after 27 years in jail, he held
	to his beliefs. **(2)**

5. How have your own experiences and beliefs helped you make a
   judgment about Nelson Mandela's character and actions?

    Sample answer: I have seen other people sacrifice for their beliefs.

    This shows that a person is selfless and determined. **(2)**

Name _____

Sugihara Syllables

Write each underlined word on the line below. Add slashes between the syllables of each word. Then write another sentence using the word correctly.

1. My father was a Japanese <u>diplomat</u> working in Lithuania.

   dip/lo/mat **(1 point)** Example: I would like to become a diplomat for

   the United States and live abroad. **(2)**

   _____

2. <u>Hundreds</u> of refugees gathered outside our house.

   hun/dreds **(1)** Example: I have hundreds of sports cards in my

   collection. **(2)**

   _____

3. They needed <u>visas</u> to leave the country.

   vi/sas **(1)** Example: Visas allow people to move from one country

   to another. **(2)**

   _____

4. My father <u>replied</u> that he would help each one of the refugees.

   re/plied **(1)** Example: When my brother asked a favor, I replied

   yes. **(2)**

   _____

5. My life changed <u>forever</u> because of my father's action.

   for/ev/er **(1)** Example: Endangered species are gone forever. **(2)**

   _____

Assessment Tip: Total **15** Points

Name _____

Long Vowels

A long vowel sound may be spelled vowel-consonant-*e* or with two vowels written together.

/ā/ g**aze**, tr**ai**t   /ē/ th**eme**, pr**ea**ch, sl**ee**ve   /ī/ str**ive**

/ō/ qu**ote**, r**oa**m   /yo͞o/ m**ute**

Write each Spelling Word under its long vowel sound.
Order of answers for each category may vary.

1. theme
2. quote
3. gaze
4. pace
5. preach
6. strive
7. trait
8. mute
9. sleeve
10. roam
11. strain
12. fade
13. league
14. soak
15. grease
16. throne
17. fume
18. file
19. toast
20. brake

/ā/ Sound

gaze **(1 point)**

pace **(1)**

trait **(1)**

strain **(1)**

fade **(1)**

brake **(1)**

/ī/ Sound

strive **(1)**

file **(1)**

/ē/ Sound

theme **(1)**

preach **(1)**

sleeve **(1)**

league **(1)**

grease **(1)**

/ō/ Sound

quote **(1)**

roam **(1)**

soak **(1)**

throne **(1)**

toast **(1)**

/yo͞o/ Sound

mute **(1)**

fume **(1)**

Theme 1: **Courage**   29
Assessment Tip: Total **20** Points

Name _____

Spelling Spree

The Third Word Write the Spelling Word that belongs with each group of words.

1. pocket, collar, <u>sleeve **(1 point)**</u>

2. association, group, <u>league **(1)**</u>

3. vapor, gas, <u>fume **(1)**</u>

4. feature, quality, <u>trait **(1)**</u>

5. crown, castle, <u>throne **(1)**</u>

6. advise, counsel, <u>preach **(1)**</u>

7. passage, excerpt, <u>quote **(1)**</u>

Code Breaker Some Spelling Words have been written in code. Use the code below to figure out each word. Then write the words correctly.

CODE: J X B M S L T O W K E G C N I Z H
LETTER: A B D E F G H I K L M N O R S T U V

8. LCMJNM <u>grease **(1)**</u>

9. ITMEM <u>theme **(1)**</u>

10. SOKM <u>file **(1)**</u>

11. SJBM <u>fade **(1)**</u>

12. XCJWM <u>brake **(1)**</u>

13. IGJNI <u>toast **(1)**</u>

14. NGJW <u>soak **(1)**</u>

15. CGJE <u>roam **(1)**</u>

Assessment Tip: Total **15** Points

Name _____

Proofreading and Writing

Proofreading Circle the five misspelled Spelling Words in this screenplay. Then write each word correctly.

Mr. Sugihara enters his home. He walks to a chair and collapses into it. He sits (muet) for a few seconds, and then he speaks.

MR. SUGIHARA: I've been filling out visas all day at an incredible (pase). I don't know how much longer I can take the (strane) . . . *(His voice begins to fade as his head droops to his chest.)*

MRS. SUGIHARA: *(She looks at her husband.)* I know, but you must think of the people. You can't just leave them to roam the countryside. They need a place to go.

MR. SUGIHARA: *(He slowly lifts his head and meets his wife's (gaiz).)* You're right, of course. I should (striv) to help as many as I can. If I don't, what will happen to them?

Spelling Words

1. theme
2. quote
3. gaze
4. pace
5. preach
6. strive
7. trait
8. mute
9. sleeve
10. roam
11. strain
12. fade
13. league
14. soak
15. grease
16. throne
17. fume
18. file
19. toast
20. brake

1. mute **(1 point)**
2. pace **(1)**
3. strain **(1)**
4. gaze **(1)**
5. strive **(1)**

✏️ **Write a Persuasive Letter** You have a chance to send Mr. Sugihara a letter on behalf of the refugees. You know he is unsure of what action to take. What will you write to convince him to help them?

On a separate piece of paper, write a persuasive letter to Mr. Sugihara. Include several reasons why he should help the refugees. Use Spelling Words from the list. Responses will vary. **(5)**

Name _____

Word-Order Sets

For each set of words, decide which two would be the guide words if all three words were on a dictionary page. On each "page," write the guide words in the correct order on the first line, and the other word on the line below.

office	ceiling	gown	refugees	emergency
offer	celery	government	refuse	embody
offside	celebration	gourmet	refrigerator	embraced

offer **(1 point)** / offside **(1)**

office **(1)**

---

ceiling **(1)** / celery **(1)**

celebration **(1)**

---

refrigerator **(1)** / refuse **(1)**

refugees **(1)**

---

gourmet **(1)** / gown **(1)**

government **(1)**

---

embody **(1)** / emergency **(1)**

embraced **(1)**

---

32   Theme 1: **Courage**
Assessment Tip: Total **15** Points

Name _____

Safety and Freedom

Conjunctions A **conjunction** is a word that connects words or sentences. The words *and*, *but*, and *or* are conjunctions.

In each sentence below, add a conjunction. Then on the line, write words or sentences to show what the conjunction joins.

Example: The escape was risky ___and___ frightening.

___words___

1. The diplomat had courage, ___and (1)___ he had compassion.

   ___sentences (1)___

2. He knew it was risky, ___but (1)___ he helped the people.

   ___sentences (1)___

3. His children could not see their friends ___or (1)___ teachers.

   ___words (1)___

4. His wife ___and (1)___ family members agreed to help.

   ___words (1)___

5. The women, men, ___and (1)___ children escaped to a safer place.

   ___words (1)___

Assessment Tip: Total **10** Points

Name _____

Should We Run, or Should We Hide?

Compound Sentences A **compound sentence** is two simple sentences joined by a comma and a conjunction (*and*, *but*, or *or*).

Add a comma followed by *and*, *but*, or *or* to combine the simple sentences below into compound sentences. Conjunctions used will vary.

> **Example:** Our escape was dangerous. We made it safely.
>
> Our escape was dangerous, but we made it safely.

1. World War II brought many hardships. People showed great courage.
   World War II brought many hardships, but people showed great courage. **(2 points)**

2. Have you read any books about that war? Did you see any movies about it?
   Have you read any books about that war, or did you see any moviesabout it? **(2)**

3. Bombs fell in many places. They did not fall in America.
   Bombs fell in many places, but they did not fall in America. **(2)**

4. My great-grandfather was in the Navy. He showed me his uniform.
   My great-grandfather was in the Navy, and he showed me his uniform.**(2)**

5. Our town built a war memorial in the park. My class went to see it.
   Our town built a war memorial in the park, and my class went to see it. **(2)**

Assessment Tip: Total **10** Points

Name _____

I Can Speak Italian, but I Can't Speak Japanese

Combining Sentences: Compound Sentences Sometimes combining short, choppy sentences into longer sentences makes your writing more interesting. Use a comma and *and*, *but*, or *or* to combine sentences.

Lee has written a letter to Aunt Lucy. Revise the letter by combining simple sentences to make compound sentences. Insert your marks on, above, and below the line, as shown in the example. The last sentence will not change. (1 point each)

, or
Tomorrow I'd like to go to the zoo︿I'd like to visit Mel.

Dear Aunt Lucy,

, but
    I think I'd like to be a diplomat someday︿I don't know

where I'd like to live. Italy would be an interesting place to

, or   , but
live︿I might live in Japan. You taught me to speak Italian︿

I don't know anyone who can teach me Japanese. Maybe I

, and
could study it in school︿I could study Japanese history too.

, and
My teacher visited Japan︿He showed us beautiful pictures.

The next time I visit, may I see your photos of Italy?

    Love,

    Lee

Name _____

Writing a Memo

Chiune Sugihara was a diplomat in Lithuania in 1940. He probably wrote different forms of business communication, such as letters, reports, and memos. A **memo** is a brief, informal message that is sent from one person to others in the same company, group, or organization.

Imagine that you are Mr. Sugihara. Plan and organize a memo to your superiors in the Japanese government about the plight of the Jewish refugees from Poland. Follow these steps: (10 points)

1. Name the person or persons to whom you are writing the memo.
2. Tell who is writing the memo.
3. Write the date.
4. Identify the subject of the memo.
5. Write the body of the memo. Begin by stating your reason for writing. Use clear, direct language and a business-like tone. Be brief but include all the important information. If you want a response, end by asking a question or by requesting that a specific action be taken.

To: _____

From: _____

Date: _____

Subject: _____

_____

_____

_____

_____

_____

Copy your memo on a separate sheet of paper and exchange it with a classmate. Then, using the format above, write a response memo from the officials in the Japanese government to Chiune Sugihara in which you deny him permission to grant visas to the Polish refugees.

36   Theme 1: **Courage**
Assessment Tip: Total **10** Points

Capitalizing and Punctuating Sentences

To communicate effectively, a writer must write sentences correctly. When you write, remember to begin all sentences with a capital letter and to capitalize the names of people and places. Also, remember to end sentences with a period, a question mark, or an exclamation mark.

Proofread the following memo from Mr. Sugihara. Look for errors in capitalizing and punctuating sentences. Use these proofreading marks to add the necessary capital letters and end punctuation. (1 point each)

⊙ Add a period.

＝ Make a capital letter.

! Add an exclamation mark.

? Add a question mark.

To: Mrs. Masue Okimoto, Office Manager

From: Mr. Chiune Sugihara

Date: August 25, 1940

Subject: Request for Office Supplies

my assistant boris Lavhas informed me that we need to restock some

office supplies will you kindly send the items listed below

  1. two hundred visas and permission forms

  2. one dozen fountain pens

  3. two dozen bottles of ink

please ship these supplies to my office in lithuania immediately

thank you for your prompt action in this matter

Name _____

Complete the Climb

Complete each sentence about mountain climbing with the correct word from the list.

Vocabulary

carabiners
pitons
foothold
desperate
improvising
belay
ice ax
overcome
functioned
fatigue

1. Metal spikes with a hole at the end through which you pass a rope are called <u>pitons **(1)**</u>.

2. Metal rings you use to attach rope to pitons are called <u>carabiners **(1)**</u>.

3. To cut into the ice and support your upper body while climbing, you might use an <u>ice ax **(1)**</u>.

4. In order to remain steady on your feet, it is important to find a secure <u>foothold **(1)**</u>.

5. If you and another climber are helping each other climb up the mountain while attached to the same rope, you are on <u>belay **(1)**</u>.

6. Do not push yourself too hard, or you may experience extreme <u>fatigue **(1)**</u>.

7. If you get lost and feel nearly hopeless that help will arrive, you feel <u>desperate **(1)**</u>.

8. If you don't have the proper equipment, you might look for other tools you have and try <u>improvising **(1)**</u>.

9. If you climb cautiously and with safety in mind, you will never have to face an obstacle you won't be able to <u>overcome **(1)**</u>.

10. Safe climbers have always <u>functioned **(1)**</u> as role models for others.

Assessment Tip: Total **10** Points

Name _____

Event Chart

1. **Page 75** At first Danielle hits the rock with Dad's hammer. Then she
   turns the hammer around and uses its claw like an ice ax. **(1)**

2. **Page 77** The hammers work. Next, Jake and Danielle
   start to climb up the icy trench. **(1)**

3. **Page 78** Danielle gets to the top of the trench first. Then she
   turns to help Jake reach the top. **(1)**

4. **Pages 80–81** Jake and Danielle are happy to be at the top. Then they realize
   they can't see a weather station anywhere. **(1)**

5. **Page 82** Crying, Jake and Danielle hug each other. Then Danielle pushes Jake
   away. Suddenly, Jake realizes that she is
   trying to show him something. **(1)**

6. **Page 84** Through the clouds, they see
   the weather station on a ridge above them. **(1)**

7. **Pages 84–85** Danielle is getting weaker. When they finally knock on the
   weather station door,
   no one answers it. **(1)**

8. **Page 86** Jake improvises by banging on the door with the hammer. As a
   result, a man finally opens the door. **(1)**

Interview with the Ice Climbers

Name _____

Complete the interview below by writing the answers Danielle and Jake would give to tell about their experience.

Q: Jake, why did you and your sister climb Mount Remington in the first place?

A: Danielle and I had to get help for our parents after our car crashed in a blizzard. I had seen a weather station on Mt. Remington on TV, so we decided to go there for help. **(1 point)**

Q: Danielle, how did you and your brother manage to climb without proper equipment?

A: We improvised. We used hammers as ice axes, screwdrivers as pitons, and a nylon leash as a carabiner. **(1)**

Q: What happened when you reached the top of the trench?

A: We were happy at first because we thought we were at the top. Then we suddenly got scared when we realized we couldn't see the weather station anywhere. **(1)**

Q: Jake, how did you and your sister feel at that moment?

A: I felt guilty for having been wrong about the weather station. Danielle was angry at me for the same reason. We were both scared of freezing to death. **(1)**

Q: What happened next that raised your spirits?

A: We realized we were on a false summit when we saw the weather station on a ridge above us. **(1)**

Q: What happened when you finally got to the weather station?

A: We banged on the door, but nobody answered. At first we thought no one was there, but then we heard faint music coming from inside. **(1)**

Assessment Tip: Total **6** Points

Name _____

Then What Happened?

Read the passage. Then complete the activity on page 42.

A Day Hike

"I'm so glad you're okay!" Elaine's dad said as he hugged her close. "But what were you thinking, wandering off like that?"

The events of the past hour came rushing back to Elaine. She had been hiking along behind her mom and dad, enjoying the mountain scenery and warm summer day. Then she had stopped to look at some wildflowers. The flowers spread away from the path and down into a meadow. Elaine had wandered off the trail and into the meadow. (While) her parents had continued hiking up the trail, Elaine had lain on her stomach, peering at hundreds of pink, yellow, and blue blossoms.

A few minutes later she had heard a sound. When she looked up, she couldn't believe her eyes. Fifty yards away stood a mountain lion, staring straight at her! Elaine had frozen, her heart pounding. Should she lie still? Should she run? Then she remembered what her parents had told her the summer before. "If you ever see a mountain lion," they had said, "stay as still as you can. Sudden moves could cause the lion to attack."

Elaine had stayed as still as she could. The lion had watched her for a moment, and then had begun to edge closer. At that moment, her mom and dad had rushed up. (As) they ran into the meadow, the lion turned and slipped away into the woods. That was when Elaine had collapsed into her father's arms.

Name _____

Then What Happened? continued

Complete the sequence chart to show the order of events in the passage on page 41. Begin the chart with an event that happened the year before the events described in the passage.

Last summer, Elaine's parents tell her to stay still if she ever sees a mountain lion. **(2 points)**

↓

The next summer, Elaine goes hiking in the mountains with her parents. **(2)**

↓

She wanders into a meadow to look at wildflowers while her parents hike up the trail. **(2)**

↓

Elaine sees a mountain lion fifty yards away. **(2)**

↓

She remembers her parents' advice and lies very still. **(2)**

↓

Her parents return and the mountain lion slips away. **(2)**

↓

Elaine's father hugs her. **(2)**

Now go back to the passage and underline the sentences that tell where two different events happened at the same time. Circle the sequence words that helped you to figure this out. (4 points)

Name _____

Prefix Clues

**Underline the word in each sentence that has the prefix *un-* or *re-*.
Then write a meaning for the word on the line below the sentence.**

Prefix	Meaning
un-	not
re-	again, back, backward

1. The hikers agreed to <u>reassemble</u> at the summit. **(1 point)**

   assemble, or meet together, again **(1)**

2. Some of them were <u>unprepared</u> for such a long hike. **(1)**

   not prepared **(1)**

3. They <u>reconsidered</u> their plan and turned back. **(1)**

   considered, or thought about, again **(1)**

4. Jake felt <u>unsteady</u> on the narrow ledge. **(1)**

   not steady **(1)**

5. He had <u>renewed</u> energy after eating a banana. **(1)**

   made new again **(1)**

6. Danielle <u>rearranged</u> the contents of her bag, looking for the map. **(1)**

   arranged again, or in a different way **(1)**

7. Only when the bag was completely <u>unpacked</u> did she find the map. **(1)**

   not packed **(1)**

8. When they <u>reexamined</u> the map, they saw that they did not have far to go. **(1)**

   examined, or looked carefully at, again **(1)**

9. Since the day was clear, they had an <u>unobscured</u> view of the valley. **(1)**

   not hidden, clear **(1)**

10. Despite the <u>unusually</u> warm weather, it was cold on the summit. **(1)**

    not what is usual or expected **(1)**

Theme 1: **Courage**   43
Assessment Tip: Total **20** Points

Name _____

More Vowel Spellings

Remember these less common spellings for some long and short vowel sounds:

/ē/ *i*-consonant-*e* (rout**ine**)   /ī/ *y* (c**y**cle)

/ĕ/ *ea* (sw**ea**t)   /ĭ/ *y* (rh**y**thm)   /ŭ/ *o*-consonant-*e* (sh**ove**)

Write each Spelling Word under its vowel sound. Order of
answers for each category may vary.

1. cycle
2. sweat
3. rhythm
4. rely
5. pleasant
6. routine
7. cleanse
8. shove
9. reply
10. meant
11. sponge
12. apply
13. threat
14. myth
15. deny
16. leather
17. rhyme
18. thread
19. meadow
20. ravine

/ē/ Sound

routine **(1 point)**

ravine **(1)**

/ĕ/ Sound

sweat **(1)**

pleasant **(1)**

cleanse **(1)**

meant **(1)**

threat **(1)**

leather **(1)**

thread **(1)**

meadow **(1)**

/ī/ Sound

cycle **(1)**

rely **(1)**

reply **(1)**

apply **(1)**

deny **(1)**

rhyme **(1)**

/ĭ/ Sound

rhythm **(1)**

myth **(1)**

/ŭ/ Sound

shove **(1)**

sponge **(1)**

Assessment Tip: Total **20** Points

Name _____

Climb or Die

Spelling **More Vowel Spellings**

Spelling Spree

Word Changes Write a Spelling Word to fit each clue.

1. Drop two letters from *really* to write a word meaning "to depend."
2. Change a letter in *moth* to write a synonym for *legend*.
3. Drop a consonant from *shovel* to write a word meaning "to push."
4. Replace a consonant in *great* with two letters to write a synonym for *danger*.
5. Change a letter in *repay* to write a synonym for *respond*.
6. Replace two letters in *circle* with one to write a shorthand word for riding a bike.
7. Add a consonant to *peasant* to write a word meaning "enjoyable."
8. Replace a consonant in *leader* with two letters to write a word that names a clothing material.

1. rely **(1 point)**
2. myth **(1)**
3. shove **(1)**
4. threat **(1)**
5. reply **(1)**
6. cycle **(1)**
7. pleasant **(1)**
8. leather **(1)**

Spelling Words

1. cycle
2. sweat
3. rhythm
4. rely
5. pleasant
6. routine
7. cleanse
8. shove
9. reply
10. meant
11. sponge
12. apply
13. threat
14. myth
15. deny
16. leather
17. rhyme
18. thread
19. meadow
20. ravine

Word Addition Write a Spelling Word by adding the beginning of the first word to the end of the second word.

9. throne	+	bread	=	thread **(1)**
10. deal	+	funny	=	deny **(1)**
11. approach	+	fly	=	apply **(1)**
12. swing	+	defeat	=	sweat **(1)**
13. rat	+	thyme	=	rhyme **(1)**
14. spoke	+	range	=	sponge **(1)**

 + = **?**

Theme 1: **Courage**   45

Assessment Tip: Total **14** Points

Name _____

Proofreading and Writing

Proofreading Circle the six misspelled Spelling Words in this travel poster. Then write each word correctly.

Spelling Words

1. cycle
2. sweat
3. rhythm
4. rely
5. pleasant
6. routine
7. cleanse
8. shove
9. reply
10. meant
11. sponge
12. apply
13. threat
14. myth
15. deny
16. leather
17. rhyme
18. thread
19. meadow
20. ravine

You Need a Vacation!

Get away from the daily (routeen) and head for the mountains! You will (clenz) your body and your mind with a week of restful hiking and climbing. Follow well-marked trails to a pleasant (meddow.) Test your climbing skills as you explore a scenic (ravene.) Delight in the beauty and (rythm) of nature. You'll discover that the mountains are the place you were (ment) to be!

1. routine **(1 point)**
2. cleanse **(1)**
3. meadow **(1)**
4. ravine **(1)**
5. rhythm **(1)**
6. meant **(1)**

✏ **Write a Comparison and Contrast** How does the portrayal of hiking and climbing in the poster above compare with the experience that Danielle and Jake had in the selection? Is one more realistic than the other? Is there anything missing from both accounts?

On a separate piece of paper, write a paragraph in which you compare and contrast the two descriptions. Use Spelling Words from the list. Responses will vary. **(6)**

Assessment Tip: Total **12** Points

Dictionary Deciphering

Read the dictionary entries. Follow each numbered instruction.
Sample answers shown.

> **des•o•late** (dĕs′ ə lĭt) *adj.* Having few or no inhabitants; deserted: *an abandoned shack on a desolate road.* —*v.* (dĕs′ ə lāt′). *des•o•lat•ed, des•o•lat•ing, des•o•lates.* To make lonely, forlorn, or wretched: *The loss of our old dog desolated us.* —**des′o•late•ly** *adv.*
>
> **im•pro•vise** (ĭm′ prə vīz′) *v.* **im•pro•vised, im•pro•vis•ing, im•pro•vis•es. 1.** To invent or perform without preparation: *The comics improvised several scenes based on audience suggestions.* **2.** To make on the spur of the moment from materials found nearby: *The hikers improvised a bridge out of fallen logs.* —**im′pro•vis′•er** *n.*
>
> **stag•ger** (stăg′ ər) *v.* **stag•gered, stag•ger•ing, stag•gers. 1.** To move or stand unsteadily; totter. **2.** To begin to lose confidence or sense of purpose; waver.
>
> **tex•ture** (tĕks′ chər) *n.* **1.** The structure of the interwoven threads or strands of a fabric: *Burlap has a coarse texture.* **2.** The appearance and feel of a surface: *The plaster gives the wall a rough texture.*

1. Write a sample sentence for the first definition of *stagger*.
   The injured animal staggered to its feet. **(2 points)**

2. Write a sentence using the noun *improviser*.
   My cousin is an improviser of dance routines. **(2)**

3. Write a sentence using the second definition of *texture*.
   The cook was pleased with the creamy texture of the dessert. **(2)**

4. Write a sentence using the adjective *desolate*.
   The house seemed desolate after my older sister went off to college. **(2)**

Name _____

After I Prepared, I Climbed the Mountain

Complex Sentences A clause contains both a subject and a predicate. An independent clause can stand by itself as a sentence. A subordinate clause cannot stand by itself as a sentence. A **complex sentence** has at least one subordinate clause and one independent clause.

A subordinate clause contains a subordinating conjunction. Here are some subordinating conjunctions:

after	because	since	when
although	before	unless	whenever
as	if	until	while

Join the two sentences using the subordinating conjunction shown in parentheses. Write the new complex sentence on the line.

1. You should not try to climb a mountain. You have prepared properly. (until)

   You should not try to climb a mountain until you have prepared properly. **(2)**

2. They begin climbing. Skilled climbers check their equipment. (before)

   Before they begin climbing, skilled climbers check their equipment. **(2)**

3. They reached the peak. They enjoyed the view. (when)

   When they reached the peak, they enjoyed the view. **(2)**

4. Danielle and Jack reached their goal. They could improvise. (because)

   Danielle and Jack reached their goal because they could improvise. **(2)**

5. I want to visit the weather station. I climb Mount Washington. (if)

   I want to visit the weather station if I climb Mount Washington. **(2)**

Assessment Tip: Total **10** Points

Before I Climbed

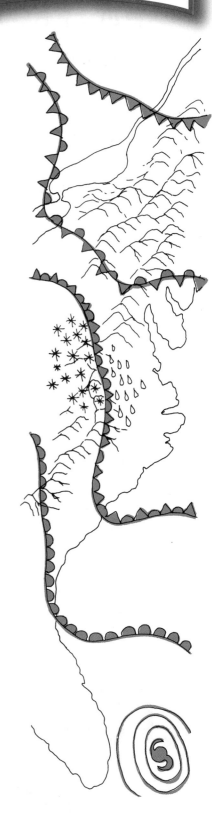

Correcting Fragments A **sentence fragment** does not express a complete thought. Correct a fragment by adding a subject or a predicate or both.

A **run-on sentence** expresses too many thoughts without correct punctuation. Correct a run-on sentence by creating separate sentences, a compound sentence, or a complex sentence.

Read the following sentence fragments or run-on sentences. Correct the problem, and write a new sentence on the line. There is more than one way to fix each sentence.

Answers will vary.

1. Because the weather can change quickly.

   Bring a warm jacket because the weather can change

   quickly. **(2 points)**

2. Meteorologists predict the daily weather, they make long-range forecasts.

   Meteorologists predict the daily weather and make

   long-range forecasts. **(2)**

3. This weather station has recorded the highest wind speeds. And the coldest temperatures in the state.

   This weather station has recorded the highest wind

   speeds and the coldest temperatures in the state. **(2)**

4. Visitors learn how a barometer works they get a tour of the weather station.

   Visitors learn how a barometer works, and they get a tour

   of the weather station. **(2)**

5. When the next storm comes.

   When the next storm comes, I will be prepared. **(2)**

   _____

Name _____

Will It Rain?

Avoiding Run-Ons A **run-on sentence** expresses too many thoughts without correct punctuation. Correct a run-on sentence by creating separate sentences, a compound sentence, or a complex sentence.

A student visited a weather station and wrote the following. Revise it by correcting run-on sentences. You might need to add punctuation, a conjunction, or both. Here are two examples: Answers will vary.

> **Incorrect:** The sky is cloudy I think it will rain.
> **Correct:** The sky is cloudy. I think it will rain.

> **Incorrect:** The sun came out it was still cold.
> **Correct:** The sun came out, **but** it was still cold.

                                                                    . A
I want to be a weather forecaster someday a big

storm would be exciting. A snowstorm can cause traffic
                    and
accidents high winds can bring down power lines. I
                                        . An
would want to be accurate an accurate forecast helps

people prepare for bad weather. I might be a scientist at
                                , or
a weather station I might work at a television station.

                                                  ,
Because I want to be a weather scientist I will study

science.   (**2 points** for each corrected sentence)

Assessment Tip: Total **10** Points

Writing a Friendly Letter

A **friendly letter** is a letter that you write to a friend to share news about what is happening in your life.

Use this page to help you plan and organize a friendly letter. Either write a letter that Jake or Danielle might have written to a friend about climbing to the Mount Remington weather station, or write a letter to a friend of yours in which you share a recent experience or adventure of your own. Follow these steps: (10 points)

1. Write a **heading** (your address and the date) and a **greeting** (*Dear* and the person's name followed by a comma).
2. Write the **body** of your letter below the greeting. Begin by writing something that shows you care about the friend to whom you are writing. At the end of the letter, ask your friend to write back soon.
3. Write an informal **closing** such as *Love* or *Your friend* followed by a comma in the lower right corner. Then sign your name under the closing.

Heading _____

_____

_____

Greeting _____

Body _____

_____

_____

_____

_____

Closing _____

Signature _____

When you finish your friendly letter, copy it onto a clean sheet of paper. If you wrote your letter to a friend, address an envelope and mail it!

Name _____

Voice

Every writer has a **voice**, or a unique way of saying things. This voice
reflects the writer's personality and manner of expression. You can express
your own personal voice in writing by using the following techniques:

► Make what you say sound like you.

► Include expressions and figures of speech you might use when speaking.
When Danielle reaches the summit of Mount Remington and does not
see the weather station, for example, she tells Jake "We're dead" to
express her feelings of hopelessness.

► Write in a way that reflects your thoughts and feelings.

**Think about how you express yourself in different situations. What do
you usually say if you are upset or frustrated? On the lines below, write
expressions and figures of speech that you might use to convey different
feelings.**

My Personal List of Expressions and Figures of Speech

(1 point) _____

(to express fear)

(1) _____

(to express relief)

(1) _____

(to express joy)

(1) _____

(to express doubt)

(1) _____

(to express sympathy)

(1) _____

(to express worry)

(1) _____

(to express confusion)

(1) _____

(to express surprise)

(1) _____

(to express helplessness)

(1) _____

(to express excitement)

**When you revise your friendly letter, use several of these expressions
and figures of speech to reflect your personal voice. By adding some
of these expressions, you can make what you say sound more like
you — as if you are speaking directly to your friend. (5)**

52   Theme 1: **Courage**
Assessment Tip: Total **15** Points

A Test of Courage

Use these words to complete the sentences below.

Vocabulary

ascent
entangled
seasoned
endeavored
rigging
ratlines
treacherous

1. Are you a _seasoned_ **(1 point)** _____ sailor, or is this your first voyage?

2. To prove that you will be an able sailor, you must climb to the top of the _rigging_ **(1)** _____.

3. To start your climb, grab one of the _ratlines_ **(1)** _____, the small ropes that form a ladder.

4. As you continue your _ascent_ **(1)** _____ upward, be careful not to become entangled in the ropes.

5. Rain and wind make the climb even more _treacherous_ **(1)** _____ than it usually is.

6. I have _endeavored_ **(1)** _____ to give you guidance, but you must find courage within yourself to make the climb.

Use two vocabulary words in a short description of what it might feel like to make the climb described above.

(2 points) _____

_____

_____

Name _____

Predictions Chart

selection details + personal knowledge + THINKING = prediction	

Selection Details page 99	**Personal Knowledge**
▶ Charlotte must climb the tallest mast to prove her worth. The climb is dangerous. Charlotte is steady, though nervous. **(1 point)**	Example: Courageous people will face challenges, despite danger. **(1 point)**

Prediction: Example: Charlotte will go through with the test. **(1)**

Selection Details page 105	**Personal Knowledge**
▶ Charlotte makes it to just below the top gallant spar. It took her thirty minutes to do what a seasoned sailor could do in two. **(1)**	Accept reasonable responses. **(1)**

Prediction: It will take Charlotte a very long time to complete the climb. **(1)**

Selection Details page 107	**Personal Knowledge**
▶ Charlotte begins her climb down. She nearly falls because she can't see where to put her feet. **(1)**	Accept reasonable responses. **(1)**

Prediction: Charlotte will probably make it down. **(1)**

Selection Details page 105	**Personal Knowledge**
▶ Captain Jaggery appears on deck. He is not cheering like everyone else. **(1)**	Accept reasonable responses. **(1)**

Prediction: Captain Jaggery will not want Charlotte to become a crew member. **(1)**

54   Theme 1: **Courage**
Assessment Tip: Total **12** Points

Name _____

A Day on the *Seahawk*

Answer the questions about the setting, characters, and plot of
The True Confessions of Charlotte Doyle.

1. Where is Charlotte when the story begins?

   below deck on the *Seahawk* **(1 point)**

2. What does she have to do to become a member of the crew?

   climb to the top of the royal yard **(1)**

3. Why doesn't Charlotte start over again after she realizes she has begun to climb the wrong set of rigging?

   She doesn't want the crew to think she is retreating. **(1)**

4. After the ship dips, how does Charlotte feel about her decision to climb?

   She worries she will not will make it down alive. **(1)**

5. How long does it take Charlotte to climb to a point on the mast that a seasoned sailor could reach in two minutes?

   thirty minutes **(1)**

6. Why is climbing near the top of the mast more difficult than climbing closer to the bottom?

   The swaying motion of the ship increases at the top of the mast. **(1)**

7. Why is climbing down the rigging more difficult than climbing up?

   Charlotte can't see where she's putting her feet. **(1)**

8. How does the crew react when Charlotte finally returns safely to the deck?

   They cheer for her. **(1)**

Theme 1: **Courage**   55

Assessment Tip: Total **8** Points

Name _____

You Guessed It!

Read the story. Then complete the activity on page 57.

The Deep End

Manning flopped around in his bed like a fish. A moment before, he had been sinking to the bottom of a swimming pool. He heard muffled shouts coming from above. He flailed his arms, but it was no use. He just kept sinking. His father's voice roused him from his dream. "Are you ready for your first day of lifeguard training?" Manning groaned.

Rough and Ready Summer Camp was just about the only place around that gave summer jobs to teenagers younger than eighteen. Manning needed money for a backpacking trip to the Rocky Mountains in the fall. He needed to buy a train ticket to Montana. He needed a new backpack and new hiking boots. He needed a job!

He had applied for the position of assistant counselor. He got the job, but was then dismayed to find out that, like all counselors at the camp, he needed to go through lifeguard training. He was a capable swimmer, but he had one discomfort that had been with him all his life: he did not like to be in deep water. In fact, being in water over his head terrified him.

At ten o'clock training began at Taft Pool. The trainer announced that first they would take a swimming test—ten laps of freestyle. "When I blow my whistle, dive in and start swimming," he said. "This is not a race," he added, "it's a test of your endurance."

Manning's heart was pounding. He knew he'd be fine in the shallow water, but what would happen when he reached the deep end? "Swimmers, on your mark!" the trainer called. Manning got into diving position. At the shrill sound of the whistle, he took a deep breath and dove. His body hit the water smoothly, and he fell into an even stroke.

"Just breathe," he told himself as he swam toward the deep end. He concentrated on his stroke. To his relief, he didn't panic as he passed the five-foot marker on the side of the pool. Nor did he panic when he passed the eight-foot marker. By the time he reached the far side of the pool, he was just hitting his best rhythm. He flipped himself around and started back toward the shallow end.

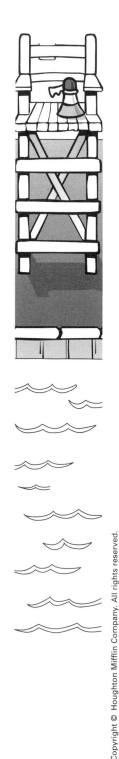

You Guessed It! continued

Answer these questions about the passage on page 56.

1. Do you think Manning will successfully complete lifeguard training? Why or why not?

   Yes. He is a capable swimmer and stays calm in the deep water.

   (2 points)

2. What information in the story might lead you to predict that Manning will not complete the training?

   He is terrified of deep water. He is nervous and doubts his own

   ability. **(2)**

3. At which point in the story might you change your prediction?

   I might change my prediction when Manning does not panic in the

   deep water. **(2)**

4. What do you think Manning will do with the money he earns as assistant counselor?

   He will buy new camping equipment and a train ticket to Montana.

   (2)

5. The following statements are generally true in real life. Which statement helps you predict that Manning will most likely succeed in lifeguard training? Circle it.

   A. People often avoid what they fear.

   B. People will often face a difficult challenge to get something they really want. **(2)**

   C. Good friends help each other through hard times.

Book Report Rewrite

Underline each contraction or possessive in this book report. Then, on the lines below, rewrite the report, replacing each contraction or possessive with its longer form. (1 point for each each underlined word)

> The True Confessions of Charlotte Doyle
> by Avi
>
> Charlotte dresses in sailor's garb and asks to be accepted as a crew member. "You're a girl" is Dillingham's reply. "What'll the captain say?" Charlotte doesn't want to think about the task she must perform, but she's determined. Charlotte's climb is terrifying, but it's nothing compared to her descent. I'd highly recommend this book to adventure lovers. The book's author has also written many other entertaining stories.

Charlotte dresses in the garb of a sailor **(1 point)** and asks to be accepted as a crew member. "You are **(1)** a girl" is the reply of Dillingham **(1)**. "What will **(1)** the captain say?" Charlotte does not **(1)** want to think about the task she must perform, but she is **(1)** determined. The climb of Charlotte **(1)** is terrifying, but it is **(1)** nothing compared to her descent. I would **(1)** highly recommend this book to adventure lovers. The author of the book **(1)** has also written many other entertaining stories.

Assessment Tip: Total **20** Points

Name _____

The /ou/, /o͞o/, /ô/, and /oi/ Sounds

Remember these spelling patterns for the /ou/, the /o͞o/, the /ô/, and the /oi/ sounds:

/ou/ *ou* st**ou**t   /ô/ *au, aw, ough, augh*

/o͞o/ *oo* bl**oo**m   v**au**lt, squ**aw**k, s**ough**t, n**augh**ty

/oi/ *oi, oy* av**oi**d, ann**oy**

Write each Spelling Word under its vowel sound.

Order of answers for each category may vary.

Spelling Words

1. bloom
2. stout
3. droop
4. crouch
5. annoy
6. vault
7. squawk
8. avoid
9. sought
10. naughty
11. mound
12. groove
13. foul
14. hoist
15. gloom
16. trout
17. noun
18. roost
19. clause
20. appoint

/ou/ Sound

stout **(1 point)**

crouch **(1)**

mound **(1)**

foul **(1)**

trout **(1)**

noun **(1)**

/o͞o/ Sound

bloom **(1)**

droop **(1)**

groove **(1)**

gloom **(1)**

roost **(1)**

/ô/ Sound

vault **(1)**

squawk **(1)**

sought **(1)**

naughty **(1)**

clause **(1)**

/oi/ Sound

annoy **(1)**

avoid **(1)**

hoist **(1)**

appoint **(1)**

Theme 1: **Courage**   59
Assessment Tip: Total **20** Points

Name _____

Spelling Spree

Find a Rhyme Write a Spelling Word that rhymes with the underlined word.

1. bloom
2. stout
3. droop
4. crouch
5. annoy
6. vault
7. squawk
8. avoid
9. sought
10. naughty
11. mound
12. groove
13. foul
14. hoist
15. gloom
16. trout
17. noun
18. roost
19. clause
20. appoint

1. If you _____ down, you can see the kangaroo's <u>pouch</u>.

2. The baseball player <u>found</u> his glove near the pitcher's _____.

3. Please <u>pause</u> while I find the _____ in this sentence.

4. I think I can see this bird's _____, if you give me a <u>boost</u>.

5. Every plant in the gardener's <u>room</u> was starting to _____.

6. Don't <u>pout</u> just because you didn't catch a _____ today.

1. crouch **(1 point)**
2. mound **(1)**
3. clause **(1)**
4. roost **(1)**
5. bloom **(1)**
6. trout **(1)**

Word Search Find nine Spelling Words in the Word Search below. Circle each word as you find it, and then write the words in order.

```
S H O I S T E R N O U N I N G A V O I D A N
S F O U L S T E G R O O V E D U N V A U L T R U
G L O O M D I A P P O I N T A N A U G H T Y A R N
```

7. hoist **(1)**
8. noun **(1)**
9. avoid **(1)**
10. foul **(1)**
11. groove **(1)**

12. vault **(1)**
13. gloom **(1)**
14. appoint **(1)**
15. naughty **(1)**

Assessment Tip: Total **15** Points

Name _____

Proofreading and Writing

Proofreading Circle the five misspelled Spelling Words in this part of a letter. Then write each word correctly.

Dear Mother,

   A most unusual event took place onboard today. Miss Charlotte Doyle, a young woman who (saught) to join the crew, managed to hoist herself to the top of the royal yard. Many of the crew had expected her to fail, and her success seemed to (anoy) more than a few of them. One sailor's response was to let his shoulders (droup) noticeably. Another let loose a rude (squak) and said, "She was just lucky." Personally, I think Miss Doyle has a (stout) heart and will be a valuable addition to the ship.

Spelling Words

1. bloom
2. stout
3. droop
4. crouch
5. annoy
6. vault
7. squawk
8. avoid
9. sought
10. naughty
11. mound
12. groove
13. foul
14. hoist
15. gloom
16. trout
17. noun
18. roost
19. clause
20. appoint

1. sought **(1 point)**
2. annoy **(1)**
3. droop **(1)**
4. squawk **(1)**
5. stout **(1)**

✏️ **Write a Character Sketch** What does Charlotte Doyle's behavior tell you about her? What do you think about her ability to make herself climb to the top of the royal yard?

On a separate piece of paper, write a character sketch in which you describe Charlotte. Use Spelling Words from the list. Responses will vary. **(5)**

Name _____

Word Family Matters

**Decide which word best completes each sentence. Write the
word in the blank.**

1. The puppy barked _horribly_ **(1 point)**_____

   when our older dog was let out at night.

2. My _advice_ **(1)**_____ to you is to hike

   with a friend.

3. I hope you _enjoy_ **(1)**_____ your school

   vacation.

4. I don't _normally_ **(1)**_____ eat six cookies

   at lunchtime.

5. Why does my brother _oppose_ **(1)**_____

   everything I say?

Now write a sentence using two words you haven't used yet.
Sample answer shown.

To my horror, my school bus went in the opposite

direction. **(3)**_____

Vocabulary

joyous
rejoice
enjoy

advice
advise
adviser

opposite
oppose
opposition

horror
horribly
horrify

normal
normally
normalize

Assessment Tip: Total **8** Points

Name _____

Charlotte and the Navy

Common and Proper Nouns A **common noun** names a person, a place, a thing, or an idea. A **proper noun** names a particular person, place, thing, or idea. Each important word in a proper noun is capitalized.

Determine which nouns in the following sentences are proper nouns and which are common nouns. List the nouns in the proper columns below the sentences.

> **Example:** New Mexico is a state in the United States.
>
> | **Proper Nouns** | **Common Nouns** |
> |---|---|
> | New Mexico | state |
> | United States | |

1. Charlotte Doyle wanted to be a sailor.
2. My big sister joined the U.S. Navy.
3. Her ship is called *The Piedmont*.
4. Last year, she sailed to Hawaii.
5. The crew is sailing in the Atlantic Ocean now.

Proper Nouns	**Common Nouns**
Charlotte Doyle **(1 point)**	sailor **(1)**
U.S. Navy **(1)**	sister **(1)**
The Piedmont **(1)**	ship **(1)**
Hawaii **(1)**	year **(1)**
Atlantic Ocean **(1)**	crew **(1)**

Name _____

Foxes and Deer

Singular and Plural Nouns A **singular noun** names one person, place, thing, or idea. A **plural noun** names more than one person, place, thing, or idea. To form the plural of most nouns, simply add -*s* or -*es* to the singular form. Some nouns have the same singular and plural forms, and some nouns have unusual plural forms. Study the examples below.

Singular	Plural	Singular	Plural
ship	ships	church	churches
waltz	waltzes	day	days
Jones	Joneses	dish	dishes
solo	solos	scarf	scarves
boss	bosses	fox	foxes
county	counties	deer	deer

Compare the spelling pattern of each singular noun below to the ones in the list above. Then write the correct plural form. You may use a dictionary.

Singular	Plural
1. box	boxes **(1)**
2. city	cities **(1)**
3. toss	tosses **(1)**
4. leaf	leaves **(1)**
5. watch	watches **(1)**
6. cap	caps **(1)**
7. ash	ashes **(1)**
8. yes	yeses **(1)**
9. zoo	zoos **(1)**
10. toy	toys **(1)**

64   Theme 1: **Courage**
Assessment Tip: Total **10** Points

Name _____

Ms. Doyle and President Kim

Capitalization and Punctuation of People's Titles A title before a person's name is capitalized. When a title is abbreviated, it is followed by a period.

> **Examples:** I will introduce **Ms.** Clara Kindowsky.
> The press interviewed **President** Carter.

Rewrite each sentence below. Use correct punctuation and capitalization for titles.

1. The sailors saluted captain Smith and lieutenant Lee.

   The sailors saluted Captain Smith and Lieutenant Lee. **(2 points)**

   _____

2. A member of the crew approached Capt Smith and dr. Tilton.

   A member of the crew approached Capt. Smith and Dr. Tilton. **(2)**

   _____

3. Dr Tilton visited ensign Johnson, who was sick.

   Dr. Tilton visited Ensign Johnson, who was sick. **(2)**

   _____

4. I recommend either mr. Kim or Mrs Ortiz for the position.

   I recommend either Mr. Kim or Mrs. Ortiz for the position. **(2)**

   _____

5. Mrs Ellison and principal Lesnikoski stood in the hallway.

   Mrs. Ellison and Principal Lesnikoski stood in the hallway. **(2)**

   _____

Name _____

Writing an Opinion Paragraph

An **opinion** is a strong belief or conclusion that may or may not be supported by facts and reasons. For example, Zachariah in *The True Confessions of Charlotte Doyle* expresses his opinion of Charlotte, saying, "You're as steady a girl as ever I've met." As you read a story, you will form your own opinions about its characters.

As you read *The True Confessions of Charlotte Doyle*, think about this question: *Do you think Charlotte should have been allowed to prove her competence as a sailor by climbing to the top of the royal yard, or should someone have stopped her from performing this hazardous feat?*

Then use this diagram to record your opinion and to write facts and examples that support it.

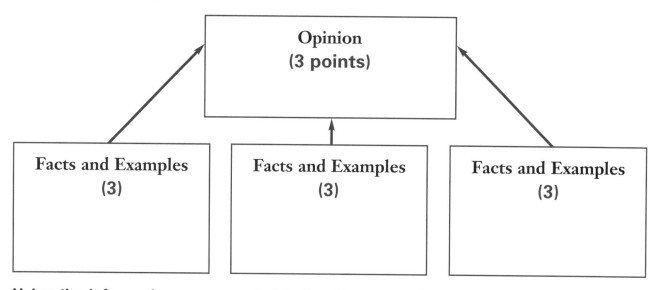

Opinion
(3 points)

Facts and Examples
(3)

Facts and Examples
(3)

Facts and Examples
(3)

Using the information you recorded in the diagram, write an opinion paragraph on a separate sheet of paper. In the first sentence, state your opinion in response to the question above. In the body of the paragraph, write two to three reasons why you think and feel the way you do. Support your opinion with facts and examples. Then end your paragraph with a concluding sentence that restates your opinion. (4)

Assessment Tip: Total **16** Points

Name _____

Combining Sentences with Appositives

One way to improve your writing is to combine two short sentences into one by using an appositive. An **appositive** is a word or group of words that immediately follows a noun and identifies or explains it. Appositives are usually set off from the rest of the sentence by commas. Here is an example of before and after:

> Charlotte Doyle was a thirteen-year-old girl. She joined the crew of the *Seahawk*.

> Charlotte Doyle, **a thirteen-year-old girl,** joined the crew of the *Seahawk*.

Revise the following sentences from Captain Jaggery's ship's log. Combine each pair of short, choppy sentences into a single sentence with an appositive.

Charlotte Doyle is a young passenger. She wants to work aboard the Seahawk.

Charlotte Doyle, a young passenger, wants to work aboard the *Seahawk*. **(3 points)**

Today two members of the crew described a test of worth that Charlotte had to pass. Zachariah and Foley are the crew members who described the test.

Today Zachariah and Foley, two members of the crew, described a test of worth that

Charlotte had to pass. **(3)**

The men asked Charlotte to climb to the top of the royal yard. The royal yard is the tallest mast of the ship.

The men asked Charlotte to climb to the top of the royal yard, the tallest mast of

the ship. **(3)**

Ewing gave Charlotte some helpful advice. He is a seasoned sailor.

Ewing, a seasoned sailor, gave Charlotte some helpful advice. **(3)**

Happily, Charlotte passed the test with flying colors. The test was a difficult physical and mental challenge.

Happily, Charlotte passed the test, a difficult physical and mental challenge, with

flying colors. **(3)**

Theme 1: **Courage**   67
Assessment Tip: Total **15** Points

Name _____

Choosing the Best Answer

Use the test-taking strategies and tips you have learned to help you answer these multiple-choice questions. You may go back to *Hatchet* if you need to. This practice will help you when you take this kind of test.

Read each question. In the answer row, fill in the circle that corresponds to the best answer.

1   What was the first clue Brian had that there was a living creature in the shelter with him?

   A   He heard it growl.

   B   He saw it in the darkness.

   C   He smelled it.

   D   He felt it touch his feet.

2   What happened when Brian kicked the porcupine?

   F   The porcupine sailed out of the shelter.

   G   The porcupine stuck quills into Brian's leg.

   H   The porcupine hid in the corner of the shelter.

   J   The porcupine knocked Brian's hatchet off some rocks.

3   What was the important rule of survival that Brain learned?

   A   Never kick at something that you can't see.

   B   A hatchet is the most valuable tool you can have.

   C   Feeling sorry for yourself doesn't work.

   D   Sleeping in a cave can be dangerous.

4   When Brain was dreaming, what did he see Terry pointing to?

   F   a park bench   **H**   a grocery sack

   G   a hatchet   **J**   a fire

ANSWER ROWS   I Ⓐ Ⓑ ●C Ⓓ **(5 points)**   3 Ⓐ Ⓑ ●C Ⓓ **(5)**

                      2 Ⓕ ●G Ⓗ Ⓙ **(5)**   4 Ⓕ Ⓖ Ⓗ ●J **(5)**

Theme 1: **Courage**   69

Name _____

Choosing the Best Answer

continued

5   What kind of tools did Brian think about making to help him push an animal away?

    A   a crutch or a broom

    B   a shovel or a rake

    C   a knife or a hatchet

    D   a staff or a lance

6   In the dream, what had Terry been trying to tell Brian?

    F   Brian could make a fire with the hatchet.

    G   Brian could find charcoal in the cave.

    H   Brian could pick wild raspberries outside the cave.

    J   Brian should never let go of the hatchet.

7   What did Brian find in his pocket that he used to get the fire started?

    A   matches

    B   a magnifying glass

    C   a twenty dollar bill

    D   charcoal

8   What was the missing ingredient that Brian needed to have a fire?

    F   oxygen

    G   sparks

    H   paper

    J   wood

ANSWER ROWS   5 Ⓐ Ⓑ Ⓒ ● **(5 points)**   7 Ⓐ Ⓑ ● Ⓓ **(5)**

                        6 ● Ⓖ Ⓗ Ⓙ **(5)**   8 ● Ⓖ Ⓗ Ⓙ **(5)**

Assessment Tip: Total **40** Points

Name _____

Spelling Review

Write Spelling Words from the list to answer the questions.
Order of answers in each category may vary.

1–8. Which eight words have the /ă/, /ĕ/, /ĭ/, /ŏ/, or /ŭ/ sound?

1. wince **(1 point)**

2. bulk **(1)**

3. depth **(1)**

4. prompt **(1)**

5. meant **(1)**

6. craft **(1)**

7. rhythm **(1)**

8. sponge **(1)**

9–30. Which twenty-two words have the /ā/, /ē/, /ī/, /ō/, /yo͞o/, /ou/, /o͞o/, /ô/, or /oi/ sound?

9. ravine **(1)**

10. squawk **(1)**

11. gaze **(1)**

12. league **(1)**

13. vault **(1)**

14. avoid **(1)**

15. theme **(1)**

16. sought **(1)**

17. throne **(1)**

18. hoist **(1)**

19. strive **(1)**

20. routine **(1)**

21. stout **(1)**

22. mute **(1)**

23. reply **(1)**

24. strain **(1)**

25. roam **(1)**

26. annoy **(1)**

27. naughty **(1)**

28. sleeve **(1)**

29. foul **(1)**

30. bloom **(1)**

Spelling Words

1. ravine
2. wince
3. squawk
4. gaze
5. league
6. vault
7. bulk
8. avoid
9. theme
10. sought
11. depth
12. throne
13. hoist
14. strive
15. routine
16. prompt
17. stout
18. mute
19. reply
20. strain
21. roam
22. meant
23. annoy
24. craft
25. naughty
26. rhythm
27. sponge
28. sleeve
29. foul
30. bloom

Theme 1: **Courage**   71
Assessment Tip: Total **30** Points

Name _____

Spelling Spree

Puzzle Play Write a Spelling Word to fit each clue.

1. a plant's flower   b l o o m **(1 point)**

2. a muscle injury   s t r a i n **(1)**

3. screech   s q u a w k **(1)**

4. a jacket's arm covering   s l e e v e **(1)**

5. a steady look   g a z e **(1)**

6. a recurring pattern of sound or movement   r h y t h m **(1)**

7. disobedient   n a u g h t y **(1)**

Now write the boxed letters in order. They will spell a mystery word that is a synonym for _courage_.

Mystery Word: b r a v e r y

Spelling Words

1. vault
2. theme
3. sleeve
4. squawk
5. meant
6. throne
7. rhythm
8. stout
9. strain
10. hoist
11. sponge
12. bloom
13. naughty
14. annoy
15. gaze

Word Switch Write a Spelling Word to replace each underlined word or word group in these sentences.

8. The gold coins were kept in a locked <u>storage area for valuables</u>. vault **(1)**

9. The <u>ruler's chair</u> was inlaid with gems. throne **(1)**

10. Movers used a crane to <u>haul up</u> the piano to the top floor. hoist **(1)**

11. We discussed the <u>subject</u> of the book. theme **(1)**

12. I <u>intended</u> to give her your message, but I forgot. meant **(1)**

13. The ship was tied to the dock with <u>strong and sturdy</u> ropes. stout **(1)**

14. The fly's constant buzzing began to <u>irritate</u> me. annoy **(1)**

15. Please <u>wipe off</u> the table. sponge **(1)**

Assessment Tip: Total **15** Points

Name _____

Proofreading and Writing

Proofreading Circle the six misspelled Spelling Words in this letter to the editor. Then write each word correctly.

As a usual (routene,)I don't write letters to newspapers. (The (bulck) of my writing is reserved for homework!) I must, though, tell the public about a very special person.

Last Saturday, the weather was really (fowle.) Since my baseball (leage) practice was canceled, I decided to test my new hiking rain gear. In the hills near town, I slipped and fell into a deep gully. Gushing rainwater swept me along, and I was struck (muete) with terror! Suddenly, a stranger's arms grabbed me and began to hoist me to solid ground. I can never thank that person enough for my rescue. From now on, I will (stryve) to be as courageous as he is!

Spelling Words
1. bulk
2. mute
3. prompt
4. craft
5. league
6. avoid
7. roam
8. ravine
9. reply
10. foul
11. depth
12. routine
13. wince
14. sought
15. strive

1. routine **(1)**   3. foul **(1)**   5. mute **(1)**

2. bulk **(1)**   4. league **(1)**   6. strive **(1)**

Just the Opposite Write the Spelling Word that means almost the opposite of each word or words.

7. to grin wince **(1)**   12. confront avoid **(1)**

8. stand still roam **(1)**   13. late prompt **(1)**

9. found sought **(1)**   14. lack of ability craft **(1)**

10. hilltop ravine **(1)**   15. to ask reply **(1)**

11. width depth **(1)**

✏— **Write an Interview Script** On a separate sheet of paper, write the script of an interview with a real or imagined hero. Use the **Spelling Review Words.** Responses will vary. **(5)**

Name _____

Comparing Poems About Friends

Choose two poems from *Poems About Friends*. Compare and contrast them by answering the questions in the chart. Add questions of your own to the chart too.

	Poem #1 Title:_____	**Poem #2** Title:_____
What is the subject of the poem?	Answers will vary. **(20 points for chart)**	
What words in the poem help you see, feel, hear, etc.?		
Does the poet use words for sound or rhyme? Give examples.		
Does the poem remind you of something from your own life? Explain.		
What is the mood or tone?		

Which poem did you like more? Why?

Answers will vary. **(5)**

_____

_____

_____

_____

Name _____

Comparing Poems About Family

Choose two poems from *Poems About Family*. Compare and contrast them by answering the questions in the chart. Add questions of your own to the chart too.

	Poem #1 Title:_____	Poem #2 Title:_____
What is the subject of the poem?	Answers will vary. **(20 points for chart)**	
What words in the poem help you see, feel, hear, etc.?		
Does the poet use words for sound or rhyme? Give examples.		
Does the poem remind you of something from your own life? Explain.		
What is the mood or tone?		

Which poem did you like more? Why?

Answers will vary. **(5)**

_____

_____

_____

Assessment Tip: Total **25** Points

Name _____

What Really Happened?

Each selection in this theme attempts to explain a mystery. After reading each selection, complete the chart below and on the next page to show what you learned about these mysteries.

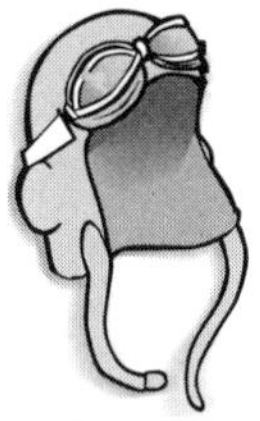

	Amelia Earhart: First Lady of Flight	The Girl Who Married the Moon	Dinosaur Ghosts
What mystery does the selection attempt to explain?	what happened to Amelia Earhart when her plane crashed **(2 points)**	what causes the moon to move across the sky and to seem to change shape **(2)**	what caused the dinosaurs at Ghost Ranch to die out **(2)**
What do you think the author's purpose was in writing the selection?	The author wanted to teach readers about Amelia Earhart and to fascinate them with the mystery of her disappearance. **(2)**	The author wanted to entertain readers by retelling a folktale about the moon. **(2)**	The author wanted to inform readers about Ghost Ranch, the dinosaurs that once lived there, and the theories about their disappearance. **(2)**
What kind of writing is the selection an example of?	nonfiction **(2)**	folktale **(2)**	nonfiction **(2)**

Name _____

What Really Happened?

	Amelia Earhart: First Lady of Flight	The Girl Who Married the Moon	Dinosaur Ghosts
How did the author attempt to explain the mystery?	The author gave several different explanations and discussed why each one might or might not be reasonable. **(2)**	The author retold a traditional story. **(2)**	The author offered several hypotheses about what caused the dinosaurs to die out, and then gave scientific facts that might help prove or disprove each theory. **(2)**
Why do you think the mystery fascinates people?	Amelia Earhart was a hero to many Americans, and people want to know what happened to her. Her disappearance was a mystery because she vanished without a trace. **(2)**	People have wondered about the sky, the moon, and the stars since the beginning of time. **(2)**	No one really knows why the dinosaurs died out. The fact that there were so many dinosaurs at Ghost Ranch and that they appeared to die suddenly makes their disappearance very mysterious. **(2)**

What are some different ways in which people try to explain mysterious events?

People sometimes try to explain mysteries by looking at facts and thinking of

several possible explanations that could be based on facts. Storytellers once

explained mysteries by telling folktales and myths. **(2)**

Assessment Tip: Total **10** Points per selection and **2** points for the final question

Name _____

A Tragic Disappearance

Use these words to complete the paragraph below.

One of the greatest mysteries in the history of
__aviation **(1 point)**__ is the __disappearance **(1)**__ of
famed pilot Amelia Earhart and her __navigator **(1)**__
Fred Noonan. When Amelia __taxied **(1)**__ down
the __runway **(1)**__ and took off toward Howland
Island on the second of July, 1937, she seemed certain to
__accomplish **(1)**__ her goal of flying around the world at
the equator. She had been giving an __accounting **(1)**__
of her experiences to newspapers, and her words were an
__inspiration **(1)**__ to millions of people everywhere.
She was also keeping a __journal **(1)**__, in which she
recorded her thoughts. During that day's flight, radio operators
lost contact with Amelia after she sent a confusing
__transmission **(1)**__ over the radio. She and Noonan
never reached their goal. It may never be known for sure
what happened.

Vocabulary

accounting
journal
runway
disappearance
aviation
taxied
inspiration
accomplish
navigator
transmission

Name _____

Fact and Opinion Chart

Passage	Fact or Opinion?	How I Can Tell
Page 148: She had read the note but believed Noonan had made an error.	Fact **(1 point)**	This statement is a fact, although Earhart's belief that Noonan made an error is her personal opinion. **(1)**
Page 148: Noonan had been right that it was necessary to turn south in order to get to Dakar.	Fact **(1)**	This fact was proven: they ended up north of Dakar because Earhart turned north instead of south. **(1)**
Page 151: Earhart's plane ran out of gas and crashed at sea.	Opinion **(1)**	No one has proven that this is true. **(1)**
Page 152: Amelia Earhart was spying for the U.S. government.	Opinion **(1)**	Some people say that there are facts to back up this claim, but nothing has ever been proven. **(1)**
Page 153: The Japanese did not let the U.S. search party into their waters, or onto the islands they controlled, to look for Amelia and Fred.	Fact **(1)**	This can be proven. **(1)**
Page 154: When Goerner showed the islanders photographs of several women, all of them picked Earhart as the woman they had seen.	Fact **(1)**	This can be proven. **(1)**
Page 154: Amelia had been brainwashed and was "Tokyo Rose."	Opinion **(1)**	This was some people's opinion, but there are not enough facts to back it up. **(1)**
Page 156: Amelia was "a tragedy of the sea."	Opinion **(1)**	This was Amelia's sister's opinion. It can't be proven that everyone would agree with her. **(1)**

Assessment Tip: Total **16** Points

Name _____

Mystery Fact Sheet

Fill in the fact sheet below with important information from the selection.

The pilot: Amelia Earhart **(1 point)**

The navigator: Fred Noonan **(1)**

The goal: to fly around Earth at its widest point, the equator **(1)**

Where their plane disappeared: over the South Pacific, between
New Guinea and Howland Island **(1)**

What Happened?

The Theories	Supporting Evidence	Evidence Against
1. They ran out of gas and crashed into the ocean.	They did not take off with very much fuel. **(1 point)**	The plane would not have sunk right away. It would have left an oil slick. **(1)**
2. They were spies for the United States.	Earhart was friends with President Roosevelt. The U.S. Navy organized the largest search in history. **(1)**	The United States government denies Earhart and Noonan were spies. **(1)**
3. Amelia was still alive.	More than 100 residents of Saipan claimed to have seen Earhart after the crash. **(1)**	Two skeletons were found, but tests showed they were not those of Earhart and Noonan. **(1)**
4. Amelia crashed on Nikumaroro.	Remains of a shoe and a piece of metal were found. Both could have belonged to Amelia. **(1)**	No one can be sure that these items belonged to Earhart. **(1)**

Assessment Tip: Total **12** Points

Focus on Facts

Read the passage. Then complete the activity on page 83.

Jacqueline Cochran, American Aviator

Jacqueline Cochran was a record-breaking female aviator. Though not as famous as Charles Lindbergh or Amelia Earhart, she certainly deserves to be.

Jacqueline was born in the early 1900s in Pensacola, Florida. She had a poor childhood in a lumber mill town. By age thirteen, she was working as a hair cutter in a beauty salon. Eventually, she moved to New York City and started her own cosmetics company. This was a courageous and admirable achievement. So that she could sell her products in more places, she learned to fly. "At that moment, when I paid for my first lesson," Cochran said, "a beauty operator ceased to exist and an aviator was born."

Soon Jacqueline was the leading female pilot in the United States. In September of 1938, with just enough gas for another few minutes of flying, she won the transcontinental Bendix Race. This was a truly incredible feat: the former beautician flew the 2,042 miles from Los Angeles to Cleveland in an amazing 8 hours, 10 minutes, and 31 seconds. She was the first person to finish the course nonstop. More than once, she was awarded the women's Harmon Trophy, the highest honor given then to American women aviators. She also broke the women's altitude record and several speed records. "I might have been born in a hovel," Jacqueline said, "but I was determined to travel with the wind and the stars."

In 1943, during World War II, Jacqueline became the leader of the Women's Airforce Service Pilots, or WASPs. These pilots did jobs such as ferrying planes, training B-17 turret gunners, testing planes at repair depots, and teaching staff pilots at navigator schools. By the end of 1944, however, Congress unfairly refused to admit the WASPs into the military and ended the program. Despite her disappointment, Jacqueline continued to fly and set records until the 1970s, when health problems forced her to stop flying. She died in 1980.

Name _____

Focus on Facts continued

Answer these questions about the passage on page 82.

1. What opinion about Jacqueline Cochran does the author give in the first paragraph?

   She deserves to be as famous as Charles Lindbergh or Amelia Earhart. **(2 points)**

2. The author includes several facts and one opinion in the second paragraph. Write them here.

   Facts: Jacqueline was born in the early 1900s in Pensacola, Florida. By age 13, she was working as a hair cutter. She moved to New York and started her own cosmetics company. She learned to fly to sell her products in more places. **(2)**

   Opinion: Opening her own cosmetics company was courageous and admirable. **(2)**

3. What opinion about Jacqueline's victory in the transcontinental Bendix Race does the author give in the third paragraph?

   It was a truly incredible feat. **(2)**

4. The author uses facts to support an opinion about Jacqueline's victory in the Bendix Race. What are they?

   She flew 2,042 miles in 8 hours, 10 minutes, and 31 seconds.

   She was the first person to finish the course nonstop. **(2)**

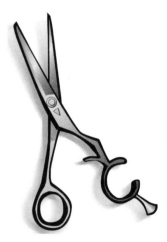

5. What opinion does the author give in the fourth paragraph?

   Congress was unfair when it refused to admit the WASPs into the military and ended the program. **(2)**

6. Rewrite the following sentence so it states a fact and not an opinion:
   Jacqueline Cochran was an amazing female aviator.

   Jacqueline Cochran was a female aviator who set many records and won several awards. **(2)**

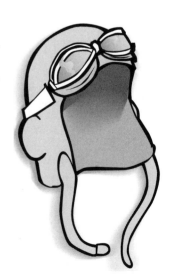

Name _____

Be a Searcher!

Amelia Earhart's plane has words on it. Circle each word that has a suffix meaning "someone who." Then use those words to complete the sentences. (**1 point** for each circled word)

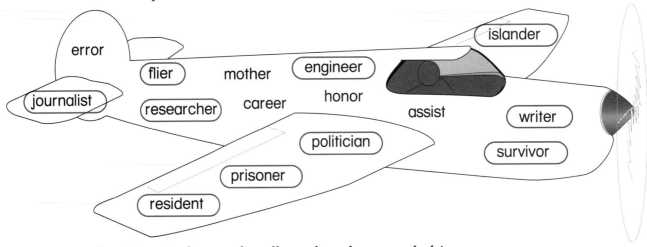

1. Years of training in how to handle a plane have made him an excellent ___flier (**1 point**)___ .

2. The ___politician (**1**)___ thanked everyone who voted for her.

3. When the war was over, each ___prisoner (**1**)___ was set free.

4. Every ___resident (**1**)___ in the town had lived there at least five years.

5. The ___islander (**1**)___ took a boat to school every day.

6. The ___writer (**1**)___ had always liked to make up stories when she was a child.

7. The ___researcher (**1**)___ is experimenting to find out how trees make oxygen.

8. The ___journalist (**1**)___ reported on the record-breaking blizzard.

9. My grandfather was the only ___survivor (**1**)___ of a house fire when he was young.

10. The ___engineer (**1**)___ designed a new plan for the factory.

Assessment Tip: Total **20** Points

Name _____

Vowel + /r/ Sounds

Remember the following spelling patterns for these vowel + /r/ sounds:

/ûr/	*ear, ur, ir*	**ear**th, **ur**ge, sk**ir**t
/ôr/	*or, our*	sc**or**n, m**our**n
/är/	*ar*	sn**ar**l
/îr/	*ier*	f**ier**ce

Write each Spelling Word under its vowel + /r/ sounds.
Order of answers for each category may vary.

1. fierce
2. sword
3. court
4. snarl
5. thorn
6. earth
7. skirt
8. chart
9. urge
10. yarn
11. whirl
12. mourn
13. rehearse
14. curb
15. earnest
16. starch
17. purse
18. birch
19. pierce
20. scorn

/ûr/ Sounds

earth **(1 point)**

skirt **(1)**

urge **(1)**

whirl **(1)**

rehearse **(1)**

curb **(1)**

earnest **(1)**

purse **(1)**

birch **(1)**

/ôr/ Sounds

sword **(1)**

court **(1)**

thorn **(1)**

mourn **(1)**

scorn **(1)**

/är/ Sounds

snarl **(1)**

chart **(1)**

yarn **(1)**

starch **(1)**

/îr/ Sounds

fierce **(1)**

pierce **(1)**

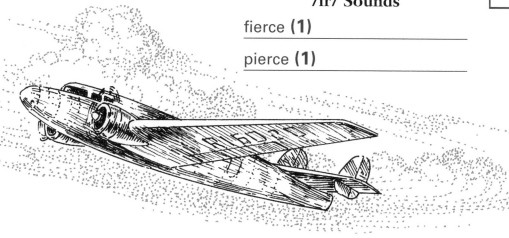

Name _____

Spelling Spree

Clues Write a Spelling Word for each clue.

1. You do this to prepare for a performance.
2. A judge presides there.
3. You step off this to cross a street.
4. A woman may wear one with a blouse.
5. A unfriendly dog may do this.
6. Some people ask the cleaner to add it to their laundry.
7. Its bark may be white and papery.
8. Kittens get tangled up in it.
9. You might find change in this.

1. rehearse **(1 point)**
2. court **(1)**
3. curb **(1)**
4. skirt **(1)**
5. snarl **(1)**
6. starch **(1)**
7. birch **(1)**
8. yarn **(1)**
9. purse **(1)**

Word Search Write the Spelling Word that is hidden in each sentence.

    Example: How is a <u>pear l</u>ike an apple? *pearl*

10. Everybody loves corn on the cob!
11. Did you hear that moaning sound?
12. The people at the pier celebrated the yacht's victory.
13. He gave me his word of honor.
14. The gardener will trim our new rosebushes.

10. scorn **(1)**
11. earth **(1)**
12. pierce **(1)**
13. sword **(1)**
14. mourn **(1)**

Assessment Tip: Total **14** Points

Spelling Words

1. fierce
2. sword
3. court
4. snarl
5. thorn
6. earth
7. skirt
8. chart
9. urge
10. yarn
11. whirl
12. mourn
13. rehearse
14. curb
15. earnest
16. starch
17. purse
18. birch
19. pierce
20. scorn

Name _____

Proofreading and Writing

Proofreading Circle the six misspelled Spelling Words in this message. Then write each word correctly.

Spelling Words

1. fierce
2. sword
3. court
4. snarl
5. thorn
6. earth
7. skirt
8. chart
9. urge
10. yarn
11. whirl
12. mourn
13. rehearse
14. curb
15. earnest
16. starch
17. purse
18. birch
19. pierce
20. scorn

While we were flying toward Howland Island, we ran into some (feirce) winds. The plane began to (wirl) out of control. It came to earth on an island that Fred and I can't find on our (cheart.) Our supplies are running low, and the only plants on the island are (thourn) bushes that bear no fruit. We (earge) anyone who finds this message to contact the United States government. A rescue operation must be organized immediately. This is in (ernest.) It is not a prank!

1. fierce **(1 point)**
2. whirl **(1)**
3. chart **(1)**
4. thorn **(1)**
5. urge **(1)**
6. earnest **(1)**

Write a Journal Entry Amelia was a unique individual who attempted a daring feat. Have you ever tried something that may have had some element of risk to it? Did anyone try to discourage you? Did you have doubts? How did you resolve the doubts? Use your own or someone else's experience to think about the idea of taking risks.

On a separate sheet of paper, write a journal entry about taking risks. Use Spelling Words from the list. Responses will vary. **(4)**

Name _____

Stress on Syllables

Read each dictionary entry. Sound out the word several times, placing stress on a different syllable each time. Circle the choice with the correct stress.

1. **ap•proach** (ə prōch′) *v.* To come near or nearer in place or time.

   AP•proach   (ap•PROACH) **(1 point)**

2. **a•vi•a•tion** (ā′ vē ā′ shən) *n.* The art of operating and navigating aircraft.

   A•vi•a•tion   a•VI•a•tion   (a•vi•A•tion)   a•vi•a•TION **(1)**

3. **cal•cu•late** (kăl′ kyə lāt′) *v.* To find or determine an answer by using mathematics.

   (CAL•cu•late)   cal•CU•late   cal•cu•LATE **(1)**

4. **con•ti•nent** (kŏn′ tə nənt) *n.* One of the seven great land masses of the earth.

   (CON•ti•nent)   con•TI•nent   con•ti•NENT **(1)**

5. **ex•haust•ed** (ĭg zôst′ əd) *adj.* Completely worn-out; tired.

   EX•haust•ed   (ex•HAUST•ed)   ex•haust•ED **(1)**

6. **fre•quen•cy** (frē′ kwən sē) *n.* The number of complete cycles of a wave, such as a radio wave, that occur per second.

   (FRE•quen•cy)   fre•QUEN•cy   fre•quen•CY **(1)**

7. **re•fu•el** (rē fyōō′ əl) *v.* To provide with fuel again.

   RE•fu•el   (re•FU•el)   re•fu•EL **(1)**

8. **re•verse** (rĭ vûrs′) *v.* To turn around to the opposite direction.

   RE•verse   (re•VERSE) **(1)**

Assessment Tip: Total **8** Points

Name _____

Amelia's Plane

Singular and Plural Possessive Nouns Possessive nouns show ownership or possession. To form the possessive of a singular noun, add an apostrophe and an -*s* (*'s*). To form the possessive of a plural noun that ends in -*s*, add only an apostrophe ('). To form the possessive of a plural noun that does not end in -*s*, add an apostrophe and an -*s* (*'s*).

> **singular noun**: dog   **singular noun**: James
> **possessive**: dog's   **possessive**: James's
> **plural noun**: boys   **plural noun**: deer
> **possessive**: boys'   **possessive**: deer's

Write the possessive form of each noun in parentheses.

1. the (plane) <u>plane's **(1 point)**</u>

   cockpit

2. the (women) <u>women's **(1)**</u> plane

3. the (planes) <u>planes' **(1)**</u> hangar

4. the (man) <u>man's **(1)**</u> binoculars

5. our (country) <u>country's **(1)**</u> flag

Assessment Tip: Total **5** Points

Amelia Earhart's Disappearance

More Possessive Nouns Remember how to form **possessive nouns**:

1. Add an apostrophe and an *-s (᾽s)* to a singular noun.
2. Add an apostrophe and an *-s (᾽s)* to a plural noun that does not end in *-s*.
3. Add an apostrophe (᾽) to a plural noun that ends in *-s*.

The following sentences use phrases that show possession or ownership. Revise each underlined phrase to use a possessive noun.

> **Example:** Lynette visited <u>the home of Amelia Earhart</u>.
>
> Lynette visited **Amelia Earhart's home**.

1. No one knows <u>the fate of Amelia Earhart</u>.

   No one knows Amelia Earhart's fate. **(2 points)**

2. Her fate has aroused <u>the interest of many people</u>.

   Her fate has aroused many people's interest. **(2)**

3. <u>The theories of researchers</u> are interesting to read.

   Researchers' theories are interesting to read. **(2)**

4. <u>The fascination of Ross</u> with Earhart's disappearance has led him to read many books.

   Ross's fascination with Earhart's disappearance has led him to

   read many books. **(2)**

5. <u>The planes of early pilots</u> seem primitive today.

   Early pilots' planes seem primitive today. **(2)**

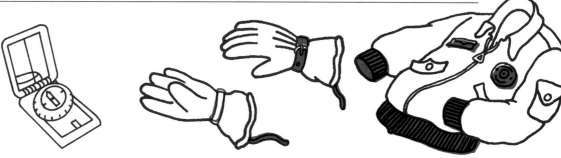

Assessment Tip: Total **10** Points

Name _____

Write to My Friend

Using Apostrophes Writers use apostrophes in possessives and in contractions. If you leave an apostrophe out, you can confuse your reader. Likewise, if you use an apostrophe incorrectly, you can also confuse your reader. Look at how apostrophes change the meaning in the examples below.

We'll see you.   Well see you.   the dog's food   the dogs' food

Proofread the following draft of a letter Lynette wrote to her friend in Kansas. Underline each error in the use of apostrophes in possessives and contractions. Then rewrite each underlined word correctly above the error.

Dear Carolyn,

      I'm **(2 points)**

      <u>Im</u> so glad that I had the chance to visit you

                         can't **(2)**

in Kansas last month. You <u>ca'nt</u> imagine how much

I miss seeing you in school every day, but the town

you now live in is beautiful. It is interesting that

                      Earhart's **(2)**

your town is also Amelia <u>Earharts</u> hometown. I

              family's **(2)**

enjoyed visiting her <u>familys'</u> house. Her story

           haven't **(2)**

inspired me, and I <u>havent</u> stopped thinking about

the mystery. What do you think really happened?

      Your friend,

      Lynnette

Name _____

Writing a News Article

Amelia Earhart's disappearance over the Pacific Ocean during her 1937 flight around the world was front-page news. Imagine you are a reporter for the *World News and Recorder*. Use the chart below to gather facts and details for a *news article* about the disappearance of Earhart's plane or about another historic event. Answer these questions: Who was involved? What happened? When, where, and why did this event occur? How did it happen?

Who? (2 points)
What? (2)
When? (2)
Where? (2)
Why? (2)
How? (2)

Now use the details and facts you gathered to write your news article on a separate sheet of paper. Write a beginning that gives the facts, yet captures the reader's attention. Present the facts you recorded in the chart in the order of most to least important. Use quotations where possible to bring this news event to life, and include a headline that will grab your reader's attention. **(3)**

Assessment Tip: Total **15** Points

Name _____

Adding Details

A good reporter uses details to hold the interest of readers and satisfy their curiosity, to clearly explain what happened, and to make the people who were involved in the event come alive.

Read the following draft of a news article. Then rewrite it on the lines below, adding details from the list to improve it. Responses may vary slightly.

Aviator Mysteriously Vanishes

American aviator Amelia Earhart and her navigator mysteriously vanished in the skies on July 2, 1937. Earhart and Noonan were attempting a west-to-east flight. Their airplane, which departed from Lae, New Guinea, was headed northeast when it disappeared.

The last radio communication with Earhart occurred in the morning with William Galten, who serves aboard the United States Coast Guard cutter.

American aviator Amelia Earhart and her navigator **Frederick Noonan** mysteriously

vanished in the skies **over the Pacific Ocean** on July 2, 1937. Earhart and Noonan

were attempting a west-to-east flight **around the world**. Their **Lockheed Electra**

airplane, which departed from Lae, New Guinea, was headed northeast **toward tiny**

Howland Island when it disappeared.

The last radio communication with Earhart occurred in the morning **at 8:47** A.M.

with **Radioman Third Class** William Galten, who serves aboard the United States

Coast Guard cutter *Itasca*. **(1 point** per detail)

Details	
Lockheed Electra	Frederick Noonan
over the Pacific Ocean	toward tiny Howland Island
Itasca	at 8:47 A.M.
around the world	Radioman Third Class

Assessment Tip: Total **8** Points

Name _____

Evaluating Your Story

Reread your story. What do you need to make it better? Use this page to help you decide. Put a checkmark in the box for each sentence that describes your story.

Loud and Clear!

☐ My setting, characters, and plot are well developed.

☐ The beginning catches the reader's attention.

☐ The dialogue is realistic and effective.

☐ I use exact nouns to make the story's action clear to the reader.

☐ The conflict is resolved in a satisfying way.

☐ There are very few mistakes.

Sounding Stronger

☐ My setting, characters, and plot are described in a vague way.

☐ The beginning could be more interesting.

☐ I need more dialogue and details.

☐ I could use more exact nouns to bring the story to life.

☐ The conflict isn't resolved well.

☐ Errors make parts of the story hard to follow.

Turn Up Volume

☐ The plot is disconnected and confusing.

☐ My beginning does not hook the reader.

☐ It's hard to tell what the characters look and sound like.

☐ The story doesn't have a clear conflict.

☐ Too many grammatical mistakes make the story hard to read.

Name _____

Using Exact Nouns

Replace each underlined noun. In exercises 1–4, circle the letter of the noun that best completes each sentence. In exercises 5–8, write in a noun of your own choice.

(**2 points** for each circled answer)

1. A lion held a mouse in its <u>hands</u> and said, "Tell me why I should not eat you, little one."

   a. legs   b. fingers   (c.) paws   d. jaws

2. "Because one day I may save you from a great <u>situation</u>," said the mouse.

   (a.) peril   b. happiness   c. accident   d. elephants

3. The lion laughed. "How could a tiny mouse such as you ever help a great <u>animal</u> such as myself?" the lion asked.

   a. mammal   (b.) beast   c. critter   d. freak

4. The lion let the mouse go and it escaped into the <u>beyond</u>.

   a. unknown   b. trail   c. cave   (d.) jungle

5. Weeks later, the mouse heard a <u>sound</u> and found a lion caught in a net.

   roar **(2)** _____

6. "Help me, little mouse," the lion cried. "I am in deep <u>adversity</u>."

   trouble **(2)** _____

7. With teeth as sharp as <u>pins</u>, the mouse ate through the net and freed the lion. "How can I ever repay you?" said the lion.

   razors **(2)** _____

8. "You already have," said the mouse. "For I am the same mouse that you caught weeks ago. You let me make an <u>exit</u> then, so I helped you now."

   escape **(2)** _____

Assessment Tip: Total **16** Points

Name _____

Spelling Words

Look for familiar spelling patterns to help you remember how to spell the Spelling Words on this page. Think carefully about the parts that you find hard to spell in each word.

Write the missing letters in the Spelling Words below.

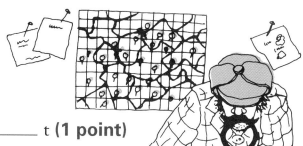

1. ton <u>i</u> <u>g</u> <u>h</u> t **(1 point)**

2. ev <u>e</u> <u>r</u> <u>y</u> where **(1)**

3. ev <u>e</u> <u>r</u> <u>y</u> body **(1)**

4. <u>a</u> <u>n</u> other **(1)**

5. bec <u>a</u> <u>u</u> <u>s</u> e **(1)**

6. <u>w</u> <u>h</u> ole **(1)**

7. p <u>e</u> <u>o</u> ple **(1)**

8. c <u>o</u> <u>u</u> <u>s</u> <u>i</u> n **(1)**

9. clo <u>t</u> <u>h</u> <u>e</u> s **(1)**

10. h <u>e</u> <u>i</u> <u>g</u> <u>h</u> t **(1)**

11. a <u>l</u> <u>w</u> <u>a</u> ys **(1)**

12. r <u>i</u> <u>g</u> <u>h</u> t **(1)**

13. m <u>i</u> <u>g</u> <u>h</u> t **(1)**

14. re <u>a</u> <u>l</u> <u>l</u> y **(1)**

15. ev <u>e</u> <u>r</u> <u>y</u> thing **(1)**

Spelling Words

1. tonight
2. everywhere
3. everybody
4. another
5. because
6. whole
7. people
8. cousin
9. clothes
10. height
11. always
12. right
13. might
14. really
15. everything

Study List On a separate sheet of paper, write each Spelling Word. Check your spelling against the words on the list.

Order of words may vary.

Assessment Tip: Total **15** Points

Name _____

Spelling Spree

Syllable Scramble Rearrange the syllables in each item to write a Spelling Word. There is one extra syllable in each item.

1. ways al all
2. oth un an er
3. cause be coz
4. ry were eve where
5. nite night to
6. ple pe peo
7. ev thing ry eve
8. bo eve ry in dy

1. always **(1 point)** _____
2. another **(1)** _____
3. because **(1)** _____
4. everywhere **(1)** _____
5. tonight **(1)** _____
6. people **(1)** _____
7. everything **(1)** _____
8. everybody **(1)** _____

Find a Rhyme Write a Spelling Word that rhymes with the underlined word and makes sense in the sentence.

9. It looks like we _____ have to find another site for the building.
10. Somebody stole the _____ eight thousand dollars!
11. There's only a slight difference between your _____ and mine.
12. When she gets _____ mad, she gets a steely look in her eyes.
13. My brother really loathes buying new _____.
14. Turn the screw to the _____ until it gets really tight.
15. I'm going to pick up a dozen donuts for my _____.

9. might **(1)** _____
10. whole **(1)** _____
11. height **(1)** _____
12. really **(1)** _____

13. clothes **(1)** _____
14. right **(1)** _____
15. cousin **(1)** _____

Theme 2: **What Really Happened?** 97
Assessment Tip: Total **15** Points

Name _____

Proofreading and Writing

Proofreading Circle the five misspelled Spelling Words in this advertisement. Then write each word correctly.

Spelling Words

1. tonight
2. everywhere
3. everybody
4. another
5. because
6. whole
7. people
8. cousin
9. clothes
10. height
11. always
12. right
13. might
14. really
15. everything

Read all about it!

You mite think you've heard the whole story behind last winter's plane crashes, but if you do, you're wrong. Do you want to know what realy happened? Then read the book that everyone everwhere is talking about! This book tells you evrything that you could want to know about why those flights went down. It just goes to show that you can't allways believe what you see on television!

1. might **(1 point)**
2. really **(1)**
3. everywhere **(1)**
4. everything **(1)**
5. always **(1)**

✏️ **Write a Tag-Team Mystery Team up with a classmate. Then, taking turns writing sentences, write a mystery story. Use Spelling Words from the list.** Responses will vary. **(5)**

Name _____

Fishing for the Right Word

Fill in each blank with a word from the box.

Vocabulary

mainland
suspicious
common room
sod
hearth
phases
kayak
sparkling
village

1. If you are in a light, one-person boat traditionally used in the Arctic, you are in a <u>kayak **(1 point)**</u>.

2. If you watch the moon each night for a month, you will observe all its <u>phases **(1)**</u>.

3. If you live in a very small settlement, you live in a <u>village **(1)**</u>.

4. If you had been alive hundreds of years ago, you might have cooked on a <u>hearth **(1)**</u>.

5. If you do not trust someone, you are <u>suspicious **(1)**</u> of that person.

6. If your roof is made of squares of soil held together with the roots of grasses, it is made of <u>sod **(1)**</u>.

7. If you are on an island, you are not on the <u>mainland **(1)**</u>.

8. If you are looking at waves on which the sun is shining, you are seeing <u>sparkling **(1)**</u> waters.

9. If you are in the part of a traditional dwelling where family members gather, you are in the <u>common room **(1)**</u>.

Name _____

Inferences Chart

Question	Evidence from the Story	Own Knowledge	Inference
Pages 172–173 What does nature mean to the cousins and their culture?	The cousins make hats and baskets from roots. They gather food from the land and ocean. **(1 point)**	Example: It is important to people who get food, clothing, and tools from the out-of-doors. **(1)**	Nature is important to the cousins and the Alutiiq culture. **(1)**
Pages 175–176 Why do you think Moon wants the most patient cousin for his wife?	Moon must work and cannot always be home. His wife gets bored. **(1)**	Example: It takes patience to be alone for a long time without getting bored. **(1)**	His wife will need to be patient in order to wait for him while he is away. **(1)**
Page 176 What is the work Moon must do?	His wife complains that he leaves every night. The cousins saw him in the sky every night. **(1)**	Example: The moon shines in the sky every night. **(1)**	He needs to shine in the sky all night. **(1)**
Pages 178–179 Why are the star people lying facedown?	They each have one sparkling eye. This section of the story takes place on the "other side" of the sky. **(1)**	Example: Stars shine down on Earth. If someone were on the "other side" of the sky, they would have to look down to see Earth. **(1)**	They are looking down so they can make the stars shine down on Earth. **(1)**
Page 180 Why does Moon's wife cover her head with a blanket and say she has a pain on her face?	Moon told her not to go into the storeroom, but she did. Now she has one of Moon's pieces of light stuck to her face.**(1)**	Example: When people do something they're not supposed to do, they usually don't want anyone to know. **(1)**	She doesn't want Moon to know she was in the storeroom trying on his masks. **(1)**

100   Theme 2: **What Really Happened?**
Assessment Tip: Total **15** Points

Name _____

Questioning the Answers

Write an answer for each question below.

1. When did the cousins fall in love with the Moon?

   one night when they were sitting on the beach, admiring the

   Moon's beauty **(1 point)**

2. What did the cousins have to do in order to become the Moon's wife?

   Moon told them to keep their eyes closed until he said they

   could open them. **(1)**

3. What happened to the cousin who opened her eye?

   She fell from the sky and lost her long hair. **(1)**

4. What did the Moon tell his wife not to do?

   look behind the blanket and in the storehouse **(1)**

5. Who were the one-eyed people whom the Moon's wife met?

   the stars **(1)**

6. What did the Moon's wife find in the storeroom?

   different masks of light for each phase of the moon **(1)**

7. What happened to Moon's wife when she tried on one of his masks?

   The mask stuck to her face. **(1)**

8. What job did the Moon give his wife?

   He told her she could carry the pieces of the moon for the

   second half of its cycle. **(1)**

Name _____

Putting Clues Together

Read the passage. Then complete the activity on page 103.

Eos and Tithonus, A Greek Myth

It was still dark when Eos, the dawn, awoke. She rose from her pink pillows and pushed her yellow bedcover aside. Pale light glowed from her hair. Eos dipped her rosy fingers into a glass and sprinkled dewdrops over the world. Then she ran outside and threw open the palace gates. She shaded her eyes as four fiery stallions pulled a golden chariot with her brother Helios, the sun, through the gates into the early morning sky. After latching the gates, Eos yawned and strolled back into the palace.

From the bedroom she heard a tiny cough. Tithonus, her husband, must be awake. "Poor dear," Eos thought, hurrying to the bedside. She caught sight of herself in the mirror and couldn't help smiling. She didn't look a day over twenty, although she was far, far older than her husband.

Eos looked everywhere for Tithonus, but she couldn't find him. At last she spied him crouching in a corner, a shriveled, tiny man about the size of a grasshopper. In fact, his wheezing sounded a little like chirping. Eos sighed sadly. "He is quite old — almost 350," she thought. It seemed only yesterday that she had glimpsed him on Earth, the handsomest young man imaginable. She had begged Zeus to make him immortal so she could marry him. Zeus had done his best, but he'd warned her that something like this might happen.

After serving Tithonus a very small breakfast, she had an idea. Why not keep him in her little handkerchief basket? A basket might keep him safe, and it was certainly a better size for him than furniture in the palace. Tithonus did not object to his new home, and Eos set the basket on the windowsill so he could enjoy the sun. That night his sad chirping lulled her to sleep. When Eos peered into the basket next morning, she thought he looked greener than he did the day before.

Name _____

Putting Clues Together   continued

Answer these questions about the story on page 102.

1. How does Eos feel about Tithonus?
   She loves him, but she feels a little sorry for him. **(2 points)**

2. What clues in the story tell you that Eos loves and pities her
   husband?
   She thinks, "Poor dear," and sighs sadly when she remembers
   his age. She takes care of him. **(2)**

3. What has happened to Tithonus that has not happened to Eos?
   Tithonus has grown old, but Eos has remained young. **(2)**

4. What seems to be happening to Tithonus? How can you tell?
   He seems to be turning into an insect. He has shrunk to the size
   of a grasshopper, chirps, and is greener than he was yesterday. **(2)**

5. What do you think Tithonus might become? Why?
   He might turn into a grasshopper. He is small and green like a
   grasshopper, and he chirps. **(2)**

6. Myths and folktales often do more than entertain. What purpose
   do you think this story has? Circle one answer. Answer shown.

   A. to teach a lesson about what is right

   B. to explain how grasshoppers came to be **(2)**

   C. to explain the movement of the sun and moon

Assessment Tip: Total **12** Points

Name _____

What's the Ending?

Read the letter. Circle the ten words with the endings -*s* or -*es*.
Write each word in the first column, and then write the base word
and the ending.

> *Dear cousin,*
>
> *We have different (lives) now, and I won't see you again. But there are many possible (husbands) in the (villages) all around you. Do you still walk on the (beaches) in the (evenings) to glimpse the moon? If you look up, you will see me in the (heavens) My husband and I share the (cycles) of the moon. He (enjoys) his work, and so do I. He (carries) the moon for the first half of each cycle, and I carry it for the second half. So, whenever the moon (glimmers) down on you, think of me.*
>
> *Your loving cousin*

(**1 point** for each part)

Word	Base word	Ending
1. lives	life	-s
2. husbands	husband	-s
3. villages	village	-s
4. beaches	beach	-es
5. evenings	evening	-s
6. heavens	heaven	-s
7. cycles	cycle	-s
8. enjoys	enjoy	-s
9. carries	carry	-es
10. glimmers	glimmer	-s

Assessment Tip: Total **30** Points

Name _____

Homophones

Words that sound alike but have different spellings and meanings are called **homophones**. When you use a homophone, be sure to spell the word that has the meaning you want.

v**ai**n	(vān)	unsuccessful, fruitless
v**ei**n	(vān)	a blood vessel

Write the homophone pairs among the Spelling Words.
(2 points for each pair)

Spelling Words

1. fir
2. fur
3. scent
4. sent
5. scene
6. seen
7. vain
8. vein
9. principal
10. principle
11. manor
12. manner
13. who's
14. whose
15. tacks
16. tax
17. hangar
18. hanger
19. died
20. dyed

Homophones

fir	fur
scent	sent
scene	seen
vain	vein
principal	principle
manor	manner
who's	whose
tacks	tax
hanger	hangar
died	dyed

Assessment Tip: Total **20** Points

Name _____

Spelling Spree

Homophone Riddles Write a pair of Spelling Words to complete each statement.

1–2. A hook to hang your coat on in an airport storage building is a _____ _____.

3–4. A dog might call the needles of a pine tree _____ _____.

5–6. The most important one in a set of rules or standards is the _____ _____.

7–8. A gift of perfume mailed to a friend is a _____ _____.

1. hangar **(1 point)**
2. hanger **(1)**
3. fir **(1)**
4. fur **(1)**

5. principal **(1)**
6. principle **(1)**
7. sent **(1)**
8. scent **(1)**

1. fir
2. fur
3. scent
4. sent
5. scene
6. seen
7. vain
8. vein
9. principal
10. principle
11. manor
12. manner
13. who's
14. whose
15. tacks
16. tax
17. hangar
18. hanger
19. died
20. dyed

Familiar Phrases Write the Spelling Word that completes each phrase or sentence. Remember to capitalize the first word in a sentence.

9. as _____ as a peacock
10. a tie-_____ shirt
11. the _____ of the crime
12. not pushpins, but _____
13. draw blood from a _____
14. federal income _____
15. Knock, knock. _____ there?

9. vain **(1)**
10. dyed **(1)**
11. scene **(1)**
12. tacks **(1)**

13. vein **(1)**
14. tax **(1)**
15. Who's **(1)**

106　　Theme 2: **What Really Happened?**
Assessment Tip: Total **15** Points

Name _____

Proofreading and Writing

Proofreading Circle the five misspelled Spelling Words in this e-mail message. Then write each word correctly.

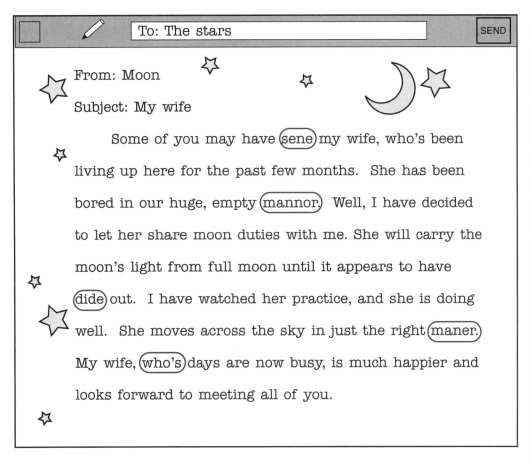

To: The stars   SEND

From: Moon

Subject: My wife

    Some of you may have (sene) my wife, who's been living up here for the past few months. She has been bored in our huge, empty (mannor.) Well, I have decided to let her share moon duties with me. She will carry the moon's light from full moon until it appears to have (dide) out. I have watched her practice, and she is doing well. She moves across the sky in just the right (maner.) My wife, (who's) days are now busy, is much happier and looks forward to meeting all of you.

1. seen **(1 point)**
2. manor **(1)**
3. died **(1)**
4. manner **(1)**
5. whose **(1)**

✏️ **Write a Job Description** Moon decided to give his wife half of his work to do, but suppose he had wanted to hire someone he didn't know. How would he have described the job in a Help Wanted ad? **(5 points)**

On a separate sheet of paper, write a job description for Moon's work. Use Spelling Words from the list. Responses will vary. **(5)**

Name _____

Match the Sounds

Match the correct definition to the boldface word. Then complete the homophone pairs below.

<u>h **(1)**</u> 1. We can **see** the moon move through its phases.

<u>e **(1)**</u> 2. The **hare** hopped in the moonlit snow.

<u>c **(1)**</u> 3. In the **past** some people worshiped the moon.

<u>b **(1)**</u> 4. The moon's light **shone** brightly.

<u>j **(1)**</u> 5. They **heard** a wolf call in the distance.

<u>i **(1)**</u> 6. Her **hair** was the color of night.

<u>f **(1)**</u> 7. The raging wind **passed** through the trees.

<u>a **(1)**</u> 8. The **herd** of deer bounded by in the woods.

<u>d **(1)**</u> 9. The path went down to the **sea**.

<u>g **(1)**</u> 10. Have you **shown** anyone that trail?

a. a group of wild animals

b. gave off light

c. the time before the present

d. ocean

e. animal like a rabbit

f. moved

g. pointed out or revealed

h. perceive through the eyes

i. strands that grow on the head

j. perceived by the ears

11. see <u>sea **(1)**</u>

12. hare <u>hair **(1)**</u>

13. past <u>passed **(1)**</u>

14. shone <u>shown **(1)**</u>

15. heard <u>herd **(1)**</u>

Assessment Tip: Total **15** Points

Name _____

We Collect Shells

Action Verbs and Direct Objects An **action verb** tells what the subject does. A **direct object** receives the action of the verb. To find the direct object in a sentence, first find the verb. Then ask who or what receives the action of the verb:

> **Jeff found a shell on the beach.** The action verb is *found*. Jeff found *what* on the beach? He found a shell. *Shell* is the direct object.

The following sentence has a **compound direct object**.

> **Karen wore her jacket and scarf to the beach.** The action verb is *wore*. Karen wore *what* to the beach? She wore her *jacket* and her *scarf*. The compound direct object is *jacket and scarf*.

Find the action verb and the direct object in each sentence below. Circle the verb and underline the direct object.

1. The older girls (collect) shells on the beach. **(2 points)**
2. Grandfather (builds) a blazing fire. **(2)**
3. Earlier, little Anna and Michael (chased) a flock of sandpipers. **(2)**
4. Grandmother (tells) stories in the moonlight. **(2)**
5. Father (wraps) Anna and Michael in a blanket. **(2)**

Name _____

Auxiliary Verbs Will Help Us

Main Verbs and Auxiliaries A **verb phrase** is made up of a main verb and an auxiliary. The **main verb** usually shows action. The **auxiliary** works with the main verb.

Common Auxiliary Verbs					
am	were	do	has	must	might
is	be	does	had	will	would
are	being	did	can	shall	should
was	been	have	may	could	

What is the main verb in each sentence below? Is there an auxiliary verb? Fill in the chart below the sentences. If there is no auxiliary verb write _none_.

1. Peggy will tell us fascinating stories.
2. She has told two stories about her life.
3. Joan and Margaret have laughed harder than ever before.
4. Should Peggy repeat that story?
5. Peggy is a great storyteller!

	Main Verb	**Auxiliary Verb**
1.	tell **(1 point)**	will **(1)**
2.	told **(1)**	has **(1)**
3.	laughed **(1)**	have **(1)**
4.	repeat **(1)**	Should **(1)**
5.	is **(1)**	none **(1)**

Assessment Tip: Total **10** Points

Name _____

Look at the Moon and Stars

Sentence Combining with Compound Direct Objects A good writer avoids writing too many short sentences, which can sound choppy. You can combine two sentences that have the same verb and different direct objects to make one sentence with a **compound direct object**.

> Nora has **binoculars**. She has a **telescope** too.
> Nora has **binoculars and a telescope**.

Here is the draft of an essay Nora is writing. Revise the draft by changing short, choppy sentences into sentences with compound direct objects. Write your version below. Answers may vary.

Ancient people told stories about the moon. They told stories about the stars too. Today we have seen people on the moon. We have seen robots on Mars. Giant telescopes in the sky take pictures of Saturn. The telescopes take pictures of other planets too. Every night, I look at the moon through a telescope. I look at stars and planets too. Someday, I'll study Mars at an observatory. I'll also study Venus. I'll be a scientist. I'll be an astronaut. I'm shooting for the stars!

Ancient people told stories about the moon and the stars.

(2 points) Today we have seen people on the moon

and robots on Mars. **(2)** Giant telescopes in the sky take pictures

of Saturn and other planets too. **(2)** Every night, I look at the

moon, the stars, and the planets through a telescope. **(2)**

Someday, I'll study Mars and Venus at an observatory. **(2)** I'll be

a scientist and an astronaut. **(2)** I'm shooting for the stars!

Name _____

Writing a Journal Entry

A **journal** is a notebook, diary, folder, or file in which you can record and save notes, lists, questions, ideas, thoughts, and feelings. For example, imagine that one of the two cousins in *The Girl Who Married the Moon* keeps a journal. She might write an entry to express her feelings about the Moon, to describe what happened when she received her chin tattoo, or to tell about such activities as weaving a basket from spruce roots or taking a sweat bath.

On the lines below, write your own journal entry for one day's events. Follow these guidelines:

► Write the date at the beginning. You may also want to note the location.

► Write in the first person, using the pronouns *I, me, my, mine, we,* and *our*.

► Describe the day's events or experiences.

► Include personal thoughts, feelings, reactions, questions, and ideas.

► Use sequence words when you narrate events.

   (5 points)

_____

_____

_____

_____

_____

_____

_____

_____

_____

_____

When you finish your journal entry, you may want to share it with a friend or a classmate.

Assessment Tip: Total **5** Points

Name _____

Using Exact Verbs

Good writers use exact verbs to bring their experiences to life. For example, exact verbs like *glow* or *sparkle* describe actions more precisely than does a common verb such as *shine*. When you write a journal entry, you can use exact verbs to create a more vivid picture of what happened.

Read this journal entry written by the cousin who became the Moon's wife in *The Girl Who Married the Moon*. Then rewrite it on the lines below, replacing the general verbs that have been underlined with more exact verbs from the list. (1 point each).

May 25, Moon's House

Today I felt incredibly bored, so I <u>looked</u> into Moon's storeroom and then <u>went</u> inside. What a surprise! Moon's storeroom is <u>filled</u> with sparkling pieces of light. I <u>found</u> all the moon phases except for the full moon. Now I know where my husband <u>hides</u> his phases.

The phases <u>shined</u> so temptingly! I <u>took</u> a piece of moon from a shelf and <u>put</u> it on my own face. Now the piece will not come off. What if Moon becomes angry?

May 25, Moon's House

Today I felt incredibly bored, so I peeked into Moon's storeroom and then sneaked inside. What a surprise! Moon's storeroom is crammed with sparkling pieces of light. I discovered all the moon phases except for the full moon. Now I know where my husband conceals his phases.

The phases glittered so temptingly! I plucked a piece of moon from a shelf and placed it on my own face. Now the piece will not come off. What if Moon becomes angry?

Exact Verbs	
conceals	peeked
placed	glittered
sneaked	discovered
plucked	crammed

Name _____

Categorizing Vocabulary

Write each word from the box under the correct category.

two kinds of scientists

paleontologist **(1 point)**

geologists **(1)**

two kinds of artifacts

fossils **(1)**

specimens **(1)**

two names for beliefs based on facts and observations

hypotheses **(1)**

theory **(1)**

a word for proof or support

evidence **(1)**

two ways soil can be removed

excavation **(1)**

erosion **(1)**

a word for a vanished species of animals or plants

extinct **(1)**

theory
erosion
paleontologist
extinct
specimens
geologists
fossils
hypotheses
evidence
excavation

Now choose at least five words from the box. Use them to write a short paragraph about searching for the remains of ancient plants and animals.

one point for each word used correctly **(5 points)**

_____

_____

_____

_____

_____

_____

Assessment Tip: Total **15** Points

Name _____

Text Organization Chart

Organization: Main Ideas and Details

A Big Find of Small Dinosaurs
What did Dr. Ned Colbert find in 1947 at Ghost Ranch, New Mexico?

dozens of dinosaur skeleton fossils **(1 point)**

What question did Dr. Colbert's discovery make scientists ask themselves?

How and why did the dinosaurs die? **(1)**

What Happened Here?
List two details about the dinosaur bones scientists found.

Accept any of the following: some skeletons complete; some

separated with missing bones; no predator tooth marks; found

among other animal skeletons; in an area 30 feet long and wide;

surrounded by red rock; not cracked from drying in the sun. **(2)**

Organization: Hypothesis and Evidence

Stuck in the Mud? **Hypothesis 1:**

got stuck in the mud while feeding at river **(1)**

Support *For* or *Against*:

Against: dinosaurs found lying on their sides, not upright

as animals who die in mud or tar pits are usually found. **(1)**

Volcanic Violence? **Hypothesis 2:**

volcanic eruption buries dinosaurs with ash and mud **(1)**

Support *For* or *Against*:

For: many animals killed by Mount St. Helens in 1980.

Against: geologists haven't found smashed silica bubbles,

usually found in volcanic rock. (1)

Name _____

What Happened to *Coelophysis*?

Scientists decided that the hypotheses below were *not* the best explanations for *Coelophysis*'s death. List the evidence *against* each one. Then answer the questions below.

Hypothesis Notes: *Why Coelophysis might have died*

Hypothesis 1: *Stuck in mud*

Evidence Against: Skeletons were found lying down. Animals who die in mud are usually found vertical. **(2 points)**

Hypothesis 2: *Volcanic eruption*

Evidence Against: The rock found around the dinosaurs does not contain the smashed silica bubbles usually found in volcanic rock. **(2)**

Hypothesis 3: *Asteroid fallout caused starvation*

Evidence Against: There is no evidence in the soil of asteroid fallout, plus the skeletons are too close together to have died of starvation. **(2)**

What two new hypotheses did scientists decide best explain *Coelophysis*'s death? drought **(1)** and flood **(1)**

How might these two hypotheses have worked together? Give evidence to support your explanation.

First, a drought killed some dinosaurs, which explains the fish skeletons, mud cracks, and curved necks of some skeletons. Then a flood killed more dinosaurs, which explains the skeletons that were found tangled and in good condition. **(2)**

Assessment Tip: Total **10** Points

Name _____

Taking Text Apart

Read the article. Then answer the questions on page 118.

Trapped in Amber

A clear golden lump sells for $27,000 at an auction. This lump of *amber*, as the material is called, started out as sap from a tree. What makes it so valuable now? Look closely — inside the amber is a small thirty-million-year-old lizard.

What Is Amber?

Amber is hardened sap from ancient trees. Over millions of years the sap has changed into a rock-hard material. Because it is beautiful and lasts many years, amber is often used in jewelry. Some amber pieces give scientists a rare opportunity to study prehistoric *inclusions* such as leaves, insects, and reptiles preserved in the once-sticky sap.

How Does Amber Form?

Picture this process. Long ago (perhaps as long ago as the age of dinosaurs), sap oozes from a tree. It hardens on the tree trunk and is covered by more sap. After many years, the tree dies and decays. It is swept into a stream and eventually ends up under the sea or beneath layers of rock. If the sap had been left out in the air, it would have rotted. Because the sap is not exposed to oxygen, however, its molecules change, forming stronger and stronger bonds. Eventually, all its oils evaporate, and it becomes hard and shiny, a beautiful golden brown. It becomes amber.

How Is Something Trapped in Amber?

It is possible today to see plants, insects, and even small reptiles from long ago preserved in amber. How did they get there? Here is one way this might have happened: an unlucky insect lands on a tree trunk that is sticky with sap. It gets stuck. More sap flows down the tree, entirely covering the bug. Over the centuries the sap slowly turns to amber. The insect dries out but otherwise stays perfectly preserved.

Name _____

Taking Text Apart continued

Answer these questions about the passage on page 117.

1. How many sections does the article have? (Don't count the introductory paragraph.)

   three **(2 points)**

2. What feature of the text helps you identify the different sections?

   the headings **(2)**

3. Reread the section under the heading *What Is Amber?* Is it organized by main idea and details, or by sequence of events?

   by main idea and details **(2)**

4. Reread the section under the heading *How Does Amber Form?* Is this section organized by main idea and details, or by sequence?

   by sequence **(2)**

5. What sequence words or phrases can you find in the second section? Write them here.

   long ago, after many years, eventually **(2)**

Name _____

Sorting Out Suffixes

**Read this field diary page. Underline each word with the suffix -*al*,
-*ive*, or -*ous*.**

> Beginning today, we will use our best <u>investigative</u> methods to figure out why so many dinosaurs died here. The area is one <u>massive</u> <u>burial</u> ground. There are so many skeletons, it looks almost <u>comical</u>, as though the dinosaurs were gathering to watch a <u>famous</u> celebrity when they died. We know that this animal was <u>carnivorous</u> because of the bones of other animals in the skeletons' bellies. Our theories may be <u>experimental</u>, but only if we are <u>creative</u> and <u>inventive</u> can we solve the mystery. Really, it is <u>marvelous</u> work.

**Now write the words you underlined. Use the paragraph above to
help you find the meaning of each word.**

1. investigative: related to investigating **(2 points)**

2. massive: very large **(2)**

3. burial: having to do with burying **(2)**

4. comical: related to comedy; funny **(2)**

5. famous: having fame **(2)**

6. carnivorous: meat-eating **(2)**

7. experimental: related to an experiment **(2)**

8. creative: good at creating **(2)**

9. inventive: good at inventing **(2)**

10. marvelous: full of marvels; wonderful **(2)**

Name _____

Final /ər/, /ən/, and /əl/

The **schwa sound,** shown as /ə/, is a weak vowel sound often found in an unstressed syllable. Remember the following spelling patterns for the /ə/ sound:

final /ər/	er, or, ar	messeng**er**, direct**or**, simil**ar**
final /n/ or /ən/	on, en	weap**on**, fright**en**
final /l/ or /əl/	le, el, al	strugg**le**, chann**el**, ment**al**

► The spelling of the final /ər/ sound in *acre* differs from the usual patterns. The final /ər/ sound in *acre* is spelled *re*.

Write each Spelling Word under its final sound. Order of answers for each category may vary.

1. struggle
2. director
3. weapon
4. similar
5. mental
6. frighten
7. channel
8. messenger
9. familiar
10. acre*
11. error
12. gallon
13. rural
14. calendar
15. elevator
16. stumble
17. youngster
18. kitchen
19. passenger
20. quarrel

Final /ər/ Sound

director **(1 point)**

similar **(1)**

messenger **(1)**

familiar **(1)**

acre **(1)**

error **(1)**

calendar **(1)**

elevator **(1)**

youngster **(1)**

passenger **(1)**

Final /n/ or /ən/ Sound

weapon **(1)**

frighten **(1)**

gallon **(1)**

kitchen **(1)**

Final /l/ or /əl/ Sound

struggle **(1)**

mental **(1)**

channel **(1)**

rural **(1)**

stumble **(1)**

quarrel **(1)**

Assessment Tip: Total **20** Points

Name _____

Spelling Spree

Match Game Match each word beginning below to an ending to form a Spelling Word. Then write each word correctly.

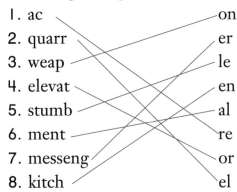

Word Beginnings
1. ac
2. quarr
3. weap
4. elevat
5. stumb
6. ment
7. messeng
8. kitch

Word Endings
on
er
le
en
al
re
or
el

1. acre **(1 point)**
2. quarrel **(1)**
3. weapon **(1)**
4. elevator **(1)**
5. stumble **(1)**
6. mental **(1)**
7. messenger **(1)**
8. kitchen **(1)**

Spelling Words

1. struggle
2. director
3. weapon
4. similar
5. mental
6. frighten
7. channel
8. messenger
9. familiar
10. acre*
11. error
12. gallon
13. rural
14. calendar
15. elevator
16. stumble
17. youngster
18. kitchen
19. passenger
20. quarrel

Syllable Spot Write the Spelling Word that includes one of the syllables in each word below.

Example: format *matter*

9. frightfully — frighten **(1)**
10. gallery — gallon **(1)**
11. passage — passenger **(1)**
12. correction — director **(1)**
13. tunnel — channel **(1)**
14. calculate — calendar **(1)**
15. fanatic — familiar **(1)**

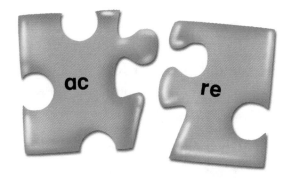

Assessment Tip: Total **15** Points

Name _____

Proofreading and Writing

Proofreading Circle the five misspelled Spelling Words in this journal entry. Then write each word correctly.

Spelling Words

July 25

    After weeks in this (rurel) area searching for dinosaur skeletons, I have finally had some success. Today, I found several skeletons (similiar) to *Coelophysis.* However, unless I made an (errer) in my measurements, these are larger and have a sturdier bone structure. The smallest, probably a (yongster,) is the most curious. It seems to have died in some sort of (strugle.) The rest of the skeletons are spread over an acre of land, and I have not had time to analyze them in detail. It looks like my work is cut out for me.

1. struggle
2. director
3. weapon
4. similar
5. mental
6. frighten
7. channel
8. messenger
9. familiar
10. acre*
11. error
12. gallon
13. rural
14. calendar
15. elevator
16. stumble
17. youngster
18. kitchen
19. passenger
20. quarrel

1. rural **(1 point)**   4. youngster **(1)**

2. similar **(1)**   5. struggle **(1)**

3. error **(1)**

✏️ **Write an Explanation** What do you think about the answer put forward in the selection for why so many dinosaur skeletons have been found at Ghost Ranch? Do you think the conclusions match the evidence? What about the possibility of new evidence suggesting another explanation?

On a separate piece of paper, write a short description of how you think the dinosaur skeletons wound up at Ghost Ranch. Use Spelling Words from the list. Responses will vary. **(5)**

Assessment Tip: Total **10** Points

Name _____

Discovering the Key

Use the spelling table/pronunciation key below to figure out how to pronounce each underlined vowel sound. Find a word in the vocabulary box with a similar vowel sound, and write that word after the sentence.

Vocabulary

blow
late
nut
reel
sail
ton

Spellings	Sample Words
a, ai, ei, ey	m**a**de, pl**ai**t, v**ei**n, th**ey**
e, ee, ie, y	th**e**se, fl**ee**t, ch**ie**f, bump**y**
o, oe, ou, ow	f**o**ld, t**oe**, b**ou**lder, sl**ow**
o, u, ou, oo	st**o**mach, c**u**t, r**ou**gh, fl**oo**d

1. Sh**ou**lder bones were found among the fossils.

   blow **(2 points)**

2. The scientists found d**o**zens of skeletons of the little dinosaur.

   nut or ton **(2)**

3. Each specimen was carefully w**eig**hed and recorded.

   late or sail **(2)**

4. The dinosaurs hunted for pr**ey** along rivers and lakes.

   late or sail **(2)**

5. Red bl**oo**d cells were made in the marrow cavity.

   nut or ton **(2)**

6. These dinosaurs had no armor to sh**ie**ld themselves from predators.

   reel **(2)**

Name _____

Dinosaurs Eat . . .

Transitive and Intransitive Verbs A **transitive verb** is an action verb
with a **direct object**, which receives the action. An **intransitive verb**
has no direct object. See the examples below.

Verb	Transitive	Intransitive
read	I **read** the book.	I **read** quickly.
sit	(none)	They **sit** on the bus.
visit	He **visits** the ranch.	He **visits** often.

**Underline the verb or verb phrase in each sentence below.
Then write *transitive* or *intransitive* after the sentence.**

1. Maurice <u>saw</u> a movie about dinosaurs. <u>transitive **(2 points)**</u>

2. I <u>researched</u> prehistoric times. <u>transitive **(2)**</u>

3. My friend <u>went</u> to the La Brea Tar Pits. <u>intransitive **(2)**</u>

4. Some dinosaurs <u>ate</u> meat. <u>transitive **(2)**</u>

5. We <u>will see</u> dinosaur bones at the museum. <u>transitive **(2)**</u>

6. Dinosaurs <u>lived</u> during the Mesozoic era. <u>intransitive **(2)**</u>

7. Some dinosaurs <u>hunted</u> other animals. <u>transitive **(2)**</u>

8. Still other dinosaurs <u>munched</u> plants. <u>transitive **(2)**</u>

9. Birds <u>may have evolved</u> from dinosaurs. <u>intransitive **(2)**</u>

10. Not all dinosaurs <u>grew</u> to become giants. <u>intransitive **(2)**</u>

Assessment Tip: Total 20 Points

Name _____

Dinosaurs Are Extinct

Being Verbs and Linking Verbs A **being verb** shows a state of being, not action. A **being verb** is called a **linking verb** when it links the subject to a predicate noun or a predicate adjective. A **predicate noun** identifies or renames the subject. A **predicate adjective** describes the subject.

Common Being and Linking Verbs				
am	was	be	become	feel
is	were	being	look	taste
are	seem	been	appear	smell

Underline the linking verb in each sentence below. After each sentence, write whether the verb links to a predicate noun or predicate adjective.

Example: Some dinosaurs <u>were</u> giants. _____predicate noun_____

1. The paleontologist <u>seems</u> excited by that stone. __predicate adjective **(2)**__

2. That stone <u>is</u> a fossil of a dinosaur. __predicate noun **(2)**__

3. The work of a paleontologist <u>looks</u> interesting to me. __predicate adjective **(2)**__

4. Fossils of ferns <u>are</u> common here. __predicate adjective **(2)**__

5. A paleontologist <u>is</u> a scientist. __predicate noun **(2)**__

Name _____

Dinosaurs Was/Were . . .

Using Forms of the Verb *be* A good writer uses the correct form of the verb *be*, especially when writing sentences with linking verbs. Study the present and past tense forms of the verb *be* in the chart below.

	Present Tense	**Past Tense**
Singular	I am	I was
	You are	You were
	She/he/it is	She/he/it was
Plural	We are	We were
	You are	You were
	They are	They were

Below is the beginning of a report written by a student who found a fossil. Write the correct form of the verb *be* above any incorrect verbs. (2 points each)

Example: I ~~were~~ (was) tired.

My brother and I ~~is~~ (are) interested in dinosaurs. Yesterday,

~~we was~~ (were) at the creek looking for fossils. My brother showed

me a good place to look. It ~~were~~ (was) a place with a lot of slate.

I didn't think we'd find anything because fossils ~~is~~ (are) hard

to find. I ~~are~~ (am) happy to tell you that I was wrong. I found

a fossil impression of a tiny snail in a piece of slate.

Assessment Tip: Total **10** Points

Name _____

Writing a Business Letter

When Ned Colbert in *Dinosaur Ghosts* began to study *Coelophysis* skeletons in 1947, he probably wrote business letters to ask paleontologists at other museums and universities around the United States for help. You write a **business letter** to request or persuade someone to do something, to apply for a job, to order a product from ads or catalogs, to ask for information, to complain about a product or service, or to express an opinion to a newspaper, radio, or TV station.

Use this page to plan and organize a business letter in which you write to either a company or a government agency requesting information. Follow these steps: (2 points each)

1. Write a **heading** (your own address and the date) in the upper right corner.
2. Write the **inside address** (the address of the person or business you are writing to) at the left margin.
3. Write a **greeting** (*Dear Sir or Madam:* or *Dear [business name]:*) at the left margin below the inside address.
4. Write the **body** of your letter below the greeting. Be brief and direct, but present all of the necessary details. If you state an opinion, support it with details. Make sure to use a formal and polite tone.
5. Write a formal **closing** such as *Sincerely, Cordially,* or *Yours truly* in the lower right corner.
6. Sign your full name under the closing. Then print or type your name below your **signature**.

When you finish your business letter, copy it onto a clean sheet of paper. Then share it with a classmate.

Name _____

Using the Right Tone

The attitude that a writer has toward a subject is called the **tone**. A writer's choice of words and details conveys his or her tone. When you write a business letter, you want to create a good impression by using the right tone. Here are some tips to follow: Use polite language. Use a more formal tone than you would use in a friendly letter. Use correct grammar, complete sentences, and well-formed paragraphs. Avoid the use of slang. Do not include personal information.

Read the following business letter from a college student to Ned Colbert. Fill in the chart below with examples of language and details that are *not* businesslike.

Dear Ned,

    Wow! I seen the cool photographs of your project in Life magazine. I do not have anything better to do, so I am interested in coming to New Mexico this summer to help with the Coelophysis excavation at Ghost Ranch. Would you tell me how to join your field crew?

    I am fascinated by the Ghost Ranch skeletons. Since I will be studying history and geology next semester, this job would give me some excellent firsthand knowledge. I am a hard worker. Ask anyone at the Ribs Palace on Route 120 where I used to work. Keep in touch.

                Sincerely,
                Dennis Sauer

Slang	Wow!, cool
Impolite Language	I do not have anything better to do
Informal Tone	Dear Ned, Keep in touch
Personal Information	Ask anyone at the Ribs Palace on Route 120 where I used to work.
Incorrect Grammar	I seen the cool photographs.

Assessment Tip: Total **8** Points

Name _____

Filling in the Blank

Use the test-taking strategies and tips you have learned to help you answer this type of multiple-choice question. This practice will help you when you take this kind of test.

Read each item. Fill in the circle in the answer row for the answer that best completes the sentence.

1 It is a fact that the first place Amelia Earhart and Fred Noonan took off from on June 1, 1937, was —

   A Karachi, India.   **C** Miami, Florida.

   B San Juan, Puerto Rico.   **D** Lae, New Guinea.

2 Many people believe that taking the telegraph key and antenna would not have helped Amelia and Fred because —

   F they would be too far away for the communications to be heard.

   G neither one of them knew Morse code.

   H they did not know how to connect the equipment.

   J there was no one on the ground who could understand their signals.

3 Newspaper reporters shared the opinion that Amelia's fans were —

   A anxious to read about her trip.

   B concerned about Amelia taking the survival equipment off the plane.

   C tired of hearing about long-distance flights.

   D afraid that it was too dangerous for Amelia and Fred to fly in bad weather.

4 It is documented that in one month of flying Amelia and Fred had gone —

   F 7,000 miles (11,300 km).   **H** 29,000 miles (46,700 km).

   G 200 miles (320 km).   **J** 22,000 miles (35,400 km).

ANSWER ROWS 1 Ⓐ ⬤Ⓒ Ⓓ **(5 points)**   3 ⬤Ⓑ Ⓒ Ⓓ **(5)**
             2 Ⓕ ⬤Ⓗ Ⓙ **(5)**   4 Ⓕ Ⓖ Ⓗ ⬤ **(5)**

Name _____

Filling in the Blank continued

5 The trip from Lae, New Guinea, to Howland Island was considered the most dangerous because —

A the plane radio would not work in this area.

B the airspace had never been mapped.

C there was no runway to land on Howland Island.

D the journey would take about 18 hours.

6 The reason Amelia and Fred did not see the smoke signals sent up by the crew of the *Itasca* might have been that —

F no one knew that the U.S. Coast Guard had a ship in the area.

G there was a problem with the Electra's radio.

H thick cloud banks blocked the view of Howland Island.

J the Electra was running out of gas.

7 Some people think that Amelia and Fred —

A were spies for the U.S. government.

B never really took the plane trip.

C returned home without any problems.

D decided to get married and live on an island in the Pacific.

8 A fact from the story is that the search for Amelia and Fred —

F was the largest in the history of the world.

G included a battleship, four destroyers, a minesweeper, and a seaplane.

H went on for many months.

J was cancelled due to bad weather around Howland Island.

ANSWER ROWS   5 Ⓐ **Ⓑ** Ⓒ Ⓓ **(5 points)**   7 **Ⓐ** Ⓑ Ⓒ Ⓓ **(5)**

6 Ⓕ Ⓖ **Ⓗ** Ⓙ **(5)**   8 Ⓕ **Ⓖ** Ⓗ Ⓙ **(5)**

130   Theme 2: **What Really Happened?**
Assessment Tip: Total **40** Points

Name _____

Spelling Review

Write Spelling Words from the list to answer the questions.
Order of answers in each category may vary.

1–24. Which twenty-four words contain the /ûr/, /ôr/, /är/, or
/îr/ sounds, or have the final /ər/, /ən/, or /əl/ sounds?

1. channel **(1 point)**
2. familiar **(1)**
3. hanger **(1)**
4. chart **(1)**
5. calendar **(1)**
6. rehearse **(1)**
7. starch **(1)**
8. purse **(1)**
9. hangar **(1)**
10. curb **(1)**
11. mourn **(1)**
12. director **(1)**
13. frighten **(1)**
14. manor **(1)**
15. thorn **(1)**
16. messenger **(1)**
17. pierce **(1)**
18. struggle **(1)**
19. manner **(1)**
20. sword **(1)**
21. similar **(1)**
22. whirl **(1)**
23. gallon **(1)**
24. rural **(1)**

25–30. Which six one-syllable words are homophones?

25. who's **(1)**
26. whose **(1)**
27. vain **(1)**
28. vein **(1)**
29. sent **(1)**
30. scent **(1)**

Spelling Words

1. channel
2. familiar
3. hanger
4. who's
5. chart
6. calendar
7. rehearse
8. starch
9. purse
10. whose
11. hangar
12. curb
13. mourn
14. director
15. frighten
16. manor
17. thorn
18. vain
19. messenger
20. pierce
21. struggle
22. sent
23. vein
24. manner
25. sword
26. similar
27. scent
28. whirl
29. gallon
30. rural

Nikumaroro

Theme 2: **What Really Happened?** 131
Assessment Tip: Total **30** Points

Name _____

Spelling Spree

Syllable Scramble **Rearrange the syllables in each item to write a Spelling Word. There is one extra syllable in each item.**

Example: er for sid con *consider*

1. sen ger mes ize _____messenger **(1 point)**_____

2. en cal men dar _____calendar **(1)**_____

3. ger iar mil fa _____familiar **(1)**_____

4. hearse in re _____rehearse **(1)**_____

5. rec na tor di _____director **(1)**_____

Word Maze **Begin at the arrow and follow the Word Maze to find ten Spelling Words. Write the words in the order you find them.**

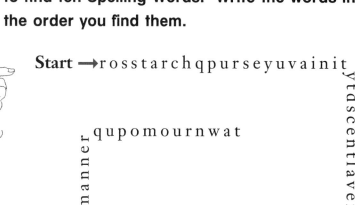

Start → r o s s t a r c h q p u r s e y u v a i n i t

6. _____starch **(1)**_____   11. _____frighten **(1)**_____

7. _____purse **(1)**_____   12. _____curb **(1)**_____

8. _____vain **(1)**_____   13. _____gallon **(1)**_____

9. _____scent **(1)**_____   14. _____manner **(1)**_____

10. _____vein **(1)**_____   15. _____mourn **(1)**_____

Spelling Words

1. familiar
2. calendar
3. mourn
4. frighten
5. gallon
6. rehearse
7. starch
8. purse
9. director
10. vain
11. messenger
12. scent
13. curb
14. vein
15. manner

Assessment Tip: Total **15** Points

Name _____

Proofreading and Writing

Proofreading Circle the six misspelled Spelling Words in this detective's journal. Then write each word correctly.

Spelling Words

> The case of Mrs. VanCash's jewels has put me into a (whurl.) At first I didn't know how to (chaurt) a course. It's been a real (struggel) for me, Sherlock McGillicuddy, to find the truth. The mystery was truly a (thorne) in my side! When the maid swore the jewels were hers, I wondered (whos) they really were. Then I solved the mystery! The maid was telling the truth. Her jewels were (simalar) to the stolen ones, but hers were fakes.

Spelling Words

1. channel
2. hanger
3. who's
4. chart
5. whose
6. hangar
7. thorn
8. pierce
9. struggle
10. sword
11. similar
12. sent
13. whirl
14. manor
15. rural

1. whirl **(1 point)**   4. thorn **(1)**

2. chart **(1)**   5. whose **(1)**

3. struggle **(1)**   6. similar **(1)**

Reporting the Facts Write the Spelling Words that best complete this television news report.

An ancient, long-bladed 7. sword **(1)** has been found in a 8. rural **(1)** area outside town. The weapon was found in an old airplane 9. hangar **(1)**. A worker picked it up, thinking it was a coat 10. hanger **(1)**. Experts believe this may be the blade used centuries ago to 11. pierce **(1)** a stone near the 12. manor **(1)** house of Sir Percy. The blade will be 13. sent **(1)** to a lab for testing. Now the question is, 14. who's **(1)** going to claim this treasure? Stay tuned to this 15. channel **(1)** !

✏ **Write a Plot Outline** On a separate sheet of paper, write a plot outline for a story about an unsolved mystery. Responses will vary. **(5)**

Name _____

Compare and Contrast

Two of the characters in these plays learn more about themselves.
Complete the chart to compare and contrast their searches and what
they find out.

	The Diary of Anne Frank	To Build a Better Mousetrap
What challenges do Anne Frank in *The Diary of Anne Frank* and the Woman in *To Build a Better Mousetrap* face?	Anne must adjust to being in hiding, never going outdoors. **(2 points)**	The Woman is frightened by the Mouse and asks for her husband's help in getting rid of it. **(2)**
How do Anne and the Woman change?	When Anne writes in her new diary, she starts to feel things are going better. **(2)**	The Woman discovers that her husband is useless, and she independently leaves for her sister's house. **(2)**

Assessment Tip: Total **4** Points per selection

Name _____

Critic's Corner

Think of a movie, play, or television show you have read or seen recently. (It can be one of the plays you have read in the *Focus on Plays* section.) Think about the characters, the setting, the plot, and other details. Write a critical review of the play, telling what you liked and didn't like about the production. Be specific. Use examples from the piece to support your points. **(10 points)**

_____
_____
_____
_____
_____
_____
_____
_____
_____
_____
_____
_____
_____
_____
_____
_____
_____
_____

Assessment Tip: Total **10** Points

Name _____

Growing Up

How do the characters in this theme grow? Add to this chart and the one on the next page after you read each story.

Answers will vary. (**10 Points** per selection)

	Where the Red Fern Grows	**Last Summer with Maizon**
Who is the main character or characters?	Billy	Margaret
What problem does the main character have?	Billy needs to save money for a pair of hound pups. This is very difficult because he lives during the Great Depression and money is scarce.	Margaret is having a hard time because her father died and her best friend moved away.
What does the main character learn about himself or herself in the story?	Billy learns that he is resourceful and that he can get what he wants if he tries. He learns that he is different from town kids.	Margaret learns that she can cope with her losses. She learns that writing can help her express her feelings.

Name _____

Growing Up

(**10 Points** per selection)

	The Challenge	**The View from Saturday**
Who is the main character or characters?	José, Estela	Nadia
What problem does the main character have?	José likes Estela, but he can't get her to notice him.	Nadia must cope with a new family member she doesn't like and with her parents' divorce.
What does the main character learn about himself or herself in the story?	José learns that girls can beat boys at sports. He learns not to brag about his abilities, especially about skills he doesn't have.	Nadia learns that she and her father are alike and that they must help each other get through the storm in their private lives.

Sometimes struggle leads to growth. How do the stories in this theme support this statement? **(2)**

All the characters grow as a result of a challenge or struggle.

_____

Assessment Tip: Total **22** Points

Name _____

Going to Market

Use the words in the box to complete the paragraph below.

> **Vocabulary**
>
> provisions
> determination
> depot
> urgency
> wares
> cheap

Several times a year, people who live in the mountains load up their wagons and travel to town to sell homemade pies, jars of jam, and other wares **(2 points)** _____. It takes determination **(2)** _____ to rise before dawn and ride such a long distance. Restaurants in town are not cheap **(2)** _____, so the mountain people usually bring their own food. They carry strips of dried meat and other provisions **(2)** _____ in their packs. The travelers feel a sense of urgency **(2)** _____ as they approach the town because they must hurry to set up their displays before shoppers from the city begin arriving at the train depot **(2)** _____.

Name _____

Generalization Chart

Generalizations	Information from the Story	Information from My Own Life
Page 242 It can take a lot of hard work to reach a goal. **(1 point)**	Page 242 Billy works hard to earn money to buy the hound pups. He traps, fishes, and gathers. **(1)**	Page 242 Example: When I wanted a new bicycle, I had to save my money for almost a year. **(1)**
Pages 243–245 When people work hard to do something difficult, their family members are proud. **(1)**	Pages 243–245 Grandpa cries after he learns how Billy earned and saved the fifty dollars. **(1)**	Pages 243–245 (Answers will vary.) **(1)**
Pages 247–248 People who are focused on a goal sometimes behave strangely. **(1)**	Pages 247–248 Biily walks around as if he is lost He misses getting a haircut. He goes off alone without telling anyone. **(1)**	Pages 247–248 (Answers will vary.) **(1)**
Page 249 Most people raised in a particular area will feel comfortable there even if they are alone. **(1)**	Page 249 Billy is not afraid to be by himself at night because he was raised in the mountains. **(1)**	Page 249 (Answers will vary.) **(1)**
Pages 249–254 Some people make fun of outsiders without bothering to get to know them. **(1)**	Pages 249–254 Several people in Tahlequah tease Billy. **(1)**	Pages 249–254 (Answers will vary.) **(1)**
Pages 255–258 After people wait for something for so long, they sometimes don't know what to do when it finally arrives. **(1)**	Pages 255–258 When Billy gets to the depot he is scared. **(1)**	Pages 255–258 (Answers will vary.) **(1)**

Assessment Tip: Total **16** Points

Name _____

A Conversation with Papa

When Billy returns from Tahlequah, he'll have to tell his parents where he's been and why. Below is a conversation he might have with his father. Use details from the story to help you fill in the words Billy might say.

Papa: Billy, where've you been? Your mother and I have been worried about you.

Billy: I went to Tahlequah. **(1 point)** _____

Papa: Why did you go there?

Billy: *(showing the bag with the hound pups)* to get these hound pups **(1)** _____

Papa: Hound pups! Who'd you buy them from?

Billy: I got them from a kennel in Kentucky. They sent them to the train depot in Tahlequah. **(2)** _____

Papa: Those pups must be worth 30 dollars apiece! How'd you pay for them?

Billy: They only cost 20 dollars each. I used money I've been saving for the past two years. **(2)** _____

Papa: Where'd you get that much money?

Billy: I earned it by selling bait and vegetables to the fishermen, collecting berries selling them to Grandpa for his store, and trapping animals for their furs. **(3)** _____

Papa: Now wait a minute. How'd you order the puppies?

Billy: Grandpa did it for me. **(1)** _____

Papa: Why did you walk to Tahlequah by yourself? Did Grandpa tell you to?

Billy: No, that was my idea. I couldn't wait for a ride into town. **(2)** _____

Name _____

Broadly Speaking . . .

Read the passage. Then complete the activity on page 143.

Dot and the Turkeys

All families were poor during the Great Depression. Dot's family was no exception. Even after selling milk and butter from the dairy farm, Ma and Pa struggled to keep food on the table for themselves and their seven children. The family's meals usually consisted of cornbread and buttermilk. Only on holidays did the children get treats such as nuts or a piece of fresh fruit. For children during the Depression, oranges were a particularly special treat. In general, families had little money for clothes, and often made their clothes by hand. Dot had no shoes and only owned one dress to wear to school, a homemade dress her older sister outgrew.

For a while Pa tried to make ends meet by raising turkeys. Ma had warned six-year-old Dot to stay away from the turkey pen. "Most turkeys are just plain mean," she said. Dot, however, was fascinated with the big birds and their drooping red wattles. She listened for hours to their clucking and gobbling and watched them strut about proudly. One day she slipped inside the pen to pet the huge, soft-looking birds. The turkeys, however, were not amused by the small girl inside their pen. The flock rushed at her and nearly smothered her. Dot's terrified screaming brought Ma and her brothers to her rescue. She never went near the turkeys again.

Name _____

Broadly Speaking . . . continued

Answer these questions about the passage on page 142.

1. The underlined sentence in the first paragraph states a generalization. Do you think it is valid or invalid? Why?

   Invalid. Some families were not poor during the Depression.

   (2 points)

2. How could you rewrite this sentence so that it states a valid generalization?

   Many families were poor during the Great Depression. **(2)**

3. What two generalizations about food are made in the first paragraph?

   A. The family's meal usually consisted of cornbread and buttermilk. **(1)**

   B. For children during the Depression, oranges were a particularly special treat. **(1)**

4. What two generalizations about clothes are made in the second paragraph?

   A. In general, families had little money for clothes. **(1)**

   B. Families often made their clothes by hand. **(1)**

5. How do the details about Dot's clothes support these generalizations?

   Dot has no shoes and only owns the dress her sister outgrew. **(2)**

6. What other generalization could you make about life during the Depression?

   Answers will vary. **(2)**

   _____

   _____

Name _____

Word Patterns in Writing

Add slashes between the syllables of each underlined word.
Then write another sentence using the word correctly. Answers will vary. Samples are shown.

1. My hands were <u>calloused</u> after raking leaves all day.

   cal/loused **(1 point)** His mother's hands were calloused

   from years of hard farm work. **(2)**

   _____

2. The girl was <u>dumbfounded</u> by the sight of the vast prairie.

   dumb/found/ed **(1)** I wanted to speak to the president,

   but I was dumbfounded by his presence. **(2)**

   _____

3. My sister and I like to tease our <u>grandfather</u> about his beard.

   grand/fa/ther **(1)** My grandfather traveled to

   Europe as a young man. **(2)**

   _____

4. At the first light of dusk, the <u>mosquitoes</u> begin biting.

   mos/qui/toes **(1)** Mosquitoes make fishing on the pond

   almost impossible. **(2)**

   _____

5. The boys saw a <u>shadowy</u> figure move in the window of the house.

   shad/ow/y **(1)** My room becomes shadowy in late afternoon. **(2)**

   _____

Assessment Tip: Total **15** Points

VCV, VCCV, and VCCCV Patterns

To spell a two-syllable word, divide the word into syllables. Look for spelling patterns, and spell the word by syllables.

Divide a VCV word after the consonant if the first syllable has the short vowel pattern. Divide the word before the consonant if the first syllable ends with a vowel sound.

VC/V **bal / ance**   V/CV **mi / nus**

VCCV words are usually divided between the consonants. They can be divided before or after two consonants that together spell one sound.

VC/CV **law / yer**   V/CCV **au / thor**   VCC/V **meth / od**

VCCCV words are often divided after the first of the three successive consonants.

When *y* spells a vowel sound, it is considered a vowel.

VC/CCV **sup / ply**

Spelling Words

1. balance
2. lawyer
3. sheriff
4. author
5. minus
6. method
7. item
8. require
9. supply
10. whisper
11. spirit
12. tennis
13. adopt
14. instant
15. poison
16. deserve
17. rescue
18. journey
19. relief
20. laundry

Write each Spelling Word under its syllable pattern.

Order of answers for each category may vary

VCV

balance **(1 point)**

sheriff **(1)**

minus **(1)**

item **(1)**

require **(1)**

spirit **(1)**

adopt **(1)**

poison **(1)**

deserve **(1)**

relief **(1)**

VCCV

lawyer **(1)**

author **(1)**

method **(1)**

whisper **(1)**

tennis **(1)**

rescue **(1)**

journey **(1)**

VCCCV

supply **(1)**

instant **(1)**

laundry **(1)**

Theme 3: **Growing Up**   145

Assessment Tip: Total **20** Points

Spelling Spree

The Third Word Write the Spelling Word that belongs with each group of words.

1. police chief, marshal, <u>sheriff</u> **(1 point)**

2. save, recover, <u>rescue</u> **(1)**

3. demand, insist, <u>require</u> **(1)**

4. editor, publisher, <u>author</u> **(1)**

5. venom, toxin, <u>poison</u> **(1)**

6. earn, merit, <u>deserve</u> **(1)**

7. liveliness, energy, <u>spirit</u> **(1)**

8. ping pong, badminton, <u>tennis</u> **(1)**

9. way, technique, <u>method</u> **(1)**

10. object, article, <u>item</u> **(1)**

Syllable Scramble Rearrange the syllables in each item to write a Spelling Word. An extra syllable is in each item.

11. jour di ney <u>journey</u> **(1)**

12. nus mi less <u>minus</u> **(1)**

13. yer pre law <u>lawyer</u> **(1)**

14. dol ance bal <u>balance</u> **(1)**

15. lief re ant <u>relief</u> **(1)**

16. a com dopt <u>adopt</u> **(1)**

17. ex ply sup <u>supply</u> **(1)**

18. dry im laun <u>laundry</u> **(1)**

19. per whis un <u>whisper</u> **(1)**

20. in port stant <u>instant</u> **(1)**

Spelling Words

1. balance
2. lawyer
3. sheriff
4. author
5. minus
6. method
7. item
8. require
9. supply
10. whisper
11. spirit
12. tennis
13. adopt
14. instant
15. poison
16. deserve
17. rescue
18. journey
19. relief
20. laundry

Assessment Tip: Total **20** Points

Proofreading and Writing

Proofreading Circle the five misspelled Spelling Words in this advertisement. Then write each word correctly.

NEEDED: People needed to (addopt) one or more puppies. They are playful and full of (spirrit,) and they require lots of love and attention. They have been living in our (londry) room, but they still need to be housebroken. We will (suply) the first two weeks of food. These are great dogs, and they (desserve) a good home. Call 555-3647.

Spelling Words

1. balance
2. lawyer
3. sheriff
4. author
5. minus
6. method
7. item
8. require
9. supply
10. whisper
11. spirit
12. tennis
13. adopt
14. instant
15. poison
16. deserve
17. rescue
18. journey
19. relief
20. laundry

1. adopt **(1 point)**
2. spirit **(1)**
3. laundry **(1)**
4. supply **(1)**
5. deserve **(1)**

Write Guidelines for Pet Care Dogs, cats, and other pets need a great deal of care. What kinds of guidelines would a new pet owner need?

Choose a type of pet. Then, on a separate sheet of paper, write a list of guidelines for caring for that pet. Use Spelling Words from the list. Responses will vary. **(5 points)**

Name _____

Synonym Sampler

Read each entry word, its definition, and its synonyms on the thesaurus page below. Then rewrite the numbered sentences using synonyms to replace the words in bold print. Sample answers shown.

> **happiness** *n.* The state or quality of feeling joy or pleasure.
>
> > **joy** A feeling of great happiness or delight.
> > **gladness** The state or quality of feeling joy or pleasure.
> > **bliss** Extreme happiness; joy.
>
> **courage** *n.* The quality of spirit that enables one to face danger or hardship; bravery.
>
> > **spirit** A mood marked by vigor, courage, or liveliness.
> > **mettle** Spirit; daring; courage.
> > **bravery** The quality or condition of showing courage.

1. Billy's **courage** helped him to reach his goal.

   Billy's spirit helped him to reach his goal. **(2 points)**

2. As he touched the pups, **happiness** welled up in Billy's heart.

   As he touched the pups, bliss welled up in Billy's heart. **(2)**

3. Billy's **happiness** was hardly contained when he knew that the pups were about to come.

   Billy's gladness was hardly contained when he knew that the pups were

   about to come. **(2)**

4. Billy needed extra **courage** to carry out his plan.

   Billy needed extra mettle to carry out his plan. **(2)**

5. Billy's **courage** as he hiked through the hills was matched by his **happiness** when he arrived.

   Billy's bravery as he hiked through the hills was matched by his joy

   when he arrived. **(2)**

Assessment Tip: Total **10** Points

Name _____

Summer Days

Verb Tenses The **tense** of a verb tells when the action takes place. The **present tense** is used when something is happening now, or happens regularly over time. The **past tense** is used when something has already happened. Here is how the verb *walk*, a regular verb, looks in these two tenses:

Present Tense	**Past Tense**
I **walk**.	I **walked**.
You **walk**.	You **walked**.
She/He/It **walks**.	She/He/ It **walked**.
We **walk.**	We **walked**.
You **walk**.	You **walked**.
They **walk**.	They **walked**.

Circle the verb in each of the following sentences. Decide whether the verb is in the past tense or the present tense, and write *past* or *present* on the line.

1. He (lived) in the Ozark Mountains. past **(1)** _____

2. Celia (fishes) in the river. present **(1)** _____

3. I (strolled) through the grass in my bare feet. past **(1)** _____

4. They (played) with Kelly's new puppy. past **(1)** _____

5. You (like) the outdoors. present **(1)** _____

Now rewrite the five sentences above. If the original verb was in the past tense, change it to the present tense. If the original verb was in the present tense, change it to the past tense.

1. He lives in the Ozark Mountains. **(1)** _____

2. Celia fished in the river. **(1)** _____

3. I stroll through the grass in my bare feet. **(1)** _____

4. They play with Kelly's new puppy. **(1)** _____

5. You liked the outdoors. **(1)** _____

Name _____

Money!

More About Verb Tenses The **present tense** of a verb is used when something is happening now or happens regularly. The **past tense** of a verb is used when something has already happened. The **future tense** of a verb is used when something is going to happen. To form the future tense, use the helping verb *will* or *shall* with the main verb.

Circle the verb in each sentence. Then write its tense on the line.

1. We (saved) our allowance for a month. past **(1)**
2. The package (will arrive) on time. future **(1)**
3. William (ordered) new track shoes. past **(1)**
4. We (will earn) money for our vacation. future **(1)**
5. Pat (saves) for the future. present **(1)**

Now rewrite each sentence using the verb tense shown.

1. **Future** We will save our allowance for a month. **(1)**
2. **Present** The package arrives on time. **(1)**
3. **Present** William orders new track shoes. **(1)**
4. **Past** We earned money for our vacation. **(1)**
5. **Future** Pat will save for the future. **(1)**

Assessment Tip: Total **10** Points

Name _____

When Did That Happen?

Choosing the Correct Verb Tense Switch tenses when you write only to tell about different times.

Dorinda wrote the following paragraph. Rewrite her paragraph using correct verb tenses. The first sentence will not change.

> Every summer I visit my aunt and uncle. They lived in a mountain valley. I will like to walk there in my bare feet and waded in the creek behind their house. Last summer, I help my aunt and uncle with their vegetable garden. It is hard work, but we all will enjoy the vegetables. Vegetables fresh from a garden will taste so much better than vegetables from a store! Now I wanted to grow vegetables at home. When spring arrives, my parents helped me plant tomatoes and green beans. Then we enjoy eating vegetables from our garden.

Every summer I visit my aunt and uncle. They **live** in a mountain valley. I **like** to walk there in my bare feet and **wade** in the creek behind their house. Last summer, I **helped** my aunt and uncle with their vegetable garden. It **was** hard work, but we all **enjoyed** the vegetables. Vegetables fresh from a garden **taste** so much better than vegetables from a store! Now I **want** to grow vegetables at home. When spring arrives, my parents **will help** me plant tomatoes and green beans. Then we **will enjoy** eating vegetables from our garden. **(10 points)**

Name _____

Writing a Problem-Solution Composition

Writing about a character's problems in a **problem-solution composition** can help you better understand characters and events in a story. In *Where the Red Fern Grows*, for example, Billy Colman faces a problem. How Billy solves his problem reveals the kind of person he is.

Brainstorm problems that Billy solves in this story as well as problems that characters solve in other stories you have read. Write three of these problems and solutions on the graphic organizer below. Answers will vary. (**2 points** for each answer.)

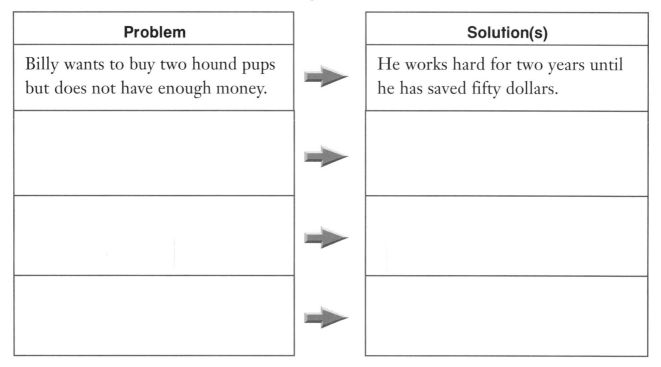

Problem		Solution(s)
Billy wants to buy two hound pups but does not have enough money.	→	He works hard for two years until he has saved fifty dollars.
	→	
	→	
	→	

Now pick one problem and its solution. On a separate sheet of paper, write your problem-solution composition. Begin with an introductory sentence that tells who or what you are writing about. Then state the problem in the first paragraph. In the second paragraph, describe how Billy or another character solves the problem. Include details that lead to the solution. Finally, end with a strong concluding sentence. (3 points)

Assessment Tip: Total **15** Points

Name _____

Organization

Good writers organize their ideas by sequence of events, by causes and effects, or by main ideas and details.

Help to unscramble this composition. Write students' ideas in a logical order in the organization outline below.

> In the winter, he traps opossums and sells their hides to fur buyers. Through hard work and determination, Billy finally realizes his dream. Billy desperately wants to buy two hound pups. Billy Colman is growing up during the Great Depression. Also, he catches crawfish and minnows and sells them to fishermen. To earn what he needs, Billy decides to work hard and save the money. However, each dog costs twenty-five dollars. During the summer, he picks berries and sells them. After two years, Billy has saved fifty dollars. Neither Billy nor his parents have fifty dollars to spend.

Paragraph 1: Introductory sentence

Billy Colman, is growing up during the Great Depression.

Problem

Billy desperately wants to buy two hound pups. However, each dog

costs twenty-five dollars. Neither Billy nor his parents have fifty dollars to spend.

Paragraph 2: Solution

To earn what he needs, Billy decides to work hard and save the money. During

the summer, he picks berries and sells them. Also, he catches crawfish and

minnows and sells them to fishermen. In the winter, he traps opossums and sells

their hides to fur buyers. After two years, Billy has saved fifty dollars.

Concluding sentence

Through hard work, and determination, Billy finally realizes his dream.

Assessment Tip: Total **20** Points

Name _____

Evaluating Your Description

Reread your description. What do you need to make it better? Use this page to help you decide. Put a checkmark in the box for each sentence that describes what you've written.

Loud and Clear!

- [ ] My description is well organized and clearly written.
- [ ] My beginning pulls the reader into the story.
- [ ] I combine sentences to make my writing more compact.
- [ ] The events are in a sequence that is easy to follow.
- [ ] The description has a satisfying ending.
- [ ] There are a few mistakes.

Sounding Stronger

- [ ] My description could be better organized.
- [ ] The beginning could be more interesting.
- [ ] I could combine more sentences to vary my writing.
- [ ] The sequence of events is confusing in parts.
- [ ] My ending could be more exciting.
- [ ] Errors make parts of the story hard to follow.

Turn Up Volume

- [ ] My description is disconnected and unorganized.
- [ ] The beginning is boring.
- [ ] I need to combine sentences to vary my writing.
- [ ] The description doesn't have an interesting ending.
- [ ] Too many mistakes make the story hard to read.

Name _____

Sentence Combining

Combine each pair of sentences to make them flow more easily. Use the joining word in parentheses. Add commas where needed. Answers may vary. Possible responses are given.

1. Tom was born in Minnesota. (AND) Tom grew up there.

   Tom was born in Minnesota and grew up there. **(1)**

2. Toby was also born in Minnesota. (BUT) He grew up in Chicago.

   Toby was also born in Minnesota, but he grew up in Chicago. **(1)**

3. Tom and Toby were twins. (AND) They had been separated at birth.

   Tom and Toby were twins, and they had been separated at birth. **(1)**

4. The twins had different last names. (BUT) They shared many traits.

   The twins had different last names, but they shared many traits. **(1)**

5. Tom owned a beagle named Willie. (OR) Toby owned a beagle named Willie.

   Tom or Toby owned a beagle named Willie. **(1)**

6. The other owned a cat named Billy. (OR) The other owned a cat name Millie.

   The other owned a cat named Billy or Millie. **(1)**

7. Both twins loved baseball. (AND) Both twins hated fishing.

   Both twins loved baseball and hated fishing. **(1)**

8. Both twins owned the same kind of truck.(BUT) Tom's was blue and Toby's was red.

   Both twins owned the same kind of truck, but Tom's was blue and Toby's

   was red. **(1)**

9. They both liked the same movie. (OR) They both hated the same movie.

   They both liked the same movie, or they both hated the same movie. **(1)**

10. Once the twins were together, they were happy. (AND)
    Once the twins were together, they would never part.

    Once the twins were together, they were happy and would never part. **(1)**

Name _____

Words Often Confused

Do cows graze in a pastor or a pasture? Is a glass ring a bauble or a bubble? It is easy to confuse words that have similar spellings and pronunciations even though the meanings are different. The Spelling Words in each pair on the list are often confused. Pay careful attention to their pronunciations, spellings, and meanings.

Spelling Words

1. bland
2. blend
3. below
4. bellow
5. pastor
6. pasture
7. moral
8. mortal
9. bauble
10. bubble
11. bisect
12. dissect
13. assent
14. ascent

Write the missing letters in the Spelling Words below.
Order of answers for 1–2, 9–10, and 13–14 may vary.

1. bl a___ nd (**1 point**)

2. bl e___ nd (**1**)

3. be l___ o___ w___ (**1**)

4. be l___ l___ ow (**1**)

5. past o___ r___ (**1**)

6. pas t___ u___ r___ e___ (**1**)

7. mor a___ l___ (**1**)

8. mor t___ a___ l___ (**1**)

9. b a___ u___ b___ le (**1**)

10. b u___ b___ b___ le (**1**)

11. b i___ s___ ect (**1**)

12. d i___ s___ s___ ect (**1**)

13. a s___ s___ ent (**1**)

14. a s___ c___ ent (**1**)

Study List On a separate piece of paper, write each Spelling Word pair. Check your spelling against the words on the list. Order of word pairs may vary. (**2**)

Assessment Tip: Total **16** Points

Name _____

Spelling Spree

Contrast Clues The second part of each clue contrasts with the first part. Write a Spelling Word to fit each clue.

1. not a descent, but an _____
2. not spicy, but _____
3. not real jewelry, but a _____
4. not a whisper, but a _____
5. not living forever, but _____
6. not a forest, but a _____
7. not to cut into unequal pieces, but to _____

1. ascent **(1)**
2. bland **(1)**
3. bauble **(1)**
4. bellow **(1)**
5. mortal **(1)**
6. pasture **(1)**
7. bisect **(1)**

Word Switch For each item below, replace the underlined definition or synonym with a Spelling Word.

8. Next week in my sister's biology class, they're going to <u>cut apart in order to study</u> frogs.
9. We were halfway up the mountain when we heard a cry for help from a <u>lower position</u>.
10. If you <u>combine completely</u> these red and yellow paints, you should get the right shade of orange.
11. Did your mom give her <u>approval</u> to our plan to go hiking?
12. The <u>minister</u> greeted the new couple the first time they walked into the church.
13. Each of Aesop's fables has a <u>lesson</u>.
14. There was a soap <u>ball of air surrounded by a thin film of liquid</u> on the surface of the dishwater.

8. dissect **(1)**
9. below **(1)**
10. blend **(1)**
11. assent **(1)**
12. pastor **(1)**
13. moral **(1)**
14. bubble **(1)**

Assessment Tip: Total **14** Points

Name _____

Proofreading and Writing

Proofreading Circle the five misspelled Spelling Words in this movie description. Then write each word correctly.

Spelling Words

1. bland
2. blend
3. below
4. bellow
5. pastor
6. pasture
7. moral
8. mortal
9. bauble
10. bubble
11. bisect
12. dissect
13. assent
14. ascent

Growing Up ★★★✦ is a welcome change from the typical, (blend) children's movie. The director manages to (bland) four stories into one film. Together, they give a picture of the often difficult (assent) from childhood to the teenage years. Each story has its own (morral,) but teaches it quietly instead of trying to bellow it from the rooftops. Movie times are listed (balow.)

1. bland **(1 point)**

2. blend **(1)**

3. ascent **(1)**

4. moral **(1)**

5. below **(1)**

✏️ **Two for One Pick four word pairs from the Spelling Word list. Then, for each pair, write a sentence using both words.** Responses will vary. **(5)**

Name _____

City Similars

Read the words in each box from *Last Summer with Maizon*. Then write two words from the list that are related in meaning. Use a dictionary if necessary.

Vocabulary

earlier
lifeless
porch
imagining
empty
past
say
platform
thinking
communicate

---

express
say **(1 point)**
communicate **(1)**

---

desolate
empty **(1)**
lifeless **(1)**

---

daydreaming
imagining **(1)**
thinking **(1)**

---

previous
earlier **(1)**
past **(1)**

---

stoop
porch **(1)**
platform **(1)**

Theme 3: **Growing Up**   159
Assessment Tip: Total **10** Points

Name _____

Inferences Chart

	Evidence from the Story	Own Experiences	Inference
How does Margaret feel about Maizon moving away? (page 279)	Maizon hasn't left yet, but Margaret has already written two letters to her. Margaret bites her cuticles. **(1 point)**	Example: I know people who chew their fingernails when they are worried about something. **(1)**	Margaret is very worried about losing her best friend. **(1)**
How does Margaret feel about her friendship with Maizon once Maizon has left? (pages 280–281)	Margaret says that they are "old friends" now. She says that Maizon kept her from doing some things. She thinks that sitting on the stoop was more fun when Maizon was still around. **(1)**	Answers will vary. **(1)**	Margaret is unsure how she feels about her friendship with Maizon. Some parts of the change seem bad, others seem good. **(1)**
How does Margaret feel about being in Ms. Peazle's class? (page 283)	She knows her essay isn't as good as she could make it. She wants very badly to stay in the class. She decides not to complain about the homework. **(1)**	Answers will vary. **(1)**	Margaret is worried that she won't make it in Ms. Peazle's class and wants to show that she belongs. **(1)**
How do you think Margaret's classmates feel about her poem? (page 286)	They stare at her blankly and remain silent when she is done reading. **(1)**	Answers will vary. **(1)**	Margaret's classmates are so moved by her poem that they don't know how to respond. **(1)**

Assessment Tip: Total **12** Points

Name _____

Story Frames

Think about what happened in *Last Summer with Maizon*. Write what happened in each part of the story by completing the story frames.

1. **On the M train:** 	**Best Friends or Old Friends?** Margaret and Maizon say good-bye. Margaret wonders whether she and Maizon are still best friends, or whether they are old friends now. **(2 points)**
2. **First Day in 6–1:** 	**The Essay** Margaret can't concentrate on the essay assignment. Ms. Peazle asks her to write it over because she thinks Margaret can do a better job. **(2)**
3. **Next Day in 6–1:** 	**The Poem** Margaret reads her poem to the class. No one says anything. Later, she gets a note from Mrs. Peazle, saying she liked it. **(2)**
4. **On the Front Stoop:** 	**What's Changed? What Hasn't?** Margaret still misses Maizon and her dad, but with the support of her neighbors and Mrs. Peazle she is starting to feel better about her loss and her ability to succeed in 6–1. **(2)**

Name _____

Reading Between the Lines

Read the passage. Then complete the activity on page 163.

The Audition

Serena ran into the girls' dressing room and locked the door behind her. "It's not fair! It's just not fair!" she cried, breaking into uncontrollable sobs. Just one week before, she had been on top of the world. She had been picked for the leading role in the spring musical. Mr. O'Toole, the choir director, had had the choir choose the parts by show of hands, after hearing the auditions for each part. "I won the part fair and square!" Serena wailed. "How dare Rebecca show up this week and ask to audition for my part! How could Mr. O'Toole have let her to do it? He's never done anything like that before! Rebecca should have been here last week if she wanted the part!"

The audition had been short, with only Serena and Rebecca performing. At first Serena hadn't been concerned. She'd won the part once, and she had figured that everyone would love her singing again. Mr. O'Toole had had everyone close their eyes again and raise their hands to vote. "The winner is Rebecca," Mr. O'Toole had announced. At that moment, the color had drained out of Serena's face as the choir applauded for Rebecca. Ashen-faced, she had bolted for the dressing room.

Name _____

Reading Between the Lines

continued

Answer the following questions about the passage on page 162.

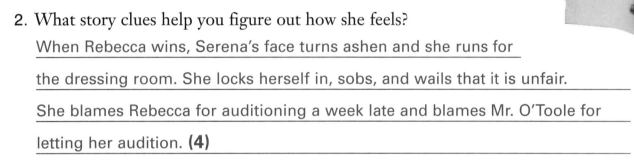

1. How does Serena feel when the choir votes for Rebecca?

   She feels surprised, upset, and cheated. She had expected

   everyone to vote for her again. She feels that she won the part

   fairly, and that it has been unfairly taken from her. **(4 points)**

2. What story clues help you figure out how she feels?

   When Rebecca wins, Serena's face turns ashen and she runs for

   the dressing room. She locks herself in, sobs, and wails that it is unfair.

   She blames Rebecca for auditioning a week late and blames Mr. O'Toole for

   letting her audition. **(4)**

3. Why do you think Mr. O'Toole allows Rebecca to audition for the role even though the choir already picked Serena? (To answer, think about what is probably important to Mr. O'Toole as the choir director.)

   He probably wants the best singer to star in the musical. **(4)**

   _____

   _____

4. How do you think Serena feels toward Rebecca at this moment in the story?

   She is angry at Rebecca for daring to audition late and for winning her part.

   She might also be jealous of her for winning more votes. **(4)**

5. What do you know from real life that can help you figure out how Serena feels toward Rebecca?

   Answers may vary. **(4)**

   _____

   _____

Name _____

Words, Inc.

For each word in column 1, write the base word in column 2 and the
ending in column 3. Check a dictionary if you are unsure about the
spelling of a base word.

	Base word	Ending
1. whispered	whisper **(1 point)**	-ed **(1)**
2. stumbled	stumble **(1)**	-ed **(1)**
3. exaggerated	exaggerate **(1)**	-ed **(1)**
4. sweating	sweat **(1)**	-ing **(1)**
5. smiling	smile **(1)**	-ing **(1)**

Write the word from the chart that best completes each sentence.

6. When Margaret was unexpectedly asked to read her poem,
   she began sweating **(1)** _____.

7. Her classmates whispered **(1)** _____ among themselves.

8. They exaggerated **(1)** _____ their reactions as she got
   ready to read.

9. Margaret stumbled **(1)** _____ over her feet on her
   way back to her desk.

10. When Margaret looked up, her teacher was smiling **(1)** _____.

Assessment Tip: Total **15** Points

Name _____

Words with *-ed* or *-ing*

Remember that when a one-syllable word ends with one vowel and one consonant, the final consonant is usually doubled before *-ed* or *-ing* is added. When a two-syllable word ends with a stressed syllable, double the final consonant before adding *-ed* or *-ing*.

map**ped**   fit**ting**   pilot**ing**   begin**ning**

Write each Spelling Word under the heading that tells how the word is changed when *-ed* or *-ing* is added.

Order of answers for each category may vary.

8270 8270

Final Consonant Doubled

mapped **(1 point)**   preferred **(1 point)**

permitting **(1)**   slipped **(1)**

beginning **(1)**   fitting **(1)**

forgetting **(1)**   knitting **(1)**

No Change

piloting **(1)**   listening **(1)**

bothered **(1)**   pardoned **(1)**

limited **(1)**   shoveled **(1)**

reasoning **(1)**   favored **(1)**

equaled **(1)**   answered **(1)**

wondering **(1)**   modeling **(1)**

Spelling Words

1. mapped
2. piloting
3. permitting
4. beginning
5. bothered
6. limited
7. forgetting
8. reasoning
9. preferred
10. equaled
11. wondering
12. slipped
13. listening
14. fitting
15. pardoned
16. shoveled
17. favored
18. knitting
19. answered
20. modeling

Assessment Tip: Total **20** Points

Name _____

Spelling Spree

Puzzle Play Write a Spelling Word to fit each clue.

(1 point each)

1. posing for a photographer (m) o d e l i n g
2. forgiven p (a) r d o n e d
3. allowing p e (r) m i t t i n g
4. flying a plane p i l o t i n (g)
5. replied (a) n s w e r e d
6. liked better p (r) e f e r r e d
7. was the same as e q u a l (e) d
8. making a sweater k n i (t) t i n g

Now write the circled letters in order. They will spell the name of a character from *Last Summer with Maizon*.

M a r g a r e t

Meaning Match Each item below contains a meaning for a base word followed by an ending. Add the base word to the underlined ending to write a Spelling Word.

Example: collect + ing = gathering

9. be suitable for + ing = fitting **(1)**
10. be for or partial to + ed = favored **(1)**
11. the ability to think + ing = reasoning **(1)**
12. disturb or annoy + ed = bothered **(1)**
13. fail to remember + ing = forgetting **(1)**
14. start + ing = beginning **(1)**
15. plan in detail + ed = mapped **(1)**

Spelling Words

1. mapped
2. piloting
3. permitting
4. beginning
5. bothered
6. limited
7. forgetting
8. reasoning
9. preferred
10. equaled
11. wondering
12. slipped
13. listening
14. fitting
15. pardoned
16. shoveled
17. favored
18. knitting
19. answered
20. modeling

Assessment Tip: Total **15** Points

Name _____

Proofreading and Writing

Proofreading Circle the five misspelled Spelling Words in this letter. Then write each word correctly.

C

Dear Leslie,

How's it going? I've been (lisening) to the tape you sent with your last letter. It's great! I really like the song you sang at the beginning. I'm sorry it's taken me so long to write. My mom (sliped) on our sidewalk last week. She was (shovelling) snow. Since then, I've been doing a lot of things around the house. I guess my time is pretty (limeted) right now. Actually, I should get going. Mom must be (wondring) why the laundry hasn't been done. I'll write again soon!

Your friend,
Carmen

Spelling Words

1. mapped
2. piloting
3. permitting
4. beginning
5. bothered
6. limited
7. forgetting
8. reasoning
9. preferred
10. equaled
11. wondering
12. slipped
13. listening
14. fitting
15. pardoned
16. shoveled
17. favored
18. knitting
19. answered
20. modeling

1. listening **(1 point)**

2. slipped **(1)**

3. shoveling **(1)**

4. limited **(1)**

5. wondering **(1)**

✏️ **Write a Poem** Margaret wrote a poem to express her feelings about her father's death. Has there been an event in your life that caused you to feel great joy or sadness?

On a separate sheet of paper, write a poem about that event and the feelings you experienced then. Use Spelling Words from the list. Responses will vary. **(5)**

Assessment Tip: Total **10** Points

Finding Word Forms

Read each entry word, its inflected forms, and its definition. Write the form of the word that best completes each sentence.

choose (chōoz) *v.* **chose, chosen, choosing, chooses.** To decide.

close (klōs) *adj.* **closer, closest.** Near in space or time.

exchange (ĭks chānj′) *v.* **exchanged, exchanging, exchanges.** To give and receive mutually; interchange.

smart (smärt) *adj.* **smarter, smartest.** Intelligent, clever, or bright.

worry (wûr′ ē) *v.* **worried, worrying, worries.** To feel uneasy or concerned about something.

1. Maizon was the _smartest_ **(2 points)** student at P.S. 102.

2. Margaret couldn't stop _worrying_ **(2)** about whether Maizon would write to her.

3. Ms. Dell and Hattie _exhanged_ **(2)** cautious looks as they talked about Maizon.

4. Hattie felt that poetry _chooses_ **(2)** where it wants to live.

5. Margaret moved _closer_ **(2)** to the women as they talked on the stoop.

Assessment Tip: Total **10** Points

Name _____

Verb Trouble

Principal Parts of Regular and Irregular Verbs The **principal parts**, or basic forms, of a verb are the present form of the verb, the present participle, the past, and the past participle. All verb tenses are formed with these basic parts.

When the past and the past participle of a verb are formed by adding -d or -ed, the verb is **regular**. When the past and the past participle of a verb are formed in some other way, the verb is **irregular**.

	Present	Present Participle	Past	Past Participle
Regular	walk	(is) walking	walked	(has) walked
Irregular	ride	(is) riding	rode	(has) ridden

Margaret is having trouble with some verbs in a poem. The troublesome verbs are listed below. Complete the verb chart by writing the missing principal parts. Use a dictionary if needed. The first one is done for you.

Present	Present Participle	Past	Past Participle
sing	**(is) singing**	**sang**	**(has) sung**
write	(is) writing **(1)**	wrote **(1)**	(has) written **(1)**
search	(is) searching **(1)**	searched **(1)**	(has) searched **(1)**
feel	(is) feeling **(1)**	felt **(1)**	(has) felt **(1)**
become	(is) becoming **(1)**	became **(1)**	(has) become **(1)**
shout	(is) shouting **(1)**	shouted **(1)**	(has) shouted **(1)**

Name _____

Score with Perfect Tenses

▶ There are three **perfect tenses**: **present perfect**, **past perfect**, and **future perfect**. Form the present perfect tense with *have* or *has* and a past participle.

▶ Form the past perfect tense with *had* and a past participle.

▶ Form the future perfect tense with *will have* and a past participle.

Complete the chart below with the verb in the proper tense. The first one has been done for you.

Verb	Present Perfect	Past Perfect	Future Perfect
work	have worked	had worked	will have worked
move	have moved	had moved	will have moved
play	have played	had played	will have played
write	have written	had written	will have written
feel	have felt	had felt	will have felt
take	have taken	had taken	will have taken

Write the correct form of the verb in parentheses ( ) in each sentence below. Use the verb forms from the chart. (2 points each)

1. Maria _____had moved_____ away before school started. (move)
   past perfect

2. At the beginning of the year, my teacher _____had worked_____ with me after school. (work)
   past perfect

3. We _____have played_____ together all day. (play)
   present perfect

4. I _____have felt_____ this way before. (feel)
   present perfect

5. In two weeks, she _____will have written_____ her report. (write)
   future perfect

Assessment Tip: Total **10** Points

Name _____

Letter Perfect Tenses

Choosing the Correct Verb Form To correctly form a perfect tense, use the **past participle** form of the verb with *have*, *has*, and *had*.

Proofread the following letter that Margaret is writing to a friend who moved away. Insert the proper verb forms where needed.

taken

Example: I had took the long route.

Hi!

heard **(1 point)**

It has been a long time since I have heared from you. Since you left,

asked **(1)**

John K. has ask me about you six times! Sarita says, "Hi." Even Ms.

said **(1)**   written **(1)**

Whitney has says she wonders how you are. J.D. has wrote you a letter, but

he has not mailed it yet.

gone **(1)**

In the past month, I have went to the movies twice. Yesterday, I saw a

seen **(1)**

TV movie called My Friend Flicka. I had seed it before but I still liked it.

taken **(1)**

Tomorrow I will have taked my fifth math quiz. We have one each week.

I plan to rake leaves and shovel snow to make money this year. By

saved **(1)**

summertime, I will have save enough to visit you. Remember last summer

went **(1)**   run **(1)**

when we goed to the beach? I had ran errands for months to earn that

money.

Your friend,

Margaret

Responding to a Prompt

In *Last Summer with Maizon*, Ms. Peazle gives her sixth-grade class a writing prompt. She asks them to write an essay about their summer vacations. A **writing prompt** is a direction that asks for a written response of one or more paragraphs.

Read the following prompts and choose one you would like to respond to.

Prompt 1
Describe a time when you had to adjust to a change.

Prompt 2
Write about a person who is important to you. Describe the person and tell why he or she is important.

Prompt 3
Describe what you look for in a friend.

Use the chart below to help you plan your response. First, list key words in the prompt such as *compare, explain, describe,* **or** *discuss.* **Next, jot down main ideas and details you might include. Finally, number your main ideas, beginning from most to least important. (15 points)**

Key Words	Main Ideas	Details

Write your response on a separate sheet of paper. Start by restating the prompt. Then write your main ideas and supporting details in order of importance from most to least important. Finally, check your response to make sure it answers the prompt. Responses will vary. **(5)**

Correcting Sentence Fragments and Run-on Sentences

Good writers check to make sure that their sentences are complete.
Rewrite the body of Maizon's letter on the lines below. Correct run-on sentences and sentence fragments so that Margaret can understand what her best friend says.

> 1234 Winding Drive Lane
> Greenfield, Connecticut 06606
> September 15
> Dear Margaret,
>
> How are you? Boarding school is okay I miss our old class. Teachers are pretty strict and they give tons of homework and they teach hard subjects. My tiny room at the end of the hall. Is already crammed with books and papers. Yesterday I met some other scholarship students. In my class. Unfortunately, none of them can jump rope.
>
> I can't wait to come home on vacation Brooklyn seems so far away. I miss you! Write soon.
>
> Your friend,
> Maizon

Responses may vary slightly. Suggested responses below. **(5 points)**

How are you? Boarding school is okay, but I miss our old class. Teachers

are pretty strict, give tons of homework, and teach hard subjects. My tiny

room at the end of the hall is already crammed with books and papers.

Yesterday I met some other scholarship students in my class.

Unfortunately, none of them can jump rope.

I can't wait to come home on vacation. Brooklyn seems so far away. I

miss you! Write soon.

Name _____

What a Racquet!

Answer each of the following questions by writing a vocabulary word.

1. Which word tells what a show-off tries to attract?
   attention **(1 point)**

2. Which word means "claimed to be great"?
   bragged **(1)**

3. Which word tells what friends do when they want you to do well? encourage **(1)**

4. Which word describes how you might feel if you accidentally walked into the wrong classroom?
   awkward **(1)**

5. Which word means the same as swiftly and rapidly?
   briskly **(1)**

6. Which word could replace was able in the sentence "Willa finally was able to return a serve"?
   managed **(1)**

7. Which word means "become aware of"?
   notice **(1)**

8. Which word means "to have a discussion"?
   conversation **(1)**

Write two new questions of your own that use at least one vocabulary word each.

9. Accept reasonable answers **(1)**

10. Accept reasonable answers **(1)**

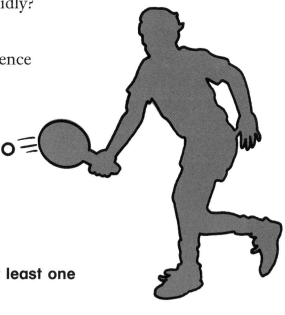

Name _____

Story Map

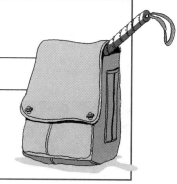

Setting	Characters
sometime during the school year at a middle school and its surrounding neighborhood in Fresno, California **(1 point)**	José, Estela **(1)**

Plot

Story problem: José wants to get Estela's attention, but after three weeks of trying he hasn't had any success. **(1)**

Events:

1: José tries impressing Estela by doing well on his history quiz and showing off his scraped chin from a bike accident. Neither effort succeeds. **(1)**

2: José notices that Estela plays racquetball and challenges her to a game, even though he's never played. She accepts after José brags he is good. **(1)**

3: José visits his Uncle Freddie to borrow his racket and get advice about playing. **(1)**

4: Estela and José play, and she beats him twenty-one to nothing. **(1)**

Resolution: José returns the racquet to his uncle. The game has left him with a bruise on his back and a broken heart. **(1)**

Name _____

Give Advice

What would you tell a friend who was thinking of lying to impress someone? Write your advice using José's experience as an example.

Lying to impress someone won't work. I know of a boy named José who wanted to impress Estela, a new girl **(1 point)** _____.

He tried studying harder to impress her with his brains **(1)** _____.

He even tried to show her a scrape on his chin **(1)** _____.

Nothing worked.

Then he saw that Estela had a raquetball racket in her backpack **(1)** _____.

That gave him the idea to challenge her to a game **(1)** _____.

Telling her that he could play racquetball was a lie, though, because he'd never played before **(1)** _____!

As soon as she said yes, José knew he was in trouble **(1)** _____.

He went to his uncle Freddy's house to borrow his racquet **(1)** _____.

Uncle Freddy was sure José would get beaten **(1)** _____.

When José met Estela at the courts, he saw right away that she was an excellent player **(1)** _____. Estela beat him

21 to nothing **(1)** _____ Instead of

impressing her, José just felt humiliated **(1)** _____.

So don't lie! Just be yourself.

Assessment Tip: Total **12** Points

Name _____

Story Building Blocks

Read the story. Then complete the story map on page 178.

The Spelling Bee

Marty had been nervous all morning. The Lincoln Middle School Spelling Bee was about to begin, and he was the representative from Ms. Higgins's sixth-grade class. Ms. Higgins had asked Marty to compete earlier in the week. He'd said yes because he was a good speller and he thought it might be fun. However, now that he was up on the stage, he wondered what he could have been thinking. "What if I make a mistake and everyone laughs at me?" he worried.

The spelling bee began. Marty's first word was *nervous*. "What a perfect word for me," he thought. He spelled the word correctly, and his classmates applauded and cheered. Marty smiled gratefully. "This isn't so bad after all," he decided.

After three rounds, only Marty and an eighth-grade girl were left. Marty's next word was *enthusiastically*. "Wow. Long word!" he thought. He started spelling the word, and then stopped. He was trying to picture the word in his mind, but he couldn't remember the last letter he had spoken! Marty made a guess and continued at the *u*. When he finished, the judge said, "I'm sorry, Marty. The word has only one *u*." The spelling bee was over. Marty had lost.

As he was packing up his books, Marty saw Ms. Higgins. He was about to apologize when she said, "Marty, what a great job! You did better than all the seventh graders and most of the eighth graders!" Marty smiled. He hadn't thought about it that way. He hadn't lost. He'd finished near the top!

Name _____

Story Building Blocks continued

Complete the story map with details from "The Spelling Bee."

Story Map

Setting	Characters
When: the day of the spelling bee **(1 point)**	**Who:** Marty, a sixth grader;
Where: Lincoln Middle School **(1)**	Ms. Higgins, his teacher; an eighth-grade girl **(2)**

Plot

Problem: Marty is afraid he will make a mistake and be laughed at. **(2)**

Events:

1. Marty worries and wonders why he agreed to be in the spelling bee. **(2)**

2. Marty spells his first word correctly, and his classmates cheer. **(2)**

3. After three rounds, only Marty and an eighth-grade girl are left. **(2)**

4. Marty pauses while spelling enthusiastically and makes a mistake. **(2)**

5. While Marty is packing up his books, he sees Ms. Higgins, who praises him. **(2)**

Resolution: Marty is proud of himself even though he didn't win. **(2)**

Assessment Tip: Total **18** Points

Name _____

Suffix Chart

Read each sentence. For each underlined word, write the base and the suffix of the word in the chart. Then use sentence clues and what you know about the meaning of each suffix to write the meaning of each word. An example is provided.

1. José's class learned how the Egyptians would <u>mummify</u> their dead.
2. Estela's racket was <u>blackened</u> by her frequent playing.
3. She <u>flattened</u> her milk carton as she finished her lunch.
4. He tried to keep his face from <u>reddening</u> with shame.
5. José didn't want to <u>dramatize</u> his feelings, even though Estela could <u>terrify</u> him on the court.

Base word	Suffix	Meaning
mummy	-ify	make into a mummy
black **(1 point)**	-en **(1)**	made black **(1)**
flat **(1)**	-en **(1)**	made flat **(1)**
red **(1)**	-en **(1)**	becoming red **(1)**
drama **(1)**	-ize **(1)**	make dramatic **(1)**
terror **(1)**	-ify **(1)**	fill with terror; make afraid **(1)**

Name _____

Endings and Suffixes

Remember that if a word ends with *e*, the *e* is usually dropped when a suffix or an ending beginning with a vowel is added. The *e* is usually not dropped when a suffix beginning with a consonant is added.

divide + ed = divid**ed**   grace + ful = grace**ful**

► In the starred words *mileage* and *manageable*, the final *e* of the base word is kept when a suffix beginning with a vowel is added.

Write each Spelling Word under the heading that tells what happens to its base word when a suffix or ending is added.
Order of answers for each category may vary.

Spelling Words

1. graceful
2. divided
3. advanced
4. privately
5. replacement
6. excitement
7. adorable
8. heaving
9. forgiveness
10. mileage*
11. barely
12. forceful
13. scarcely
14. blaming
15. entirely
16. usable
17. sincerely
18. amusement
19. lifeless
20. manageable*

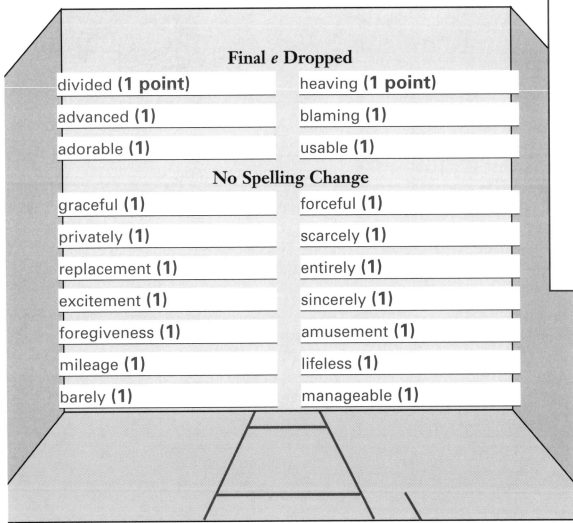

Final *e* Dropped

divided **(1 point)**	heaving **(1 point)**
advanced **(1)**	blaming **(1)**
adorable **(1)**	usable **(1)**

No Spelling Change

graceful **(1)**	forceful **(1)**
privately **(1)**	scarcely **(1)**
replacement **(1)**	entirely **(1)**
excitement **(1)**	sincerely **(1)**
foregiveness **(1)**	amusement **(1)**
mileage **(1)**	lifeless **(1)**
barely **(1)**	manageable **(1)**

Assessment Tip: Total **20** Points

Name _____

Spelling Spree

Adding Suffixes or Endings Write the Spelling Word that has each base word below. The spelling of a base word may change.

Spelling Words

1. graceful
2. divided
3. advanced
4. privately
5. replacement
6. excitement
7. adorable
8. heaving
9. forgiveness
10. mileage*
11. barely
12. forceful
13. scarcely
14. blaming
15. entirely
16. usable
17. sincerely
18. amusement
19. lifeless
20. manageable*

1. use   usable **(1 point)**

2. forgive   forgiveness **(1)**

3. grace   graceful **(1)**

4. adore   adorable **(1)**

5. sincere   sincerely **(1)**

6. heave   heaving **(1)**

7. mile   mileage **(1)**

8. life   lifeless **(1)**

9. replace   replacement **(1)**

10. scarce   scarcely **(1)**

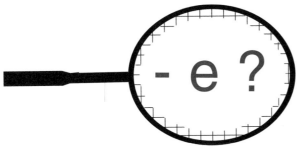

Contrast Clues The second part of each clue contrasts with the first part. Write a Spelling Word to fit each clue.

11. not united, but   divided **(1)**

12. not partly, but   entirely **(1)**

13. not basic, but   advanced **(1)**

14. not publicly, but   privately **(1)**

15. not impossible, but   manageable **(1)**

Assessment Tip: Total **15** Points

Name _____

Proofreading and Writing

Proofreading Circle the five misspelled Spelling Words in this script for a scene from a movie. Then write each word correctly.

Setting: A basketball court, with a boy and girl playing.

LUCY: *(She makes a forcefull move to the basket and scores. Her face lights up with exitement.)* Yes!

DANIEL: *(His chest is heaving.)* That was a lucky lay-up. You barly got past me. If it wasn't for these old, worn-out shoes . . .

LUCY: *(She looks at Daniel with amusment.)* Quit blamming your shoes. It's my ball. The score's ten to ten. Next point wins.

DANIEL: Hold on! Let me catch my breath. . . . Okay, let's go.

LUCY: *(She gets the ball and shoots a graceful jump shot, which goes in.)* That's game, little brother!

1. graceful
2. divided
3. advanced
4. privately
5. replacement
6. excitement
7. adorable
8. heaving
9. forgiveness
10. mileage*
11. barely
12. forceful
13. scarcely
14. blaming
15. entirely
16. usable
17. sincerely
18. amusement
19. lifeless
20. manageable*

1. forceful **(1 point)**
2. excitement **(1)**
3. barely **(1)**
4. amusement **(1)**
5. blaming **(1)**

✏ **Write a Challenging Invitation** Are you especially good at a sport or game? Is there someone whom you'd like to challenge to be your competitor?

On a separate sheet of paper, write an invitation challenging a friend to compete against you in your chosen sport or game. Use Spelling Words from the list. Responses will vary. **(5)**

Assessment Tip: Total **10** Points

Name _____

Using Parts of Speech

Read the dictionary entries. For each word, write two sentences, using the word as a different part of speech in each sentence.

► **palm** (päm) *n.* The inside surface of the hand. *–tr.v.* **palmed, palming, palms.** To conceal an object in the palm of the hand.

► **quiz** (kwĭz) *tr.v.* **quizzed, quizzing, quizzes.** To test the knowledge of by asking questions. *–n., pl.* **quizzes.** A short oral or written examination.

► **strain** (strān) *v.* **strained, straining, strains.** *–tr.* To exert or tax to the utmost. *–n.* An injury resulting from excessive effort or twisting.

► **whip** (wĭp) *v.* **whipped, whipping, whips.** *Informal.* To defeat; outdo. *–n.* A flexible rod or thong attached to a handle, used for driving animals.

1. The girl's palms were sweating when she finished her speech. **(1)**

   The practical joker palmed a buzzer and surprised us all when we

   shook hands. **(1)**

2. The science teacher will quiz us this afternoon on chapter 10. **(1)**

   I did well on the quiz she gave us last week. **(1)**

3. Reading in the sunshine always strains my eyes. **(1)**

   The doctor checked Ramon's muscle strain in his leg. **(1)**

4. My grandmother can whip me at marbles any day. **(1)**

   Grandpa used to drive cattle with a whip. (1)

Name _____

The Challenge

Grammar Skill More
Irregular Verbs

The Irregular Verb Challenge

Irregular verbs have the past or past participle formed, not by adding -*ed* or -*d*, but in some other way. You must memorize the forms of irregular verbs. Here are five irregular verbs to study.

Present	Past	Past Participle
become	became	become
feel	felt	felt
go	went	gone
see	saw	seen
take	took	taken

Now cover the chart above, and complete the exercise below. Fill in the blank in each sentence with either the past or the past participle form of the verb in parentheses. Remember that there must be a helping verb in order to use the past participle form.

1. Bob had become **(1)** _____ a skilled tennis player. (become)

2. He took **(1)** _____ his racket to the court. (take)

3. He felt **(1)** _____ confident. (feel)

4. Bob's friends had seen **(1)** _____ him play many times. (see)

5. Last week they went **(1)** _____ to a big tournament with him. (go)

184   Theme 3: **Growing Up**
Assessment Tip: Total **5** Points

Name _____

In Agreement

The verb in a sentence must agree in number with its subject. In the
present tense, if the subject is singular, add *-s* or *-es* to the verb. Do not
add *-s* or *-es* if the subject is *I* or *you* or if the subject is plural.

**Kyle has started a conversation with Rosa,
the new girl in his class. To find out what
they are saying, choose from among these
verbs to fill in the blanks. Make each verb
agree with its subject.**

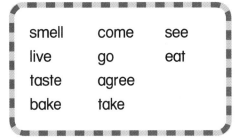

smell	come	see
live	go	eat
taste	agree	
bake	take	

Kyle: This tomato soup <u>tastes **(1 point)**</u> salty.

Rosa: You <u>come **(1)**</u> from Ohio, don't you?

Kyle: Yes. My cousin still <u>lives **(1)**</u> in Ohio.

Rosa: My cousin does too! He <u>goes **(1)**</u> to college
there.

Kyle: I <u>see **(1)**</u> my cousin during the holidays.

Rosa: Our cafeteria chef <u>bakes **(1)**</u> cookies every Friday.

Kyle: They <u>smell **(1)**</u> terrific!

Rosa: Chris and Kelly always <u>eat **(1)**</u> six cookies each.

Kyle: Our homework <u>takes **(1)**</u> a long time to do.

Rosa: I <u>agree **(1)**</u> with you!

Theme 3: **Growing Up**   185
Assessment Tip: Total **10** Points

Name _____

Writing Challenge

Verbs That Agree The people below are facing challenges.
Complete each sentence by writing an appropriate verb to
describe each scene. Be sure that subjects and verbs agree.

Answers will vary, but subjects
and predicates should agree in
number.

1. Mark and Laura **(2)** _____.

2. A girl with three rings **(2)** _____.

3. Mary **(2)** _____.

4. Latasha and Bill **(2)** _____.

5. Roberto **(2)** _____.

Assessment Tip: Total **10** Points

Name _____

Writing a Character Sketch

A **character sketch** is a written profile that tells how either a real person or a character like Estela or José looks, acts, thinks, and feels.

Think about a real person or a story character from a selection you have read whom you would like to write about. Then use the web below to help you brainstorm details about this character's physical appearance and personality traits. (10 points for chart)

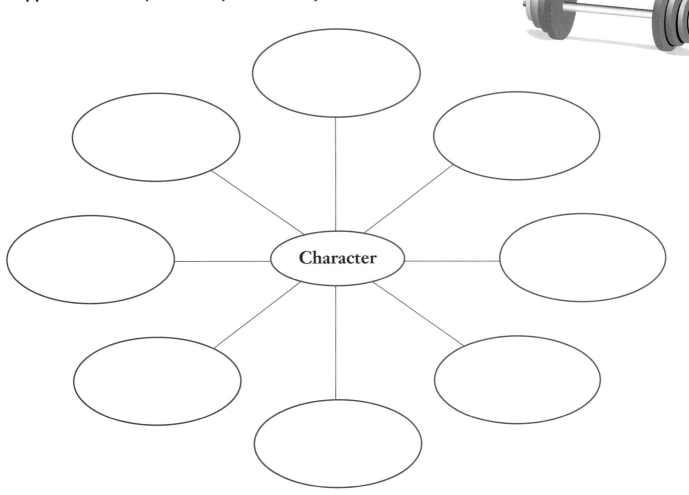

Character

On a separate sheet of paper, write your character sketch. Begin with an anecdote or quote about the character. Then write a sentence that summarizes the character's most significant traits. Next, give two or three details from the web that support your summary. Conclude by restating the traits that are most significant. (5 points)

Name _____

Using Exact Nouns and Verbs

Which noun, *sport* or *racquetball*, is more exact? Which verb, *held* or *gripped*, is more exact? A good writer avoids using vague nouns and verbs. Exact nouns and verbs like *racquetball* and *gripped* will make your writing clearer and help readers get a more vivid mental picture of the people, places, and events you describe.

Imagine José gives Uncle Freddie a play-by-play account of his racquetball game with Estela. Read the following portion of his account. Circle vague nouns and pronouns and inexact verbs. Then replace them with more exact verbs and nouns from the list below. Write the exact verbs and nouns above the words you circled.
(1 point each)

Exact Verbs and Nouns

whizzed
smashed
winner
court
scored
racquetball
racket
sprinted
left ear
swatted

smashed racquetball
Estela (hit) the (thing) hard against the front wall.

scored   winner
She (got) her first point. Then she served another (one.)

whizzed   left ear sprinted
Point 2. Her third serve (flew) by my (head.) I (ran) top

court
speed right off the paved (playing area!) Point 3. Now I

swatted
really had to concentrate. This time I (swung) at her

racket
serve, but my (equipment) slipped from my fingers. Four

to zip.

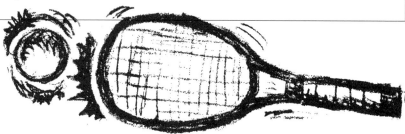

Turtle Patrol Puzzle

Words are missing in the sentences. Fill each blank with a vocabulary word. Then follow the directions to help you find the letters that need to be unscrambled to answer the question below.

Vocabulary

subtle
resettling
volunteers
interfering
commute
hover
permitted

1. If you go back and forth between two places, you
   <u>commute</u> **(1 point)** .

   Directions: Circle the fifth letter.

2. If you are moving to a new place, you are
   <u>resettling</u> **(1)** .

   Directions: Circle the first and seventh letters.

3. If something is not very obvious, it is
   <u>subtle</u> **(1)** .

   Directions: Circle the first and second letters.

4. If you remain in one place in the sky, you
   <u>hover</u> **(1)** .

   Directions: Circle the third and fourth letters.

5. If something is allowed, it is <u>permitted</u> **(1)** .
   Directions: Circle the fifth and eighth letters.

6. If you and your friends offer to do something, you are
   <u>volunteers</u> **(1)** .

   Directions: Circle the third and ninth letters.

7. If you are too curious about other people's business, you are
   <u>interfering</u> **(1)** .

   Directions: Circle the seventh letter.

What do turtle patrols try to do during big storms?

h (e) l p   t (u) (r) t (l) (e) (s)

s (u) (r) v (i) (v) (e) **(1)**

Name _____

Problem-Solution Chart

Problem	Solution
If tall buildings hide the horizon's light, baby turtles head toward the city lights instead of the sea, and many die.	Turtle volunteers guide the baby turtles to the sea. **(2 points)**
Nadia is jealous when she learns that Dad wants to be listed on Margaret's permit. She feels left out.	Nadia decides that, from now on, she will not go on any more turtle walks. **(2)**
Dad knows that Nadia is upset and jealous of the time he spends with Margaret and the turtles.	Dad invites Nadia to go to Walt Disney World and bring a friend. **(2)**
A storm hits the Florida Coast, and the turtles are in danger.	Nadia decides to stay behind and help the turtles instead of going to Disney World. **(2)**
Dad and Nadia realize that, like the turtles, they too need help settling into their new lives.	They agree that there will be times when they need a lift from each other. **(2)**

Assessment Tip: Total **10** Points

Name _____

How Does Nadia Feel?

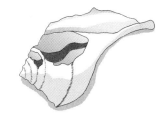

The following questions ask about how Nadia feels about her new family situation in *The View from Saturday*. **Answer each one.**

Why does it upset Nadia to learn that Margaret set up her mother's job interview?

She feels that she has been spied on by Ethan because he did not tell her that he knew her. She is angry with Margaret for helping her mother start a new life apart from her father. **(2 points)**

Why does Nadia's father decide to take her to Disney World?

He realizes Nadia feels hurt and neglected, and wants to show her that he cares about her. **(2)**

How does Nadia feel about her grandfather's remarriage and her new family at first?

She is very unhappy about the new situation. She is resentful of the time her father spends with Margaret and Ethan. **(2)**

Why does Nadia decide not to go to Disney World?

She decides it's more important to stay and help rescue the hatchlings during the storm than to spend time just having fun. **(2)**

What connection does Nadia discover between her life and the lives of the sea turtles?

She realizes that, like the hatchlings, she and her father have been stranded in a difficult situation by the "storm" in their private lives. She also realizes that she, like the turtles, will learn to commute between her two new homes, with her father's help. **(2)**

Name _____

What Would You Do?

Read the story. Then complete page 193.

The Tag-Along

Ben whooped with joy as he rode down the hill on his mountain bike. He heard Ann shout with glee as she started down the same trail. When he glanced over his shoulder, however, Ben noticed that someone else was following them. It was Joyce. Ben felt annoyed.

Joyce had arrived in their class a few months ago. She was new to town and didn't know anyone. That became a problem for Ben when Joyce decided she wanted to become Ann's friend. For the past few weeks, no matter where Ben and Ann went, Joyce always seemed to show up a few minutes later.

Last week, Joyce came across Ben and Ann as they read comic books in Ben's tree house. She watched them for a while, but Ben did not invite her to join them. Yesterday, when Ann and Ben went swimming at the local pool, Joyce showed up and put her towel down right next to theirs.

Ben wanted to resolve the situation one way or another. He stopped his bike and waited for Joyce to catch up. He decided he was going to tell Joyce to stop following Ann around.

Name _____

What Would You Do? continued

**Complete the chart and answer the questions based on
"The Tag-Along."** Sample answers shown.

Character	Problem	Solution
Joyce	She is new in town and doesn't know anyone. **(2 points)**	She decides she wants Ann to be her friend and starts following her around. **(2)**
Ben	He is annoyed by Joyce interfering in his friendship with Ann. **(2)**	He decides he will tell Joyce to stop following Ann. **(2)**

1. Is Joyce's way of dealing with her problem a good one?
   Why or why not?

   No. Following other people around when you have not been

   invited is not a good way to make friends. **(4)**

   _____

2. How else can Joyce handle her problem?

   She can tell Ann that she likes her and would like to be her friend.

   She can also invite Ann to do something with her. **(4)**

   _____

3. Do you think Ben handles his problem in the best way possible?
   Explain your answer.

   No. He should ask Ann what she wants to do about Joyce before

   he acts. He could also invite Joyce to join them rather than being

   annoyed with her for tagging along. **(4)**

Name _____

Prefix Puzzle

Each of the words in the eggs begins with the prefix *in-, im-,* or *con-*.
Find the word that matches each clue and write it in the letter spaces.

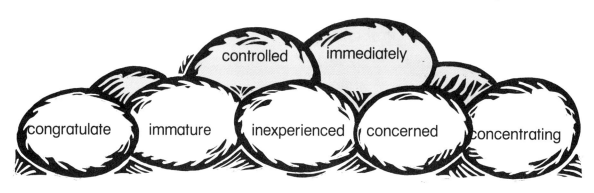

1. worried; anxious; troubled

   c o n c e r n e d **(2)**

2. held in check; restrained

   c o n t r o l l e d **(2)**

3. not fully grown or developed

   i m m a t u r e **(2)**

4. taking place at once; happening without delay

   i m m e d i a t e l y **(2)**

5. to express joy or good wishes to someone for an achievement

   c o n g r a t u l a t e **(2)**

6. thinking very hard; focusing attention on something

   c o n c e n t r a t i n g **(2)**

7. not having knowledge or experience

   i n e x p e r i e n c e d **(2)**

**Read the tinted letters down. Write the word, which means "to travel
regularly between one place and another." (2)**

commute
_____

Assessment Tip: Total **16** Points

Name _____

Prefixes: *in-* and *con-*

A **prefix** is a word part added to the beginning of a base word or a word root to add meaning. A **word root** is a word part that has meaning but cannot stand alone.

The prefix *in-* is spelled *im* before a base word or a word root beginning with *m* or *p*. The prefix *con-* is often spelled *com* before the consonant *m* or *p*.

Prefix + Base Word
incomplete, **im**polite
contest

Prefix + Word Root
involve, **im**mense
control, **com**ment, **com**pete

To spell words with these prefixes, find the prefix, the base word or word root, and any ending. Spell the word by parts.

Write each Spelling Word under the spelling of its prefix.
Order of answers for each category may vary.

Spelling Words

1. computer
2. impolite
3. control
4. include
5. immigrant
6. compete
7. consumer
8. involve
9. immediate
10. comment
11. infection
12. concert
13. import
14. conversation
15. community
16. incomplete
17. immense
18. contest
19. inactive
20. complicate

in-

include **(1 point)**

involve **(1)**

incfection **(1)**

incomplete **(1)**

inactive **(1)**

con-

control **(1)**

consumer **(1)**

concert **(1)**

conversation **(1)**

contest **(1)**

im-

impolite **(1)**

immigrant **(1)**

immediate **(1)**

import **(1)**

immense **(1)**

com-

computer **(1)**

compete **(1)**

comment **(1)**

community **(1)**

complicate **(1)**

Theme 3: **Growing Up**   195
Assessment Tip: Total **20** Points

Name _____

Spelling Spree

Alphabetizing Write the Spelling Word that fits alphabetically between the two words in each group.

1. indoors, __infection **(1 point)**__, inform

2. contract, __control **(1)**__, convene

3. compromise, __computer **(1)**__, comrade

4. income, __incomplete **(1)**__, increase

5. compass, __compete **(1)**__, complain

6. inability, __inactive **(1)**__, incentive

7. consonant, __consumer **(1)**__, contain

8. concern, __concert **(1)**__, conduct

Base Word/Word Root Match Write the Spelling Word that has the same base word or word root as each word below.

9. detest   __contest **(1)**__

10. export   __import **(1)**__

11. exclude   __include **(1)**__

12. duplicate   __complicate **(1)**__

13. emigrant   __immigrant **(1)**__

14. politeness   __impolite **(1)**__

15. immunity   __community **(1)**__

196   Theme 3: **Growing Up**
Assessment Tip: Total **15** Points

Name _____

Proofreading and Writing

Proofreading Circle the five misspelled Spelling Words in these instructions. Then write each word correctly.

Instructions for Permitted Volunteers

1. Watch the hatching quietly. Keep (conversasion) to a minimum.

2. Don't (involv) yourself in the hatching process. Let the turtles do it!

3. The turtles' (inmediate) goal is to reach the water. Don't get in their way.

4. You will seem (immence) to the hatchlings. Don't stand too close to them.

5. Take notes about the results of the hatching. Include figures for all the eggs as well as for any dead or half-pipped turtles. Add a (coment) about anything unusual.

Spelling Words

1. computer
2. impolite
3. control
4. include
5. immigrant
6. compete
7. consumer
8. involve
9. immediate
10. comment
11. infection
12. concert
13. import
14. conversation
15. community
16. incomplete
17. immense
18. contest
19. inactive
20. complicate

1. conversation **(1 point)**
2. involve **(1)**
3. immediate **(1)**
4. immense **(1)**
5. comment **(1)**

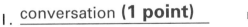

Write a Personal Narrative Have you ever taken part in a project or program as a volunteer? What was the experience like?

On a separate piece of paper, write a personal narrative about a time when you served as a volunteer. Use Spelling Words from the list. Responses will vary. **(5)**

Name _____

Connotation Correction

You are writing a screenplay for the selection, and the director would like to see some changes. Rewrite each sentence replacing the underlined word with a word from the box that has a negative connotation. Then rewrite it again using a word with a positive connotation. If you don't know the meanings of the words, use a dictionary to find them.

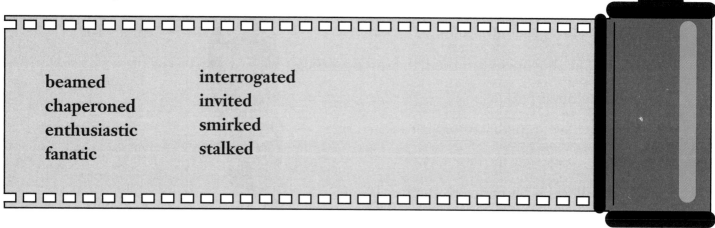

beamed   interrogated
chaperoned   invited
enthusiastic   smirked
fanatic   stalked

1. People who volunteer to help turtles can be <u>excited</u> about their work.

   People who volunteer to help turtles can be fanatic about their work. **(1 point)**

   People who volunteer to help turtles can be enthusiastic about their work. **(1)**

2. Nadia <u>asked</u> Ethan about the comments he had heard.

   Nadia interrogated Ethan about the comments he had heard. **(1)**

   Nadia invited Ethan to tell about the comments he had heard. **(1)**

3. The volunteers <u>followed</u> the turtles as they moved from the beach to the sea.

   The volunteers stalked the turtles as they moved from the beach to the sea. **(1)**

   The volunteers chaperoned the turtles as they moved from the beach to the sea. **(1)**

4. Ethan <u>smiled</u> during the performance of *Phantom of the Opera*.

   Ethan smirked during the performance of *Phantom of the Opera*. **(1)**

   Ethan beamed during the performance of *Phantom of the Opera*. **(1)**

Assessment Tip: Total **8** Points

Name _____

Up in the Sky

sit, set; lie, lay; rise, raise Some verb pairs can be confusing. Below are the definitions of three such pairs of words.

> **sit**—to rest in an upright position
> **set**—to put or place an object
>
> **lie**—to rest or recline
> **lay**—to put or place an object
>
> **rise**—to get up or go up
> **raise**—to move something up

Complete the sentences below by filling in the blanks with the correct verb in parentheses ( ) .

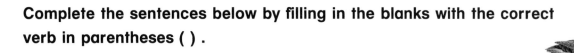

1. (sits/sets) A robin __sits **(1 point)**__ on its nest.

2. (lie/lay) I __lie **(1)**__ on my back to watch geese fly overhead.

3. (rises/raises) Mario __rises **(1)**__ from his chair when the flock flies over.

4. (sits/sets) That bird watcher __sets/set **(1)**__ down his binoculars.

5. (rise/raise) I __rise **(1)**__ at dawn when I go bird watching.

6. (lie/lay) I will __lay **(1)**__ my backpack on the grass.

7. (sit/set) We __set **(1)**__ out food for the migrating birds.

8. (lies/lays) She __lies **(1)**__ under the tree listening to the chirping birds.

9. (sit/set) I __set **(1)**__ the fallen baby bird back in its nest.

10. (rise/raise) I __raise **(1)**__ my binoculars to my eyes.

Name _____

Dog Days

lend, borrow; let, leave; teach, learn Here are the definitions of three more easily confused word pairs:

lend—to give
borrow—to take

let—to permit
leave—to go away

teach—to give instruction
learn—to receive instruction

Complete the sentences below by filling in the blanks with the correct verb in parentheses ( ).

1. Sadie <u>borrows **(1 point)**</u> from Mr. Karol a book on dog training. (lends/borrows)

2. She <u>learns **(1)**</u> from the book how to train puppies. (teaches/learns)

3. Sadie and her puppy, Kipper, <u>leave **(1)**</u> for dog obedience school. (let/leave)

4. The instructor <u>teaches **(1)**</u> Sadie how to handle her dog. (teaches/learns)

5. Sadie <u>lets **(1)**</u> me take Kipper to obedience school one day. (lets/leaves)

6. The instructor <u>lends **(1)**</u> me a better leash. (lends/borrows)

7. Kipper <u>learns **(1)**</u> to sit on command. (teaches/learns)

8. We <u>leave **(1)**</u> for home. (let/leave)

9. My parents <u>let **(1)**</u> me have a puppy. (let/leave)

10. I <u>learn **(1)**</u> to be responsible for her well-being. (teach/learn)

Assessment Tip: Total **10** Points

Name _____

Autumn in New England

Choosing the Correct Verb **Proofread the following passage written
by a girl on her way to New England in the fall. Correct each
incorrect verb form.**

lent
Example: The libarian borrowed me a book.
^

let **(1)**   sitting **(1)**
Please leave me explain something. I like setting on Florida
^   ^

beaches, but when it is autumn, I'd rather head to New England.

teach **(1)**   raise **(1)**
Teachers learn me better and I rise my hand more often when it is cool
^   ^

sit **(1)**
outside. I look forward to seeing the trees turn red and gold. I set in
^

lets **(1)**
newly raked leaves and watch the sky. Sometimes my mother leaves me
^

teaches **(1)**
make hot chocolate with marshmallows, and I wonder who learns
^

set **(1)**
squirrels to gather nuts. When I come home, I sit my books on my desk
^

lay **(1)**
and lie my good school clothes over a chair. By February I will want to
^

borrow **(1)**
lend a little warmth from Florida, and by June I will be ready to fly south
^

again, but in autumn, I am a New England girl.

Name _____

Writing a Speech

In *The View from Saturday*, Nadia gives an informal speech to persuade her father to let her help Grandpa with the sea turtles. Now you will write your own speech. Choose a topic listed below or come up with an idea of your own.

► Write a speech in which the mayor of the Florida town where Nadia lives thanks the turtle volunteers for their efforts.

► Write a speech to persuade local residents to clean up a beach or park.

► Write a speech to inform a group of children about what the turtle patrol's job is and why it is important.

Use the chart below to help you get started. First, identify the purpose of your speech—to entertain, to persuade, to inform, or to thank—and the audience to whom you will speak. Then jot down facts about the situation and reasons why you feel a certain way about it. Before you begin to write, number your ideas, in the order you in which you will present them. (15 points for chart)

Purpose	Audience	Facts and Reasons

Write your speech on a separate sheet of paper. At the beginning, mention whom you are addressing and the purpose of your speech. Then present your facts and reasons in a logical order. Finally, end with a conclusion that sums up or restates the purpose. (5)

Assessment Tip: Total **20** Points

Name _____

Audience

Speech writers not only keep in mind their purpose for writing but also the **audience** they are addressing. Their audience affects what they say and how they say it. When you write a speech, you need to use language and examples that will best reach your audience.

Read each of the following excerpts from different speeches. What audience do you think the speech writer most likely had in mind when writing the speech? Choose a possible audience from the list and write it on the lines.

Audiences

family members

voters

environmental club
  members

real-estate developers

turtle patrol volunteers

pet owners

residents of Florida

biologists

young children

fishing industry
  representatives

1. The Plum Beach condominium will offer lucky owners wonderful views from each unit, including a close look at this area's marine life.

   real-estate developers **(2 points)**

2. Although small turtles used to be commonly available, stores no longer sell them. If you want to observe sea life at home and up close, you might consider buying tropical fish.

   pet owners **(2)**

3. Thank you so much for a job well done! You greatly contributed to this year's successful turtle patrol. Most importantly, you have helped Florida's sea turtles.

   turtle patrol volunteers **(2)**

4. Sea turtles face extinction. Some are hunted for their meat, and turtle eggs are sold as a delicacy. Tragically, beach-front development has also destroyed the traditional breeding grounds of some species.

   environmental club members **(2)**

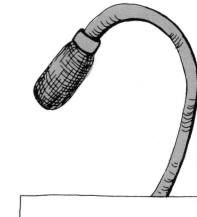

Name _____

Writing a Personal Response

Use the test-taking strategies and tips you have learned to help you answer this kind of question. Then read your response and see how you may improve it. This practice will help you when you take this kind of test.

Write one or two paragraphs about one of the following topics.

a. In *Where the Red Fern Grows*, the narrator saved the money he earned over a two-year period to buy some hunting dogs. Tell about a time when you had to work for a long time to reach a goal. What was the goal? How did you reach it? How long did it take? How did you feel while you were working toward the goal and after you reached it?

b. The narrator of *Where the Red Fern Grows* shared his happiness with his little sisters by giving them some of the candy he brought home. Write about a time when you have shared your happiness with someone. What were you happy about? Who did you share your happiness with? What did you do to share your happiness?

Answers will vary. **(15 points)**

_____

_____

_____

_____

_____

_____

_____

_____

_____

_____

Name _____

Writing a Personal Response continued

Read your answer. Check to be sure that it

- focuses on the topic
- is well organized
- has supporting details
- includes vivid and exact words
- has few mistakes in capitalization, punctuation, grammar, or spelling

Now pick one way to improve your response. Make your changes below.

Answers will vary. **(5)** _____

_____

_____

_____

_____

_____

_____

_____

_____

_____

_____

_____

_____

_____

Assessment Tip: Total 20 Points

Name _____

Spelling Review

1–30. **Write each Spelling Word.** Order of answers may vary.

1. conversation **(1 point)**
2. supply **(1)**
3. minus **(1)**
4. impolite **(1)**
5. graceful **(1)**
6. author **(1)**
7. beginning **(1)**
8. forgiveness **(1)**
9. immediate **(1)**
10. forgetting **(1)**
11. slipped **(1)**
12. method **(1)**
13. answered **(1)**
14. relief **(1)**
15. consumer **(1)**
16. heaving **(1)**
17. amusement **(1)**
18. include **(1)**
19. advanced **(1)**
20. listening **(1)**
21. adorable **(1)**
22. scarcely **(1)**
23. excitement **(1)**
24. control **(1)**
25. balance **(1)**
26. complicate **(1)**
27. preferred **(1)**
28. involve **(1)**
29. community **(1)**
30. lawyer **(1)**

Spelling Words

1. conversation
2. supply
3. minus
4. impolite
5. graceful
6. author
7. beginning
8. forgiveness
9. immediate
10. forgetting
11. slipped
12. method
13. answered
14. relief
15. consumer
16. heaving
17. amusement
18. include
19. advanced
20. listening
21. adorable
22. scarcely
23. excitement
24. control
25. balance
26. complicate
27. preferred
28. involve
29. community
30. lawyer

Name _____

Spelling Spree

Contrast Clues The second part of each clue contrasts with the first part. Write a Spelling Word to fit each clue.

1. not remembering, but <u>forgetting</u> **(1 point)**

2. not boredom, but <u>excitement</u> **(1)**

3. not plus, but <u>minus</u> **(1)**

4. not simplify, but <u>complicate</u> **(1)**

5. not asked, but <u>answered</u> **(1)**

6. not distress, but <u>relief</u> **(1)**

7. not retreated, but <u>advanced</u> **(1)**

Code Breaker Parts of some Spelling Words have been written in code. Use the code below to figure out each word. Then write the words correctly.

@ = con	¤ = or	$ = ed	# = ing	* = ate
% = ance	+ = im	Ø = er	& = ation	¶ = ly

Spelling Words

1. relief
2. author
3. forgetting
4. consumer
5. slipped
6. conversation
7. minus
8. immediate
9. advanced
10. complicate
11. scarcely
12. heaving
13. answered
14. balance
15. excitement

8. + medi * <u>immediate</u> **(1)**

9. slipp $ <u>slipped</u> **(1)**

10. bal % <u>balance</u> **(1)**

11. @ sum Ø <u>consumer</u> **(1)**

12. heav # <u>heaving</u> **(1)**

13. scarce ¶ <u>scarcely</u> **(1)**

14. @ vers & <u>conversation</u> **(1)**

15. auth ¤ <u>author</u> **(1)**

Assessment Tip: Total **15** Points

Name _____

Proofreading and Writing

Proofreading Circle the five misspelled Spelling Words in these rules. Then write each word correctly.

Rules for Growing Up

You can learn a lot by (lissening) to what older people say.
Never be (impalite) to anyone. Keep your temper under (controal).
This might (invollve) biting your tongue once in a while, but it's
worth doing. If you hurt someone's feelings, ask for (forgivness.)

1. listening **(1 point)**
2. impolite **(1)**
3. control **(1)**
4. involve **(1)**
5. forgiveness **(1)**

Write the Spelling Words that best complete this discussion.

Question: All of you must be 6. beginning **(1)** to
think about your futures. What kinds of jobs do you
7. include **(1)** in your thinking?

Amy: I'd like to be a comedian! I love to see the 8. amusement **(1)**
on people's faces when I tell jokes.

Jaime: I'm 9. graceful **(1)**, so I might be a dancer.
Later, if I 10. preferred **(1)** to, I could teach dance.

Laura: As a vet, I'd have a steady 11. supply **(1)** of
12. adorable **(1)** animals in my life!

Dion: I would like to be a 13. lawyer **(1)**, like my mom. She
helps people in the 14. community **(1)** fight for their rights.

Bart: I'll invent a fast 15. method **(1)** for growing up!

Write a Song **On a separate sheet of paper, write
a song about growing up. Use Spelling Review Words.** Responses will vary. **(5)**

Theme 3: **Growing Up** 209
Assessment Tip: Total **20** Points

Name _____

Discovering Ancient Cultures

The selections in this theme will take you on a journey to the world of long ago. After reading each selection, complete the chart below to show what you learned.

	What is the location of the culture described in the selection?	When did the events described in the selection take place?
Lost Temple of the Aztecs	Mexico	in the early 1500s
The Great Wall	China	toward the end of the Ming dynasty, from about 1600–1800
The Royal Kingdoms of Ghana, Mali, and Songhay	Africa	in the eleventh century A.D.

Assessment Tip: Total **10** Points per selection

Name _____

Discovering Ancient Cultures

	What was remarkable about the culture described in the selection?
Lost Temple of the Aztecs	The Aztecs built huge temples and beautiful cities. They were fierce, powerful warriors. They were expert jewelers and they had a very accurate calendar.
The Great Wall	The Chinese built an immense wall of pounded earth and stone. It is the longest structure ever built.
The Royal Kingdoms of Ghana, Mali, and Songhay	The people of ancient Ghana were prosperous. They traded with people far away for exotic items. Gold was plentiful, and many people were wealthy. Even the farmers lived well.

What have you learned about ancient cultures in this theme?

Sample answer: Ancient cultures were very different from one another; people long

ago created incredible things.

Assessment Tip: Total **10** Points per selection and **2** Points for the final question

Name _____

In the Time of the Aztecs

Words are missing in the sentences. Fill each blank with a word from the box.

Vocabulary

intricate
sites
empire
conquered
adorned
metropolis
tributes
causeways

1. If you rule over many lands, you rule over an
   empire **(1 point)** _____.

2. If you live in a very large city, you live in a
   metropolis **(1)** _____.

3. If you travel on raised pathways across marshlands,
   you travel on causeways **(1)** _____.

4. If you have defeated another nation in a war and won
   control over it, you have conquered **(1)** _____ that nation.

5. If a building has carvings that are carefully done and show great
   detail, it has intricate **(1)** _____ carvings.

6. If you have decorated an emperor or empress with jewelry, you have
   adorned **(1)** _____ that person.

7. If you deliver valuable goods to a foreign ruler who holds control of
   your nation, you give tributes **(1)** _____ to that ruler.

8. If you visit several places where archaeologists have found relics, you
   have visited archaeological sites **(1)** _____.

Theme 4: **Discovering Ancient Cultures**   213
Assessment Tip: Total **8** Points

Author's Viewpoint Chart

Passage from Selection	Whom It Tells About	Viewpoint
"one of the most famous and tragic rulers in history" (page 365)	Moctezuma	positive
Should they be destroyed or treated as guests? Moctezuma decided to welcome the strangers. (page 365)	Moctezuma **(1 point)**	positive **(1)**
Moctezuma was filled with fear and confusion at these unnatural happenings. (page 370)	Moctezuma **(1)**	rather negative **(1)**
Cortés looked at everything they had given him. "Are these your gifts of welcome?" he asked. "Is this all you have brought?" (page 374)	Cortés **(1)**	negative **(1)**
Cortés ordered his men to fasten irons around the messengers' ankles and necks. (page 374)	Cortés **(1)**	negative **(1)**
"You will do as I say," said Cortés. (page 374)	Cortés **(1)**	negative **(1)**
A few months later Moctezuma, against the advice of his chiefs, welcomed Cortés and his army as friends. (page 375)	Moctezuma **(1)**	negative **(1)**
The next year the Spaniards seized treasure and attacked the Aztecs during a festival. (page 375)	Cortés **(1)**	negative **(1)**
In May 1521 Cortés returned to attack Tenochtitlán and claimed victory after leaving the city in ruins. (page 375)	Cortés **(1)**	negative **(1)**

Assessment Tip: Total **16** Points

Name _____

Anniversary Speech

**The year is 2019. It is the 500th anniversary of the arrival of Cortés at
Veracruz. You have been chosen to give a speech honoring all who
played a part in the momentous events of that year and the following
two. Plan your speech by completing these statements:**

1. We remember the Aztecs for (name at least two things) <u>their great empire, their</u>
   <u>technology, and the beautiful city they built.</u> **(2 points)**

2. We remember Tenochtitlán for (name at least two things) <u>its site in the middle of</u>
   <u>a lake, its majestic monuments, its large size and population, and its beautiful</u>
   <u>gardens.</u> **(2)**

3. We remember Moctezuma II for <u>his decision to welcome Cortés, which lead to</u>
   <u>the downfall of the Aztec empire.</u> **(2)**

4. We remember Hernando Cortés for <u>his greed, his cruelty, and his conquering of</u>
   <u>the Aztecs.</u> **(2)**

5. We wonder if the Aztec society would have survived, if only Moctezuma hadn't
   mistaken Cortés for <u>the Aztec god Quetzalcoatl.</u> **(2)**

6. We are glad that the Great Temple of the Aztecs was rediscovered because
   <u>it reminds us of the greatness of that vanished civilization and the mistakes</u>
   <u>in history that we do not want to repeat.</u> **(2)**

Name _____

To Be Fair . . .

Read the passage. Then complete the activity on page 217.

Cabeza de Vaca's Journey

Álvar Núñez Cabeza de Vaca ranks among the greatest explorers who ever lived. In 1528, he joined a Spanish expedition headed to the New World to look for cities filled with gold and other riches.

When the expedition's five ships arrived on the coast of Florida, their leader proposed that they begin an overland exploration. Cabeza de Vaca disagreed with this dangerous and foolish plan but was too proud to stay behind. The landing party never found any cities of gold. Instead, the men lost contact with their ships and became stuck in the Florida swamps. In an effort to find their ships, they built crude boats and set sail. A hurricane separated Cabeza de Vaca's boat from the others and blew it to Texas, where it was destroyed. One by one, his companions died, leaving him alone.

Over the next four years, Cabeza de Vaca survived on his own, a superhuman achievement. He learned to live off the land and helped different native groups trade with each other. Then one day he miraculously came across three other members of the original expedition, who were now enslaved by a native group. He helped these men to escape, and together they wandered through what today is Mexico and the American Southwest. At one point, he healed a Native American man shot by an arrow. News of this feat traveled quickly, and soon many people came to him to be healed. Everywhere he and his companions went, they were welcomed and greeted with gifts.

Finally, the men crossed paths with four Spanish soldiers, who took them to a Spanish city on the Pacific Coast. Cabeza de Vaca returned to Spain to a hero's welcome. He told the king that he would like to go back to the New World. The king asked him to return as an aide to the new governor of Florida, but he refused because he had vowed never again to follow anyone else's orders. By sticking to his principles, he once again showed himself to be a truly great man.

To Be Fair . . . continued

Answer the questions below about the passage on page 216.

1. What is the author's view of Cabeza de Vaca? The author thinks he is a great explorer, capable of great feats, and a man of principle. **(4 points)**

2. Would you say the author is biased toward Cabeza de Vaca? Why or why not? Yes. The author excessively praises Cabeza de Vaca's personal qualities and accomplishments. **(4)**

3. Do you think the facts in the article support the author's statement that Cabeza de Vaca "showed himself to be a truly great man"? Why or why not? Sample answer: No. The author says that Cabeza de Vaca's greatness is based on his sticking to his principles. But in the beginning of the article, he lets his pride get in the way of his judgment when he joins the overland exploration. **(4)**

4. In his writings, Cabeza de Vaca describes native peoples in an unfavorable way. Why do you think the author does not include this information in the article? The author leaves this information out because it does not support the author's view of Cabeza de Vaca as a great man. **(4)**

Name _____

Aztec Artifacts

**Circle the suffixes *-ic*, *-al*, and *-ure* in the underlined words in the
sentences below.**

1. The museum had original Aztec artifacts on display for the public. **(2)**

2. These national treasures of Mexico would only be in the United States
   for a short time. **(1)**

3. The arrival of many visitors made the museum crowded by ten o'clock. **(1)**

4. Visitors could not touch the stone artifacts because they were protected
   by a rope enclosure. **(1)**

5. A plaque told of the historic importance of the Aztecs' tragic defeat by Cortés in
   the year 1521. **(2)**

6. A letter that showed Cortés's authentic signature was on display in a
   glass case. **(2)**

7. A professional archaeologist was also there to answer questions about
   her work. **(1)**

**Now, choose five underlined words and use them correctly in sentences
of your own.** Accept responses that use the word correctly. **(1 point each)**

1. _____

2. _____

3. _____

4. _____

5. _____

Assessment Tip: Total **15** Points

Name _____

The /sh/ Sound

The /sh/ sound is usually spelled with two letters. When you hear the /sh/ sound, think of the patterns *sh*, *ti*, *ci*, and *ss*.

/sh/   poli**sh**   mo**ti**on   offi**ci**al   mi**ss**ion

Write each Spelling Word under its spelling of the /sh/ sound. Order of answers for each category may vary.

1. glacier
2. motion
3. pressure
4. direction
5. caution
6. partial
7. ancient
8. polish
9. station
10. shallow
11. official
12. edition
13. musician
14. mention
15. mission
16. portion
17. session
18. selfish
19. establish
20. cushion

sh

polish **(1 point)**

shallow **(1)**

selfish **(1)**

establish **(1)**

cushion **(1)**

ti

motion **(1)**

direction **(1)**

caution **(1)**

partial **(1)**

station **(1)**

edition **(1)**

mention **(1)**

portion **(1)**

ci

glacier **(1)**

ancient **(1)**

official **(1)**

musician **(1)**

ss

pressure **(1)**

mission **(1)**

session **(1)**

Theme 4: **Discovering Ancient Cultures**   219

Assessment Tip: Total **20** Points

Name _____

Spelling Spree

Adding the /sh/ Sound Write a Spelling Word by adding
the correct spelling of the /sh/ sound to the incomplete
word in each phrase below.

1. the second edi‾ti **(1)**‾on of a book

2. a drop in air pre‾ss **(1)**‾ure

3. the ‾sh **(1)**‾allow end of the pool

4. a large por‾ti **(1)**‾on of food

5. a par‾ti **(1)**‾al eclipse of the sun

6. a comfortable seat cu‾sh **(1)**‾ion

7. a musi‾ci **(1)**‾an in a band

Spelling Words

1. glacier
2. motion
3. pressure
4. direction
5. caution
6. partial
7. ancient
8. polish
9. station
10. shallow
11. official
12. edition
13. musician
14. mention
15. mission
16. portion
17. session
18. selfish
19. establish
20. cushion

Word Detective Write a Spelling Word for each clue.

8. a "river" of ice
9. inconsiderate of others
10. a meeting
11. very old
12. where you board a train or bus
13. a synonym for *movement*
14. to found or set up
15. the state of being careful

8. _glacier_ **(1)**

9. _selfish_ **(1)**

10. _session_ **(1)**

11. _ancient_ **(1)**

12. _station_ **(1)**

13. _motion_ **(1)**

14. _establish_ **(1)**

15. _caution_ **(1)**

Assessment Tip: Total **15** Points

Name _____

Proofreading and Writing

Proofreading Circle the five misspelled Spelling Words in this letter. Then write each word correctly.

Spelling Words

To the Royal Governor:

You will be pleased to know that our (mishun) has been successful so far. After leaving Cuba, we sailed in a westerly (direccion) until making landfall. We were quickly able to (astablish) that a great empire lay farther inland. Later, we received some (offical) visitors from this empire. Among their gifts to us were gold and precious stones, which were shined to a very high polish. In return, we demonstrated the power of our guns to them. This they will no doubt (mension) to their lord back in the capital. We believe this country possesses great riches, and we are confident of success.

Your servant,
Hernando Cortés

1. glacier
2. motion
3. pressure
4. direction
5. caution
6. partial
7. ancient
8. polish
9. station
10. shallow
11. official
12. edition
13. musician
14. mention
15. mission
16. portion
17. session
18. selfish
19. establish
20. cushion

1. mission **(1 point)**   4. official **(1)**

2. direction **(1)**   5. mention **(1)**

3. establish **(1)**

✎ **Write an Explanation** The Aztecs had a calendar just for keeping track of special religious days. Have you ever crossed off on a calendar the days leading up to a holiday? What is your favorite holiday?

On a separate piece of paper, write about your favorite holiday. Remember to name the holiday and tell why it is your favorite. Use Spelling Words from the list. Responses will vary. **(5)**

Theme 4: **Discovering Ancient Cultures**   221
Assessment Tip: Total **10** Points

Name _____

Expand the Meaning

**Read the news article and the clues below it. Find the word that
answers each of the ten clues. Be careful! The meaning of the word
in the article is different from the meaning in the clue. Circle each
word in the article and write it on the line next to the clue.**

Amazing Recent Events

Lots of news should interest readers this week. Our ruler,
Moctezuma, received word that an important stranger with light
skin has appeared near the city wall. For years Moctezuma
visited the Great Temple hoping that Quetzalcoatl would return
there, even though no one knows the spot where this will
happen. Strange stories of recent events in our rich country also
signal that a change is near.

1. more unusual _stranger_ **(1 point)**

2. the flat area at the side of the head _temple_ **(1)**

3. a stain _spot_ **(1)**

4. a tool for drawing lines and measuring length _ruler_ **(1)**

5. the floors of a building _stories_ **(1)**

6. empty pieces of land _lots_ **(1)**

7. seemed _appeared_ **(1)**

8. heavy and sweet _rich_ **(1)**

9. not heavy _light_ **(1)**

10. a charge for borrowing money _interest_ **(1)**

Assessment Tip: Total **10** Points

Many Ways to Describe

Descriptive adjectives:	what kind, how many, which one	Visitors, **old** and **young**, are awed by **ancient** ruins.
Demonstrative adjectives:	which one	**These** postcards show **those** sites. **This** photograph was taken at **that** place.
Articles:		**The** people built a temple. It was uncovered in **an** excavation.

Adjectives Identify the adjectives in each sentence. Write each adjective on the correct line under each sentence. Hint: Every sentence does not contain every kind of adjective, and some sentences may contain more than one of a kind.

1. The Aztecs used a circular stone calendar.

   descriptive adjectives: circular, stone **(1 point)**

   articles: the, a **(1)**   **demonstrative adjectives:** (none) **(1)**

2. They created a great empire.

   descriptive adjectives: great **(1)**

   articles: a **(1)**   **demonstrative adjectives:** (none) **(1)**

3. Those workers found that temple and made an important discovery.

   descriptive adjectives: important **(1)**

   articles: an **(1)**   **demonstrative adjectives:** those, that **(1)**

4. It was a magnificent building.

   descriptive adjectives: magnificent **(1)**

   articles: a **(1)**   **demonstrative adjectives:** (none) **(1)**

5. That temple was in the capital city.

   descriptive adjectives: capital **(1)**

   articles: the **(1)**   **demonstrative adjectives:** that **(1)**

Name _____

It's Only Proper!

A **proper adjective** is formed from a proper noun and always begins with a capital letter.

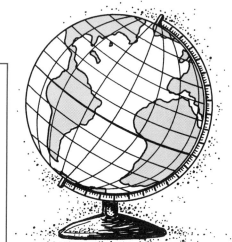

Proper noun	Ending	Proper adjective
Germany	-an	German poetry
Chile	-an	Chilean fruit
China	-ese	Chinese art
Japan	-ese	Japanese language
Sweden	-ish	Swedish bread
Ireland	-ish	Irish music

Proper Adjectives Complete each sentence. Write the proper adjective formed from the proper noun in parentheses. Use a dictionary if you need to.

1. Nancy read about an <u>Alaskan **(1 point)**</u> sled race. (Alaska)

2. Tim prepared an <u>Italian **(1)**</u> meal for us. (Italy)

3. A trifle is an <u>English **(1)**</u> dessert. (England)

4. Our class saw <u>African **(1)**</u> art at the museum. (Africa)

5. This <u>Chinese **(1)**</u> vase is extremely old. (China)

6. The design on that <u>Portuguese **(1)**</u> dish is lovely. (Portugal)

Assessment Tip: Total **6** Points

First or Last?

A good writer can change the position of adjectives to make sentences more effective. Here is an example:

Awkward: The letter was long and interesting, and he read it twice.
Improved: He read the long, interesting letter twice.

Below are some of the postcard messages Keesha has sent from Europe. Rewrite the second sentence of each one, changing the position of adjectives to make the sentence more effective.

1. Greetings from France! The paintings in the Louvre are beautiful, and I want to see them all!

   I want to see all the beautiful paintings in the Louvre! **(2 points)**
   _____

2. Greetings from Germany! Here is the place where the Berlin Wall once stood, and it is lively and interesting.

   Here is the lively and interesting place where the Berlin Wall once stood. **(2)**
   _____

3. Greetings from Ireland! The countryside is green, and I am enjoying hiking in it.

   I am enjoying hiking in the green countryside. **(2)**
   _____

4. Greetings from Spain! The days are sunny and warm, and I swim.

   I swim on the warm, sunny days. **(2)**
   _____

5. Greetings from Italy! The ruins are ancient, and I am learning about them.

   I am learning about the ancient ruins. **(2)**
   _____

Writing an Explanation

Lost Temple of the Aztecs explains who the Aztecs were and why they were conquered by Spanish explorers in 1519. The purpose of a written **explanation** is to explain

▶ who or what something is

▶ what is or was important about something or someone

▶ how something works or worked

▶ the steps of a process

▶ why something happens or happened

Fill in the graphic organizer to help you plan and organize an explanation that answers this question: *Why did Moctezuma decide to welcome the strangers as friends rather than treat them as enemies?* **Write this topic in the center box of the graphic organizer. Then list reasons and supporting details from the selection that explain why this event happened. (2 points each)**

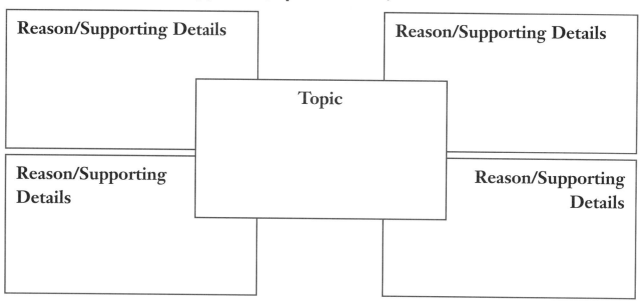

Reason/Supporting Details

Reason/Supporting Details

Topic

Reason/Supporting Details

Reason/Supporting Details

Now write a two- to three-paragraph explanation on a separate sheet of paper, using the information you recorded. In the first sentence or paragraph, clearly state the topic. Provide enough reasons to help readers understand the subject, and give details to clarify each reason. Be sure to define any unfamiliar terms the first time you use them. End with a conclusion. (5)

Assessment Tip: Total **15** Points

Name _____

Eliminating Unnecessary Words

Good writers revise their writing to eliminate unnecessary words and repeated ideas that can make their writing seem awkward.

Unnecessary Word: The two of them were **both** running track.

Revised: The two of them were running track.

Read the following paragraph. Cross out unnecessary words and repeated phrases. Then write the revised paragraph on the lines below. You may want to revise and combine sentences to make the paragraph read more smoothly.

> My mother, Mom, is an anthropologist. She studies ancient civilizations. She also teaches on the subject too. Both my sister and I, the two of us want to be anthropologists when we're grown-up adults. I'm taking a course at the Natural History Museum after school. The course at the Natural History Museum is on ancient Egyptian civilizations. I'm learning about Egypt. In addition to learning about Egypt, I'm reading some books right now on the Inca culture of Peru. Peru is in South America.

Revised paragraphs will vary. Sample paragraph given.

My mother is an anthropologist. She studies ancient civilizations and teaches on the subject. My sister and I want to be anthropologists when we're adults. I'm taking a course on ancient Egyptian civilizations at the Natural History Museum after school. In addition to learning about Egypt, I'm reading some books right now on the Inca culture of Peru in South America. **(10 points)**

Name _____

Evaluating Your Research Report

Reread your research report. What do you need to make it better? Use this page to help you decide. Put a checkmark in the box for each sentence that describes your research report.

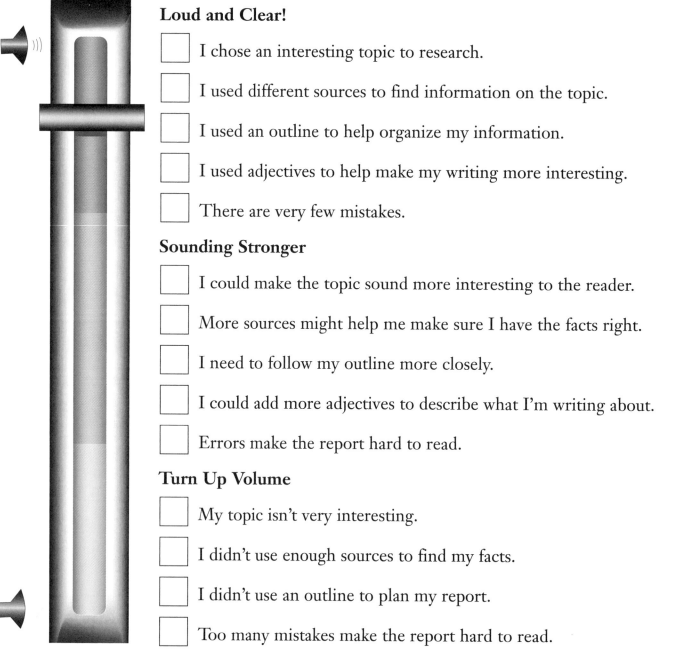

Loud and Clear!

☐ I chose an interesting topic to research.

☐ I used different sources to find information on the topic.

☐ I used an outline to help organize my information.

☐ I used adjectives to help make my writing more interesting.

☐ There are very few mistakes.

Sounding Stronger

☐ I could make the topic sound more interesting to the reader.

☐ More sources might help me make sure I have the facts right.

☐ I need to follow my outline more closely.

☐ I could add more adjectives to describe what I'm writing about.

☐ Errors make the report hard to read.

Turn Up Volume

☐ My topic isn't very interesting.

☐ I didn't use enough sources to find my facts.

☐ I didn't use an outline to plan my report.

☐ Too many mistakes make the report hard to read.

Name _____

Using Adjectives

Adjectives are words that modify nouns or pronouns. Choose the best adjective to complete each sentence.

1. The __c (1)__ Mayan civilization flourished long ago in Central America.
   a. humorous   b. popular   c. ancient   d. youthful

2. The Maya built __a (1)__ temples and pyramids.
   a. gleaming   b. roasting   c. rotting   d. grinding

3. The Maya were one of the __b (1)__ cultures in the western hemisphere to develop a writing system.
   a. biggest   b. first   c. heaviest   d. second

4. The Mayan writing system included symbols for sounds as well as __d (1)__ symbols.
   a. baseball   b. murky   c. heavy   d. picture

5. The Maya also invented the zero in their __b (1)__ system.
   a. geology   b. number   c. religious   d. government

6. __d (1)__ crowds came to see the Maya play a ball game called pokta-pok.
   a. Careless   b. Rippled   c. Microscopic   d. Immense

7. The game seems to have been an __a (1)__ combination of basketball, soccer, and volleyball.
   a. exciting   b. inner   c. outer   d. empty

8. At their peak, __c (1)__ cities of the Maya had populations of 50,000 or more.
   a. tall   b. fruitless   c. major   d. empty

9. In the year 909 the Mayan civilization suffered a __d (1)__ defeat from which it never recovered.
   a. popular   b. clever   c. colorful   d. devastating

Theme 4: **Discovering Ancient Cultures**   229
Assessment Tip: Total **9** Points

Name _____

Spelling Words

Is ice slick or sleek? Is a friend an alley or an ally? It is easy to confuse words that have similar spellings and pronunciations even though the meanings are different. The pairs of Spelling Words in the box are often confused. Pay careful attention to their pronunciations, spellings, and meanings.

Write the missing letters in the Spelling Words below.

Order of answers for 3–4, 11–12, and 13–14 may vary.

1. de <u>c</u> ent **(1 point)**

2. de <u>s</u> <u>c</u> ent **(1)**

3. <u>a</u> ffect **(1)**

4. <u>e</u> ffect **(1)**

5. de <u>s</u> ert **(1)**

6. de <u>s</u> <u>s</u> ert **(1)**

7. sl <u>i</u> ck **(1)**

8. sl <u>e</u> <u>e</u> k **(1)**

9. all <u>e</u> <u>y</u> **(1)**

10. all <u>y</u> **(1)**

11. confid <u>e</u> nt **(1)**

12. confid <u>a</u> nt **(1)**

13. hur <u>d</u> le **(1)**

14. hur <u>t</u> le **(1)**

Spelling Words

1. decent
2. descent
3. affect
4. effect
5. desert
6. dessert
7. slick
8. sleek
9. alley
10. ally
11. confident
12. confidant
13. hurdle
14. hurtle

Study List On a separate piece of paper, write each Spelling Word. Check your spelling against the words on the list.

Order of words may vary.

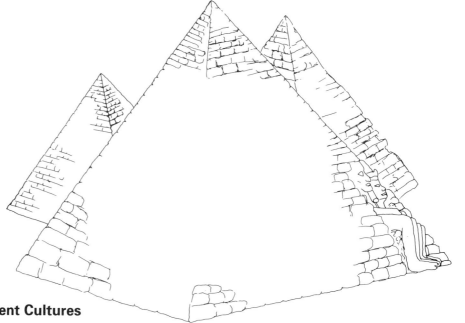

Assessment Tip: Total **14** Points

Spelling Spree

Word Switch **Write a Spelling Word to replace each underlined definition in the sentences below.**

1. For the <u>part of the meal that comes after the main course</u>, we had a choice of chocolate cake or blackberry pie.
2. The speech the governor gave was <u>reasonably good</u>, although it went on a little too long.
3. The cold weather will <u>cause a change</u> in the garden.
4. When I need someone to talk to, I'm glad I have a <u>person entrusted with secrets</u> like Anna.
5. If you get involved in a conflict, it's helpful to have a <u>person who joins with another to achieve a goal</u>.
6. After a day of traveling through <u>the area that gets little rainfall</u>, the caravan reached an oasis.
7. The horse was groomed until its coat was <u>smooth and glossy</u>.

Spelling Words

1. decent
2. descent
3. affect
4. effect
5. desert
6. dessert
7. slick
8. sleek
9. alley
10. ally
11. confident
12. confidant
13. hurdle
14. hurtle

1. dessert **(1 point)**
2. decent **(1)**
3. affect **(1)**
4. confidant **(1)**
5. ally **(1)**
6. desert **(1)**
7. sleek **(1)**

The Third Word **Write a Spelling Word that belongs with each group of words.**

8. slippery, icy, _____
9. sure, certain, _____
10. result, outcome, _____
11. fall, plunge, _____
12. rush, speed, _____
13. lane, passageway, _____
14. obstacle, difficulty, _____

8. slick **(1)**
9. confident **(1)**
10. effect **(1)**
11. descent **(1)**

12. hurtle **(1)**
13. alley **(1)**
14. hurdle **(1)**

Assessment Tip: Total **14** Points

Name _____

Proofreading and Writing

Proofreading Circle the five misspelled Spelling Words in this archaeologist's diary entry. Then write each word correctly.

1. decent
2. descent
3. affect
4. effect
5. desert
6. dessert
7. slick
8. sleek
9. alley
10. ally
11. confident
12. confidant
13. hurdle
14. hurtle

September 16th.

The ruins we've found out here in the (dessert) appear to be part of a lost city. Dr. Boxer is (confidint) that this city was part of a previously undiscovered ancient culture. I try not to let his opinion (afect) me too much as I investigate. The past few days have been spent excavating what appears to be an (aley) off one of the main streets. The building stones that we have found are still in (descent) shape. It looks as though the climate has had surprisingly little effect on them. I remain extremely curious about this place's past.

1. desert **(1 point)**
2. confident **(1)**
3. affect **(1)**
4. alley **(1)**
5. decent **(1)**

Write Context Sentences Choose three word pairs from the Spelling List. Then write three pairs of sentences, one for each word. Responses will vary. **(5)**

Assessment Tip: Total **10** Points

Name _____

Words on the Wall

Vocabulary

domain
massive
craftsmen
terrain
extravagance
laborers
dynasty
durable
steppe
nomadic
excluding

Read each description. Then write one or two words from the box that match that description.

terms for land

terrain **(1 point)**

steppe **(1)**

descriptive terms for objects

massive **(1)**

durable **(1)**

terms for workers

laborers **(1)**

craftsmen **(1)**

descriptive term for people

nomadic **(1)**

term for territory ruled over

domain **(1)**

term for reign of one group

dynasty **(1)**

action word for "keeping out"

excluding **(1)**

term for lavishness and excess

extravagance **(1)**

Theme 4: **Discovering Ancient Cultures**   233
Assessment Tip: Total **11** Points

Name _____

Cause and Effect Chart

Cause		Effect
Mongol warriors threatened to overpower the Chinese.	→	Chinese emperors constructed a wall to keep the Mongols out. **(1 point)**
Stone was scarce in western China. **(1)**	→	Laborers built the western part of the Great Wall from packed dirt.
The Great Wall had to be guarded against the Mongols.	→	Forts for soldiers to live in were built all along the wall. **(1)**
The Great Wall demanded great sacrifices of the Chinese people, yet their leaders lived extravagant lives.	→	The Chinese people became angry with their leaders and began to rebel against them. **(1)**
The Ming dynasty had been disliked by its own people.	→	The Manchus easily won support for the new Qing dynasty. **(1)**
The Manchus drove the Mongols away. The Qing emperors ruled both sides of the Great Wall. **(1)**	→	The Great Wall was no longer needed for defense.

Name _____

The People Behind the Great Wall

Each entry below names a group of people who were important in the history of the Great Wall. Next to each entry write a sentence or two telling about that group and its role.

Ming Leaders They built most of the Great Wall under their 300-year rule. Many Chinese people were not happy with them. **(2 points)**

Mongols They were nomadic warriors. The Chinese built the wall to keep them out. **(2)**

Laborers and Craftsmen Unskilled laborers built the parts of the wall made of packed earth. Skilled craftsmen built the parts made of stone. **(2)**

Chinese Soldiers They guarded, helped build, and even lived on the wall. **(2)**

Chinese People They were taxed by the Ming government to pay for the wall and forced to work on it. They eventually rebelled against the Ming rulers. **(2)**

Manchus They were a powerful nomadic tribe who took over the Ming throne when the Chinese people rebelled. **(2)**

Name _____

How It Started

Read the following passage. Then complete the activity on page 237.

The Egyptian Pyramids

The pyramids of Egypt are among the wonders of the ancient world. Many were built as tombs for the Egyptian pharaohs, or kings. Because the pharaohs were considered to be gods living on earth, their tombs had to be very special places.

The greatest Egyptian pyramid is the Great Pyramid of Khufu, built more than 4,500 years ago. The Great Pyramid is one of three pyramids set along the Nile River at Giza. It was built to hold the remains of Khufu, a pharaoh who ruled Egypt for twenty-three years, beginning in 2589 B.C. The pyramid is around 480 feet tall with sides that measure 760 feet long at the base. It is one of the largest structures ever built.

The Egyptians built the pyramids out of giant stone blocks that weighed several tons each. This stone came from rock quarries many miles away. It had to be floated down the Nile on barges and then moved into place using logs, levers, and pulleys. This took enormous effort! As many as twenty thousand workers helped build the Great Pyramid over a period of twenty years.

The Egyptians also built temples near the pyramids. They believed that the pharaoh's spirit traveled between the earth and the heavens, and that it continued to watch over them and help them in their lives. To nourish the pharaohs' spirits, they filled the temples and tombs with food and valuable objects. This wealth attracted grave robbers, however, who looted the tombs, even in ancient times. Later Egyptian leaders built their tombs in rock cliffs, making entry more difficult.

Name ______________________________

How It Started continued

Complete the chart below to show the missing cause or effect. Refer to the passage on page 236.

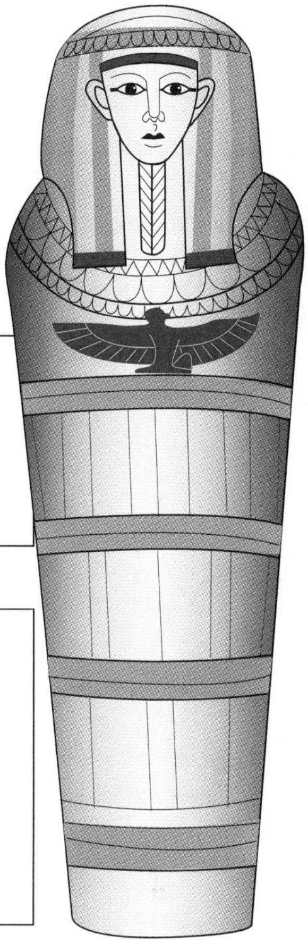

	Cause		Effect
Paragraph 1	Egyptians considered their pharaohs to be gods living on earth.	→	They built special tombs for their pharaohs. **(4 points)**
Paragraph 3	The rock quarries from which the stones were cut were many miles away from where the pyramids were built.	→	Workers had to float the stones down the Nile River on barges. **(4)**
Paragraph 4	A. The Egyptians believed that the pharaohs' spirits traveled between heaven and earth. **(4)**	→	They built temples for worshipping pharaohs after death and filled both the temples and tombs with food and valuable objects.
	B. Grave robbers looted the tombs. **(4)**	→	Later Egyptian leaders built their tombs in rock cliffs.

Assessment Tip: Total **16** Points

Name _____

Suffix Search

Circle the suffixes -*ion* and -*ation* in the underlined words in the blocks.

1. The Great Wall marked the separation between the Ming and the Mongol territories. **(1 point)**

2. A huge gate was the place of connection between two sections of the Great Wall. **(2)**

3. The Ming government got money to build the Great Wall through years of taxation of the Chinese people. **(1)**

4. The Chinese people finally staged a rebellion because they were tired of the Ming government's lying and corruption. **(2)**

Now, use four of the underlined words above in sentences of your own.

Accept sentences that use the words correctly. **(4)**

_____

_____

_____

_____

_____

Assessment Tip: Total **10** Points

Name _____

Adding *-ion* or *-ation*

The suffixes *-ion* and *-ation* can change verbs into nouns.
If the verb being changed ends with *e*, drop the *e* before
adding *-ion* or *-ation*.

connect, connec**tion**   situate, situa**tion**

admire, admir**ation**

**Write each pair of Spelling Words under the heading that
shows the spelling change when *-ion* or *-ation* is added.**
Order of answers for each category may vary.

No Spelling Change

construct **(1 point)**   attract **(1)**

construction **(1)**   attraction **(1)**

connect **(1)**

connection **(1)**

Final *e* Dropped

combine **(1)**   examine **(1)**

combination **(1)**   examination **(1)**

cooperate **(1)**   contribute **(1)**

cooperation **(1)**   contribution **(1)**

admire **(1)**   explore **(1)**

admiration **(1)**   exploration **(1)**

situate **(1)**

situation **(1)**

Name _____

Spelling Spree

Spelling Words

Questions **Write a Spelling Word to answer each question.**

1. What does a magnet have for iron?
2. What do people do when they want to work well together?
3. What does a teacher give you to test your knowledge of a subject?
4. What is the opposite of *repel*?
5. When you hear static during a telephone call, you have a bad what?
6. What do you have for your favorite role model?
7. What is another word for *build*?

1. attraction **(1 point)**
2. cooperate **(1)**
3. examination **(1)**
4. attract **(1)**
5. connection **(1)**
6. admiration **(1)**
7. construct **(1)**

Syllable Scramble **Rearrange the syllables to write a Spelling Word. There is one extra syllable in each numbered item.**

Example: de tion in spec   *inspection*

8. nect ble con   connect **(1)**
9. bu con ant tion tri   contribution **(1)**
10. plo at ex ra tion   exploration **(1)**
11. bine dent com   combine **(1)**

The Third Word **Write the Spelling Word that belongs with each group of words.**

12. like, appreciate, _____
13. teamwork, collaboration, _____
14. investigate, examine, _____
15. place, locate, _____

12. admire **(1)**
13. cooperation **(1)**
14. explore **(1)**
15. situate **(1)**

Spelling Words

1. construct
2. construction
3. connect
4. connection
5. combine
6. combination
7. cooperate
8. cooperation
9. attract
10. attraction
11. admire
12. admiration
13. situate
14. situation
15. examine
16. examination
17. contribute
18. contribution
19. explore
20. exploration

Proofreading and Writing

Proofreading Circle the five misspelled Spelling Words in this proclamation. Then write each word correctly.

The imperial architect is pleased to announce that the (construcktion) of our Emperor's wall is going splendidly. However, much work remains to be done. The (combanation) of building materials must be just right. Then we must connect all the separate parts into one solid barrier. The Chinese people are now called upon to (contribuet) more labor to this effort. The Mongol (situashun) on our northern border continues to worsen. The barbarians constantly (examin) our defenses to find weaknesses. Therefore, we must build a wall that has none. Let all people unite in this glorious endeavor!

Spelling Words

1. construct
2. construction
3. connect
4. connection
5. combine
6. combination
7. cooperate
8. cooperation
9. attract
10. attraction
11. admire
12. admiration
13. situate
14. situation
15. examine
16. examination
17. contribute
18. contribution
19. explore
20. exploration

1. construction **(1 point)**
2. combination **(1)**
3. contribute **(1)**
4. situation **(1)**
5. examine **(1)**

Write a Report You are on an inspection tour of the Great Wall. You must write a report to the chief architect on the conditions along the wall. How would you describe the usefulness of the wall against Mongol attacks? Are there any suggestions you would make?

On a separate sheet of paper, write a report giving an update on the state of affairs along the Great Wall. Use Spelling Words from the list.
Responses will vary. **(5)**

Name _____

Sentences with Synonyms

Read each sentence below. Find a word in the box that is a *synonym* for each underlined word. Rewrite the sentences using the synonyms.

Vocabulary

ancient	crests	distant	earth	elaborate
grueling	patrolled	plunged	survive	withdrew

1. Some walls were built with pounded <u>dirt</u>, an <u>old</u> building technique.

   Some walls were built with pounded earth, an ancient building

   technique. **(2 points)**

2. Soldiers <u>checked</u> the wall in a <u>detailed</u> defense system.

   Soldiers patrolled the wall in an elaborate defense system. **(2)**

3. The wall snaked along the <u>tops</u> of hills and <u>fell</u> down into rivers.

   The wall snaked along the crests of hills and plunged down

   into rivers. **(2)**

4. Many workers did not <u>outlive</u> the <u>exhausting</u> conditions.

   Many workers did not survive the grueling conditions. **(2)**

5. The Mongols <u>retreated</u> to <u>remote</u> parts of the steppe.

   The Mongols withdrew to distant parts of the steppe. **(2)**

Assessment Tip: Total **10** Points

Name _____

Compare Us!

Comparing with Adjectives Use the **comparative** form (*-er* or *more*) of an adjective to compare two persons, places, ideas, or things. Use the **superlative** form (*-est* or *most*) to compare three or more. Look at this chart of spelling changes that happen when *-er* or *-est* is added to some words.

Spelling changes with *-er* and *-est*			
► Do not add another *e* to **adjectives ending in** *e*.	nice	nic**er**	nic**est**
► You usually double the final consonant of **adjectives that end in a consonant after a single vowel.**	flat	flat**ter**	flat**test**
► Change the final *y* to *i* in **adjectives ending in** *y*.	busy	bus**ier**	bus**iest**

Complete each sentence with the correct form of the adjective in parentheses. Remember to use *more* or *most* with long adjectives.

1. My family built a <u>larger **(1 point)**</u> snow fort this year than last year. (large)

2. Our neighbors tried to build a <u>bigger **(1)**</u> one than ours. (big)

3. We made the fort on the <u>coldest **(1)**</u> day of the year. (cold)

4. It was the <u>most fantastic **(1)**</u> snow fort ever built! (fantastic)

5. I hope tomorrow is not <u>sunnier **(1)**</u> than today. (sunny)

6. If the snow melts, we'll lose the <u>most ambitious **(1)**</u> snow fort we've ever made! (ambitious)

Name _____

Good News or Bad?

Comparing with *good* and *bad* The adjectives *good* and *bad* are irregular. They do not take the endings -*er* or -*est*, and the words *more* or *most* are not added to them. Study their special comparative forms in this chart.

	Positive	**Negative**
Adjective:	I have **good** news.	I have **bad** news.
Comparative form:	The news is **better** today.	Today's news is **worse**.
Superlative form:	This is the **best** news I've ever heard.	This is the **worst** news I've ever heard.

Fill in the blank with the correct form of *good* if the word in parentheses ( ) is *positive* and the correct form of *bad* if the word in parentheses is *negative*.

1. Signal fires were once a <u>good **(1 point)**</u> means of communication. (positive)

2. Now we have <u>better **(1)**</u> ways of getting in touch than ever before. (positive)

3. This is the <u>worst **(1)**</u> telephone connection I've ever had! (negative)

4. Receiving a scrambled message is <u>worse **(1)**</u> than no message at all. (negative)

5. Sending electronic mail is the <u>best **(1)**</u> way of all to keep in touch with friends who live far away. (positive)

6. No one likes to get <u>bad **(1)**</u> news. (negative)

Assessment Tip: Total **6** Points

Name _____

What Good Form!

Using the Correct Forms of Adjectives It is important for a good
writer to use the correct form of an adjective. Here are examples of some
common mistakes writers make with adjectives:

Error: As the years went by, they found a **more better** way to build the wall.

Correct: As the years went by, they found a **better** way to build the wall.

Error: Some rulers were **benevolenter** than others.

Correct: Some rulers were **more benevolent** than others.

Error: What is the **older** place you have ever seen?

Correct: What is the **oldest** place you have ever seen?

**Beth has written a draft of a letter to her friend Nell about an
enjoyable visit to the art museum. In her enthusiasm, she has
made some mistakes with her adjectives. Find the five incorrect
adjective forms in her letter, and write them correctly on the
lines below.** Order of answers may vary.

Dear Nell,

Yesterday I visited the (greater) art museum I've ever

seen. It was (gooder) than the one we went to last month.

The works from China were the (impressivest) ones. Many

of the works are very old. A (beautifuler) statue of a young

man with two birds was more than 2000 years old! Can

you imagine seeing anything (ancienter)? If an American

statue is 200 years old, we think that is amazing.

1. greatest **(1 point)**

2. better **(1)**

3. most impressive **(1)**

4. beautiful **(1)**

5. more ancient **(1)**

Name _____

Writing a Paragraph of Information

In *The Great Wall*, you learned about the building of China's Great Wall. A **paragraph of information** like this one from the selection presents facts in a logical order.

> Tens of thousands of workers were involved in building the Great Wall. The army provided many laborers. Soldiers became construction workers, and generals became architects and engineers. Peasants were required to work on the wall. They worked for months at a time for little or no pay. Criminals served their sentences doing hard labor on the wall.

Use this graphic organizer to build your own paragraph of information about another human structure.

Topic
(2 points)
_____

_____

Topic Sentence

(2)
_____

_____

Supporting Sentences

(4)
_____

_____

_____

_____

Now write your paragraph of information on a separate sheet of paper. Include a topic sentence, usually the first sentence in the paragraph, that tells what the entire paragraph is about. Arrange several supporting sentences in a logical order, and make sure all of the sentences contain facts about the topic. (4)

Assessment Tip: Total **12** Points

Name _____

Elaborating with Adjectives

Adjectives like *strong* and *difficult* describe nouns and pronouns help readers picture people, places, ideas, and things that are being described. A good writer uses adjectives in sentences to make his or her writing clearer and more vivid.

Read these sentences about the Great Wall. Then add adjectives from the box to make each sentence more interesting. Answers will vary.

fierce	tall	massive	incredible	long	smoky	heavy
hardworking	well-trained	costly	high	swift	skillful	curious

1. The Chinese built a <u>long **(1 point)**</u> wall to protect their country from the <u>fierce **(1)**</u> Mongols.

2. In the eastern mountains, the <u>massive **(1)**</u> wall was made of mud bricks and <u>heavy **(1)**</u> blocks.

3. Thousands of <u>skillful **(1)**</u> and <u>hardworking **(1)**</u> laborers spent years and years working on the wall.

4. A million <u>well-trained **(1)**</u> soldiers defended the Great Wall against <u>swift **(1)**</u> Mongol horsemen.

5. Stationed in <u>tall **(1)**</u> watchtowers, guards built <u>smoky **(1)**</u> fires to send a warning about an approaching enemy.

6. Ming emperors imposed <u>high **(1)**</u> taxes to help pay for the <u>costly **(1)**</u> project.

7. Today, many <u>curious **(1)**</u> tourists come to view this <u>incredible **(1)**</u> structure from the ancient world.

A Desert Journey

Use these desert words to complete the journal entry below.

Vocabulary

oasis	entourage	vicinity	primary
flourishing	bartering	goods	caravans

Today is the thirty-fourth day of our journey. Having enough water to survive is the ___primary **(1 point)**___ concern when crossing the Sahara. We reached the cool waters of this ___oasis **(1)**___ just before sunset and immediately allowed our camels to drink. We are one of seven ___caravans **(1)**___ made up of people and camels here tonight. Most of the camels are heavily laden with ___goods **(1)**___. Some of the different traders have already begun ___bartering **(1)**___ with each other for items they want. Trade is ___flourishing **(1)**___ in this region, with gold, salt, and exotic goods in high demand in so many places. We heard that a prince stopped here with a huge ___entourage **(1)**___ just two days ago. Too bad we did not get to see that splendid group! Still, we are told that equally wondrous sights await us in the ___vicinity **(1)**___ of the city Jenne.

Assessment Tip: Total **8** Points

Name _____

Topic, Main Idea, and Details Chart

Topic: Life in the medieval Kingdom of Ghana **(2 points)**

Section 1
Main Idea: Ghana's secret gold mines produced gold for use and trade. **(1)**

Key Details: 1. Gold was common and plentiful in Ghana. **(1)**

2. The location of the gold mines was kept secret. **(1)**

3. Archaeologists are still searching for the mines. **(1)**

Section 2
Main Idea: Wangaran miners used dumb bartering to protect their gold. **(1)**

Key Details: 1. Merchants and miners traded without speaking. **(1)**

2. Miners chose death over betraying the location of the mines. **(1)**

3. Trade was Ghana's lifeblood, so soldiers protected caravans. **(1)**

Section 3
Main Idea: Trade caravans carried goods through Ghana and beyond. **(1)**

Key Details: 1. Camels were essential for desert travel. **(1)**

2. Traveling in large groups provided safety and resources. **(1)**

3. Caravans traveled during the coolest parts of the day. **(1)**

Section 4
Main Idea: Daily life in the city differed from life in small villages. **(1)**

Key Details: 1. City people had expensive belongings and ate exotic food. **(1)**

2. Eighty percent of people lived in small farming compounds. **(1)**

3. The whole community was one big extended family. **(1)**

Name _____

Trader's Log— Trans-Saharan Route

Use information from *The Royal Kingdoms of Ghana, Mali, and Songhay* to complete the following log of a trader who is traveling in a caravan.

Destination: Koumbi Saleh, in the empire of <u>Ghana **(1 point)**</u>

Method of travel: <u>camel caravan **(1)**</u>

Reason for traveling: to trade for <u>gold **(1)**</u>, Ghana's most plentiful and valuable resource

Two items brought to trade : <u>accept: honey, jewelry, tools, metal</u> and leather goods, birds, livestock, horses, cloth, silk, furs **(2)**

Length of journey: <u>forty days **(1)**</u>

Two types of traveling companions: <u>accept: other traders, slaves,</u> bodyguards, scholars, ambassadors, poets, musicians **(2)**

Daytime schedule: <u>travel about three miles per hour from oasis to</u> oasis; stop for prayer periods; stop at caravanserai during hottest part of day **(2)**

Evening activities: <u>occasional travel; usually travelers sleep while</u> guards stand watch **(2)**

Three interesting facts about Soninke village life: <u>Everyone is one</u> big family; families work together on farm compounds; advanced farming skills; men and women share work; houses made of mud or wood and stone **(3)**

Assessment Tip: Total **15** Points

What's the Big Idea?

Read the following passage. Then complete the activity on page 252.

Civilizations of Mesoamerica

Before Europeans arrived in the Americas, Mesoamerica (which includes Mexico and Central America) was home to several advanced civilizations. Three of the main groups were the Olmecs, the Maya, and the Aztecs.

The Olmecs were the first to create an advanced civilization. Around 1200 B.C. they began to build cities and create a trade network in the jungles of southeastern Mexico, along the Gulf of Mexico. They carved giant stone heads, some weighing as much as forty-four tons. By 400 B.C. their culture was in decline, but their achievements influenced other civilizations to come.

By A.D. 250 another powerful culture, the Maya, had emerged in Mesoamerica. The Maya built great stone cities, or ceremonial centers, in the lowland jungles and mountain highlands of southern Mexico and northern Central America. Mayan cities, including Palenque, Tikal, and Copán, featured elaborate pyramids, temples, and palaces. The Maya built irrigation canals for their fields. They also developed a writing system, a calendar, and advanced knowledge of mathematics and astronomy. After A.D. 900 their culture began to decline, though Mayan peoples continue to live in the region to this day.

The third great civilization of Mesoamerica was the Aztec. It emerged in the dry highlands of central Mexico after A.D. 1200. The Aztecs built a great city, Tenochtitlán, on an island in a large lake in the Valley of Mexico. They were also great warriors. By the early 1500s they had conquered many neighboring groups and had created a large empire. When the Spanish arrived in Mexico in 1519, they were astounded by the wealth and achievements of the Aztec empire.

Name _____

What's the Big Idea? continued

Answer these questions about the passage on page 251.

1. What is the topic of the passage? the civilizations of Mesoamerica
   (1 point)

2. The topic and main idea of the second paragraph are listed below.
   Fill in the supporting details.

Topic: the Olmec civilization

Main Idea: The Olmecs were the first to create an advanced civilization.

Details: Around 1200 B.C. they began building cities and creating a

trade network.

They carved giant stone heads weighing up to forty-four tons.

Their culture influenced future civilizations. **(3)**

3. On the lines below, write the topic, main idea, and details of the third and
   fourth paragraphs.

Third Paragraph

Topic: the Mayan civilization **(1)**

Main Idea: By A.D. 250 the Maya
emerged in Mesoamerica as a
powerful culture. **(3)**

Details: They built great stone cities
with pyramids, temples, and
palaces. They built irrigation canals,
developed a writing system and a
calendar, and knew math and
astronomy. **(3)**

Fourth Paragraph

Topic: the Aztec civilization **(1)**

Main Idea: The Aztecs were the
third great civilization of
Mesoamerica. **(3)**

Details: This culture emerged in the
central Mexican highlands after
A.D. 1200. The Aztecs built a great
city on a lake. They were powerful
warriors, created a large empire,
and achieved great wealth. **(3)**

252   Theme 4: **Discovering Ancient Cultures**
Assessment Tip: Total **18** Points

Name _____

Recognizing Unstressed Syllables

Read each sentence. Sound out the underlined word several times, placing stress on a different syllable each time. Circle the choice with the correct unstressed and stressed syllables. Unstressed syllables are written in lowercase letters and stressed syllables are written in capital letters.

1. In bartering, the buyer and the seller reach an agreement that is satisfactory to both sides. **(1 point)**

   SAT•is•fac•to•ry   sat•IS•fac•to•ry   (sat•is•FAC•to•ry)

2. In a caravan, camels are loaded with merchandise and supplies.

   (MER•chan•dise)   mer•CHAN•dise   mer•chan•DISE **(1)**

3. Royal patrols guaranteed safe passage to all visitors to ancient Ghana.

   GUAR•an•teed   guar•AN•teed   (guar•an•TEED) **(1)**

4. Smaller towns were surrounded by walls with moats or pits in front of them.

   SUR•round•ed   (sur•ROUND•ed)   sur•round•ED **(1)**

5. Families in ancient Ghana worked cooperatively on the land.

   CO•op•er•a•tive•ly   (co•OP•er•a•tive•ly)   co•op•er•a•TIVE•ly **(1)**

6. Village leaders allocated land to each family according to need.

   (AL•lo•cat•ed)   al•LO•cat•ed   al•lo•cat•ED **(1)**

7. Farmers used dikes and earthen dams for irrigation.

   ir•RI•ga•tion   (ir•ri•GA•tion)   ir•ri•ga•TION **(1)**

8. The women cooked, ate, worked, and entertained together.

   EN•ter•tained   en•TER•tained   (en•ter•TAINED) **(1)**

Theme 4: **Discovering Ancient Cultures**   253
Assessment Tip: Total **8** Points

Name _____

Unstressed Syllables

To spell a two-syllable or three-syllable word, divide the word
into syllables. Look for familiar spelling patterns. Be sure to
note the spelling of any unstressed syllables, and then spell the
word by syllables.

prob / lem (prŏb´ ləm)   **po / si / tion** (pə zĭsh´ ən)

**Write each Spelling Word under the heading that gives the
number of its syllables.** Order of answers for each category
may vary.

1. company
2. success
3. position
4. problem
5. policy
6. difficult
7. document
8. quality
9. surprise
10. physical
11. crisis
12. awake
13. example
14. ignore
15. accept
16. parallel
17. admiral
18. desire
19. garage
20. ambulance

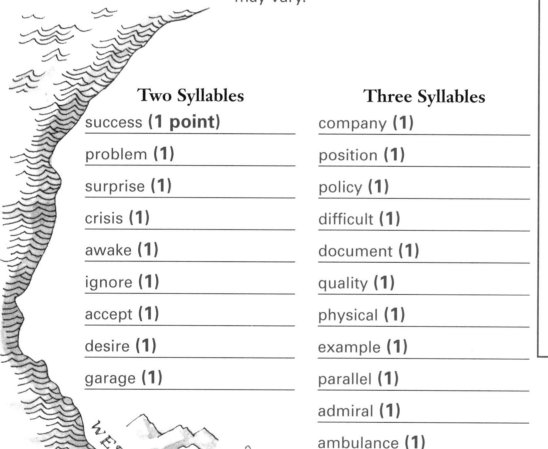

Two Syllables

success **(1 point)**

problem **(1)**

surprise **(1)**

crisis **(1)**

awake **(1)**

ignore **(1)**

accept **(1)**

desire **(1)**

garage **(1)**

Three Syllables

company **(1)**

position **(1)**

policy **(1)**

difficult **(1)**

document **(1)**

quality **(1)**

physical **(1)**

example **(1)**

parallel **(1)**

admiral **(1)**

ambulance **(1)**

WEST AFRICA

Assessment Tip: Total **20** Points

Name _____

Spelling Spree

Phrase Fillers Write the Spelling Word that best completes each phrase.

1. a government _____ on automobile safety

2. to set a good _____

3. a patient's _____ condition

4. to solve a _____

5. to reach the rank of _____

6. a _____ birthday party

7. a parking _____

8. rushed to the hospital in an _____

1. policy **(1 point)**   5. admiral **(1)**

2. example **(1)**   6. surprise **(1)**

3. physical **(1)**   7. garage **(1)**

4. problem **(1)**   8. ambulance **(1)**

Spelling Words

1. company
2. success
3. position
4. problem
5. policy
6. difficult
7. document
8. quality
9. surprise
10. physical
11. crisis
12. awake
13. example
14. ignore
15. accept
16. parallel
17. admiral
18. desire
19. garage
20. ambulance

Code Breaker Some Spelling Words have been written in code. Use the code below to figure out each word. Then write the words correctly.

CODE: I S T P W A C D J R H V E L G M Y B
LETTER: a c d e f g i l m n o p q r s t u y

9. GYSSPGG success **(1)**   13. CARHLP ignore **(1)**

10. ISSPVM accept **(1)**   14. VILIDDPD parallel **(1)**

11. TPGCLP desire **(1)**   15. SLCGCG crisis **(1)**

12. VHGCMCHR position **(1)**

Theme 4: **Discovering Ancient Cultures**   255
Assessment Tip: Total **15** Points

Name _____

Proofreading and Writing

Proofreading Circle the five misspelled Spelling Words in
this travel report. Then write each word correctly.

I write these words because my employers desire
a brief (documint) of my recent trading expedition.
Our (compeny) of merchants made the desert crossing
in good time. We were all (awak) several hours before
sunrise each day and did most of our traveling before
the sun got too hot. It is a (diffacult) journey, but the
sights to be seen at the end of it make it well
worthwhile. The cities of the kingdom of Ghana are
bustling with many thousands of people. Goods of
high (qualty) fill the marketplaces. There are excellent
trading opportunities here.

1. company	
2. success	
3. position	
4. problem	
5. policy	
6. difficult	
7. document	
8. quality	
9. surprise	
10. physical	
11. crisis	
12. awake	
13. example	
14. ignore	
15. accept	
16. parallel	
17. admiral	
18. desire	
19. garage	
20. ambulance	

1. document **(1 point)**   4. difficult **(1)**
2. company **(1)**   5. quality **(1)**
3. awake **(1)**

✏️ **Write a Paragraph of Information** From reading the selection,
what do you know about daily life in the medieval kingdom of Ghana?
What was it like to travel across the desert in a trade caravan?

**On a separate piece of paper, write a paragraph about one aspect of
life in the Kingdom of Ghana. Use Spelling Words from the list.**
Responses will vary. **(5)**

Assessment Tip: Total **10** Points

Prefix and Suffix Chart

Read the journal entry. Underline each word that has a prefix or suffix listed in Chart 1. Then fill in Chart 2 with your underlined words.

The <u>miners</u> of ancient Ghana traded their gold by bartering. Sometimes they would find the merchants' goods <u>unacceptable</u>, and the merchants would <u>reoffer</u> more goods. Often, though, the system moved <u>smoothly</u> and the bartering was <u>successful</u>.

Chart 1			
Suffixes	**Meanings**	**Prefixes**	**Meanings**
-er, -or -ful -ly	a person who does full of in a specified way	re- un-	again or back not

Chart 2		
Word	**Base Word and Suffix**	**Meaning**
1. miners 2. smoothly 3. successful	mine ___ + er ___ smooth ___ + ly ___ success ___ + ful ___	a person who mines **(2 points)** in a smooth way **(2)** full of success **(2)**
Word	**Base Word and Prefix**	**Meaning**
4. unacceptable 5. reoffer	un ___ + acceptable ___ re ___ + offer ___	not acceptable **(2)** offer again **(2)**

Name _____

Tell Me How!

Adverbs   An **adverb** can modify, or describe, a verb or an adjective. An adverb that modifies a verb tells *how, where, when,* or *to what extent.* An adverb that modifies an adjective tells *to what extent.* Look at the example sentences. What word does each adverb in dark type modify?

>   **How:** They **carefully** <u>guarded</u> the secret mines.
>   **Where:** You must <u>go</u> **west** to reach the American deserts.
>   **When:** The people <u>worked</u> **daily**.
>   **To what extent:** I **really** <u>like</u> the book about Ghana.
>   **To what extent:** It is a **very** <u>interesting</u> book.

Under each sentence write the adverb, the word it modifies, and *Verb* or *Adjective* to tell what kind of word it modifies.

1. Trade was very important in ancient Ghana.

   very, important, Adjective **(3 points)**

2. Merchants traveled safely in groups.

   safely, traveled, Verb **(3)**

3. A full-time cameleer usually managed the camels.

   usually, managed, Verb **(3)**

4. The camels could be quite stubborn.

   quite, stubborn, Adjective **(3)**

5. The caravans traveled south.

   south, traveled, Verb **(3)**

6. They regularly pushed their way across the desert.

   regularly, pushed, Verb **(3)**

7. It must have been an extremely dangerous journey.

   extremely, dangerous, Adjective **(3)**

8. Temperatures in the desert could become dangerously high.

   dangerously, high, Adjective **(3)**

Assessment Tip: Total **24** Points

Name _____

Time to Compare

Comparing with Adverbs Like adjectives, **adverbs** can be used to make comparisons. Use the **comparative** form (*-er*) to compare two things. Use the **superlative** form (*-est*) to compare three or more. Use *more* or *most* with adverbs that end with *-ly*.

Comparative
Andrea digs **faster** than Mike.
Brian swims **more quickly** than you.

Superlative
Tony digs **fastest** of all.
He swims **most quickly** of us all.

Some adverbs have completely different forms of comparison. Study the chart.

Adverb	Comparative	Superlative
well	better	best
badly	worse	worst
little	less	least
much	more	most

Write the comparative or superlative form of the adverb in parentheses ( ) to complete each sentence correctly.

1. I wonder <u>more frequently **(1 point)**</u> about the past than I do about the future. (frequently)

2. I'm going to work <u>harder **(1)**</u> on my history lesson this week than I did last week. (hard)

3. The archaeologist was the <u>most **(1)**</u> interesting speaker of all at the assembly. (much)

4. I was <u>less **(1)**</u> interested in the historian's speech than in hers. (little)

5. She went <u>deepest **(1)**</u> of all into details about working in the field. (deep)

6. I may think <u>more seriously **(1)**</u> now about studying archaeology than before. (seriously)

Theme 4: **Discovering Ancient Cultures** 259
Assessment Tip: Total **6** Points

Name _____

Adverbs at Work!

Adjective or Adverb? Good writers are careful to use adverbs, not adjectives, to tell *how much* or *to what extent* about adjectives. Review the examples below.

> **Incorrect:** She plays **real** well.
> **Correct:** She plays **really** well.
>
> **Incorrect:** The stew was **extreme** delicious.
> **Correct:** The stew was **extremely** delicious.

Brigitte has written a play about an imaginary medieval kingdom. Here is part of the script. Proofread it to change adjectives to adverbs where necessary. Write the correct word above each mistake.

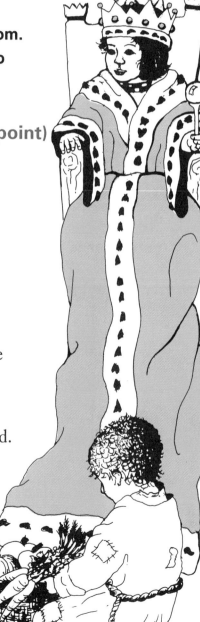

King Snoof: Loyal subject, what have you brought me so eager? eagerly **(1 point)**

Garnid the Serf: Good and kind king, I have gladly brought
really **(1)**
this real big basket full of crops from my field.

King Snoof: You must have had a tremendous good harvest this tremendously **(1)**

year, serf.

Garnid the Serf: Yes, King Snoof! Your fierce brave soldiers have fiercely **(1)**

protected your kingdom and our crops.

King Snoof: Now, serf, sing me an extreme sweet tune of the land. extremely **(1)**

Garnid the Serf: But, sire, I carry no sweet tune in my
tightly **(1)**
tight woven basket!

King Snoof: Then, sorry serf, sing a sour one!

Writing a Comparison and Contrast Paragraph

In *The Royal Kingdoms of Ghana, Mali, and Songhay,* the authors compare and contrast the roles played by men and women in Soninke village life. For example, both men and women made baskets and pots, but men served in the military while women harvested and processed crops. One way to explore how things are alike and different is by writing a **comparison and contrast paragraph**. Comparing shows how things are alike, and contrasting shows how they are different.

Use the Venn diagram to help you compare and contrast travel in the days of the camel caravans with travel in modern times.

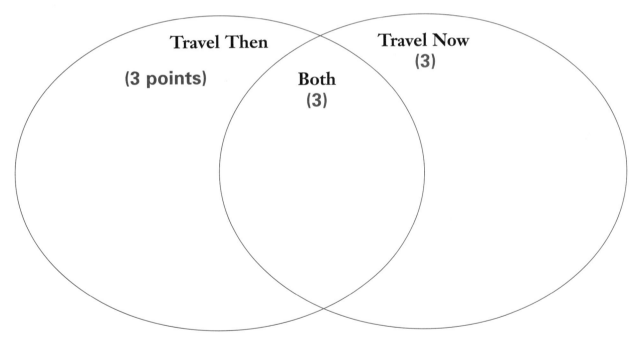

Travel Then

(3 points)

Both
(3)

Travel Now
(3)

On a separate sheet of paper, write a compare-contrast paragraph about travel today and travel in ancient North Africa. In the opening sentence, clearly state the subject being compared and contrasted. In the supporting sentences, group details that compare and details that contrast in a clear manner. Use clue words such as *both* or *likewise* to help readers identify likenesses, and *on the other hand* or *only* to help them identify differences. (3)

Name _____

Combining Sentences with Adjectives

Adjectives describe nouns and pronouns. You can improve your writing by combining repetitive adjectives into a single sentence.

> Ancient Ghanaians had **golden** jewelry. They also had **golden** thread.
> Ancient Ghanaians had **golden** jewelry and thread.

You can also combine several short, choppy sentences with different adjectives into a list of adjectives in one sentence.

> The journey was **long**. The trip was **difficult**, too. It was often **dangerous**.
> The journey across the Sahara was **long, difficult,** and **dangerous**.

Revise this paragraph. Combine repetitive adjectives into a single sentence, or combine several short, choppy sentences with different adjectives into a list of adjectives in one sentence.

Men and women played important roles in Soninke village life. Working together, Soninke men and women shared essential tasks. They did daily chores that were essential, too. For example, both made useful baskets. Men and women made pots and utensils that were useful as well. On the other hand, men and women had separate responsibilities. The men hunted, farmed, and served in the military. They used iron to make tools and weapons that were strong. The tools and weapons were durable. They were sharp. The women in the village cooked plain meals. Their dishes were also nutritious.

Men and women played important roles in Soninke village life.

Working together, Soninke men and women shared essential tasks and

daily chores. For example, both made useful baskets, pots, and

utensils. On the other hand, men and women had separate

responsibilities. The men hunted, farmed, and served in the military.

They used iron to make tools and weapons that were strong, durable,

and sharp. The women in the village cooked plain and nutritious meals.

Assessment Tip: Total **20** Points

Name _____

Vocabulary Items

Use the test-taking strategies and tips you have learned to help you complete each analogy with the correct answer. Take the time you need to think about each analogy and the answer choices. This practice will help you when you take this kind of test.

Read each analogy below. Then fill in the circle for the best answer at the bottom of the page.

1   <u>Emperor</u> was to <u>China</u> as _____ is to the <u>United States</u>.

   A   China

   B   United States

   C   rulers of countries

   D   president

2   The <u>Great Wall</u> was to the <u>Chinese people</u> as a _____ was to the <u>early American settlers</u>.

   F   wall

   G   fort

   H   horse

   J   sheriff

3   _____ were to the <u>Chinese guards</u> as <u>telephones</u> are to <u>people today</u>.

   A   Swords

   B   Letters

   C   Smoke signals

   D   Mailboxes

ANSWER ROWS   1 Ⓐ Ⓑ Ⓒ ⬤ᴰ **(5 points)**   3 Ⓐ Ⓑ ⬤ᶜ Ⓓ **(5)**

                                    2 Ⓕ ⬤ᴳ Ⓗ Ⓙ **(5)**

Name _____

Vocabulary Items continued

4 Mongol was to threat as the Great Wall was to _____.

    F defense

    G taxes

    H cannons

    J airplanes

5 Soldier was to construction worker as _____ was to architect.

    A horse

    B general

    C criminal

    D brick

6 Gate is to the Great Wall as _____ is to a house.

    F porch

    G window

    H door

    J roadway

ANSWER ROWS 4 ● (F) (G) (H) (J) **(5)** 6 (F) (G) ● (H) (J) **(5)**
    5 (A) ● (B) (C) (D) **(5)**

Assessment Tip: Total **30** Points

Name _____

Spelling Review

1–30. Write each Spelling Word. In words that have the /sh/ sound, underline the letters that spell that sound.

Order of answers may vary.

1. establi<u>sh</u> **(1 point)**
2. cooperate **(1)**
3. edi<u>ti</u>on **(1)**
4. admira<u>ti</u>on **(1)**
5. surprise **(1)**
6. accept **(1)**
7. combine **(1)**
8. difficult **(1)**
9. musi<u>ci</u>an **(1)**
10. offi<u>ci</u>al **(1)**
11. <u>sh</u>allow **(1)**
12. ambulance **(1)**
13. posi<u>ti</u>on **(1)**
14. connec<u>ti</u>on **(1)**
15. par<u>ti</u>al **(1)**
16. exam<u>pl</u>e **(1)**
17. mi<u>ss</u>ion **(1)**
18. pre<u>ss</u>ure **(1)**
19. crisis **(1)**
20. <u>ph</u>ysical **(1)**
21. problem **(1)**
22. construct **(1)**
23. combina<u>ti</u>on **(1)**
24. success **(1)**
25. connect **(1)**
26. an<u>ci</u>ent **(1)**
27. cu<u>sh</u>ion **(1)**
28. construc<u>ti</u>on **(1)**
29. admire **(1)**
30. coopera<u>ti</u>on **(1)**

Spelling Words

1. establish
2. cooperate
3. edition
4. admiration
5. surprise
6. accept
7. combine
8. difficult
9. musician
10. official
11. shallow
12. ambulance
13. position
14. connection
15. partial
16. example
17. mission
18. pressure
19. crisis
20. physical
21. problem
22. construct
23. combination
24. success
25. connect
26. ancient
27. cushion
28. construction
29. admire
30. cooperation

Theme 4: **Discovering Ancient Cultures**   265
Assessment Tip: Total **30** Points

Name _____

Spelling Spree

Headline Help Write the Spelling Word that means the opposite of the underlined word in each headline. Begin each word with a capital letter.

1. <u>Solution</u> Surfaces at Archaeological Dig Site
   Problem **(1 point)**

2. Thousand-Year-Old Artifacts Found in <u>Deep</u> Pit
   Shallow **(1)**

3. Protecting the Great Wall from Vandals Proves <u>Easy</u>
   Difficult **(1)**

4. Experts <u>Reject</u> Award for Preserving Historic City
   Accept **(1)**

5. <u>Modern</u> Aztec Stone Discovered in Mexico
   Ancient **(1)**

6. Workers Uncover <u>Total</u> Remains of Mummy
   Partial **(1)**

7. <u>Mental</u> Fitness Helps Dig Workers Handle Desert Heat
   Physical **(1)**

8. Archaeologists Meet with <u>Failure</u> on African Dig Success **(1)**

Tongue Twisters Write the Spelling Word that completes each tongue twister.

9. Milly the muddled musician **(1)** made many mistakes.

10. Cousin Carl can't combine **(1)** cucumbers and carrots.

11. Adrian will always admire **(1)** Aunt Alice's albums.

12. Sarah spilled soup when startled by Sam's silly surprise **(1)** .

13. Ed's early edition **(1)** of the encyclopedia was expensive.

14. A calico cat is curled up on the couch cushion **(1)** .

15. Amber asked for an ambulance **(1)** after the accident.

Spelling Words

1. ambulance
2. physical
3. admire
4. difficult
5. musician
6. edition
7. surprise
8. accept
9. problem
10. ancient
11. partial
12. success
13. combine
14. cushion
15. shallow

Assessment Tip: Total **15** Points

Name _____

Proofreading and Writing

Proofreading Circle the six misspelled Spelling Words in this report. Then write each word correctly.

It can be exciting to (estabalish) facts about an ancient culture. Often it is necessary to set up an (oficial) camp. The exact (pesition) of the camp can be based on old records. One useful activity is to (construckt) a model of a building that may have existed. Another is to study an (exsample) of the tools the people used. A (combonation) of study and exploration is needed.

1. establish **(1 point)**	4. construct **(1)**
2. official **(1)**	5. example **(1)**
3. position **(1)**	6. combination **(1)**

Write the Spelling Words that best complete this log entry.

August 16

I am filled with 7. admiration **(1)** for my fine crew. With their help and 8. cooperation **(1)**, we are able to resolve each new 9. crisis **(1)** quickly. We are working under some 10. pressure **(1)**, but we are coping.

Our goal, or 11. mission **(1)**, is to study the methods of 12. construction **(1)** used to build an old temple. I hope to find a 13. connection **(1)** between the temple and the buildings in the north. If I can prove that the styles 14. connect **(1)** with one another, it will be a great discovery. Now, if the weather would only 15. cooperate **(1)**!

✏️ **Write a News Report** **On a separate sheet of paper, write a news report. Use the Spelling Review Words.** Responses will vary. **(5)**

Spelling Words

1. crisis
2. example
3. position
4. cooperate
5. cooperation
6. admiration
7. combination
8. connection
9. connect
10. construction
11. construct
12. mission
13. pressure
14. establish
15. official

Name ______________________________

Mythical Elements

Fill in the chart below, describing the basic elements of each myth.

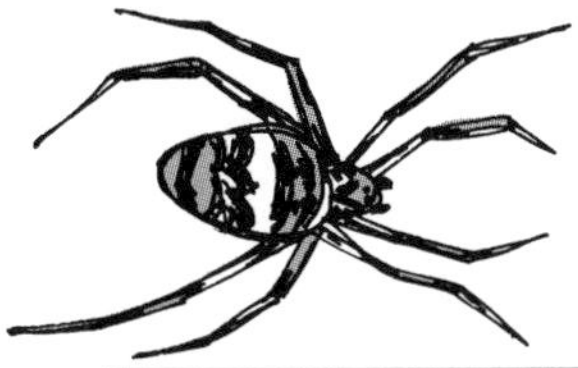

	Arachne the Spinner	**Guitar Solo**	**How Music Was Fetched out of Heaven**
Central Conflict	Athene and Arachne try to prove who is the most skilled weaver. **(2 points)**	Zin's magic guitar is scaring the fish away and making his neighbor angry. **(2)**	The earth has no music. **(2)**
Setting	ancient Greece **(2)**	The countryside of Mali, where six rivers join. **(2)**	ancient Mexico, on earth and in heaven **(2)**
Superhuman Character(s)	Athene **(2)**	Zin-Kibaru, the water spirit **(2)**	Tezcatlipoca, Quetzalcoatl, the Sun, the musicians **(2)**
Human Characters (if any)	Arachne **(2)**	Faran, Faran's mother **(2)**	the men, women, and children on earth **(2)**
Fantasy Elements	Old lady turns into Athene. Athene changes Arachne into a spider. **(2)**	magic guitar; walking fish; talking animals; magic words. **(2)**	Quetzalcoatl journeys to the Sun. The Sun can talk, and the winds are called in "like hounds." **(2)**

Which myth did you like the most? Why?

Answers will vary. **(2)**

Assessment Tip: Total **32** Points

Name _____

Describe Your Mythical Character

Every myth must have at least one superhuman character. Choose someone real, and imagine that person as a mythical character. Describe this character.

Answers will vary. **(10 points)**

_____

_____

_____

_____

_____

Show what this character looks like.

Assessment Tip: Total **10** Points

Name _____

Doers and Dreamers

The real people profiled in this theme aimed high and reached their goals despite obstacles. After reading each selection, complete the chart below to show what you learned.

	Who is this selection about?	What kind of writing is the selection an example of?
A Kind of Grace	It is about Jackie Joyner-Kersee, an athlete who excels at track events. **(2.5 points)**	an autobiography **(2.5)**
Under the Royal Palms	It is about a writer named Alma Flor Ada and her childhood in Cuba. **(2.5)**	a memoir **(2.5)**
Chuck Close Up Close	It is about an artist named Chuck Close, who is famous for his huge portraits. **(2.5)**	a biography **(2.5)**

Assessment Tip: Total **10** Points per selection and **2** points for the final question

Name _____

Doers and Dreamers

	What examples of "dreaming" did you read about in this selection?	What examples of "doing" did you read about?
A Kind of Grace	First Jackie dreamed of being a good runner, and then she got the idea that she could be a good jumper. **(2.5)**	Jackie practiced her running even though she didn't win any races. She set up a sand pit in her yard so she could practice jumping, and she taught herself how to jump. **(2.5)**
Under the Royal Palms	The author's mother dreamed of having her own business. The author's father dreamed of a family project everyone could do together. **(2.5)**	The family bought a jewelry store. They also worked together to create figurines that people in their village could afford to buy. **(2.5)**
Chuck Close Up Close	Chuck Close showed great imagination in his huge portraits. After he became paralyzed, he dreamed of working as an artist again. **(2.5)**	Chuck Close explored many new techniques for making art. After his illness he worked hard to learn to paint again. **(2.5)**

What have you learned about being a "doer" and a "dreamer" in this theme?

Sample answer: It is important to have high hopes and goals. It is also important to

work hard for what you want. **(2)**

Assessment Tip: Total **10** Points per selection and **2** points for the final question

Name _____

Running Riddles

Answer each track riddle with a vocabulary word from the box.

1. You're called this when you do the unexpected, not when you blend in with the crowd.
   unconventional **(1 point)**

2. You might feel this way when you fail to meet your goals, not when you've achieved a personal best.
   discouraged **(1)**

3. You do best in these races with short, quick strides, not long, graceful strides. sprints **(1)**

4. You need this for running distances, but not for a short race.
   endurance **(1)**

5. You hear these kinds of words from friends after a loss, but not after a win. consoling **(1)**

6. When you are a member of this, you are one of many people on a team, not one alone. squad **(1)**

7. You do drills constantly in practice to achieve this, but you lose it quickly if you start taking it easy.
   conditioning **(1)**

8. These are periods of practice, but they could be meetings of other kinds as well. sessions **(1)**

> ## Vocabulary
>
> sessions
> sprints
> unconventional
> endurance
> discouraged
> conditioning
> squad
> consoling

Name _____

K-W-L Chart

Sample answers shown.

What I <u>K</u>now	What I <u>W</u>ant to Know	What I <u>L</u>earned
Jackie Joyner-Kersee is a track and field star who has won six Olympic medals. **(1 point)**	In what events has she competed? **(1)**	She has competed in the 440-yard run, the long jump, the pentathlon, and the heptathlon. **(1)**
Jackie lost her first race. **(1)**	What did she do to get better? **(1)**	She practiced every day and ate right. **(1)**
Jackie wanted to try the long jump. **(1)**	Did she ever tell her coach she wanted to try jumping? **(1)**	She practiced jumping at home, then one day jumped while her coach was watching. He was amazed and helped her practice jumping from then on. **(1)**
Title IX required public schools to give girls and boys equal opportunities to participate in sports. **(1)**	How did this help Jackie? **(1)**	Mr. Ward and Mr. Fennoy used the money they received to form track teams in which Jackie participated. **(1)**

Assessment Tip: Total **12** Points

Name _____

Interview with an Athlete

Below are questions an interviewer might ask Jackie Joyner-Kersee. Read each question and write the answer you think Jackie would give.

Interviewer: How old were you when you joined your first track team?

Jackie: I was ten. **(1 point)**

Interviewer: What made you decide to join?

Jackie: I saw a notice about it on the bulletin board at my local Community Center. **(1)**

Interviewer: I understand that your first coach, Percy, had to end the team because most of the girls dropped out. What did you do then?

Jackie: I began to run with a new team of girls at Franklin Elementary. **(1)**

Interviewer: Who was your new coach?

Jackie: George Ward. **(1)**

Interviewer: How did you finish in your first race?

Jackie: I finished last. **(1)**

Interviewer: What did you do to become a better runner?

Jackie: I went to practice every day and made sure I ate right. **(1)**

Interviewer: Did you participate in a track and field event besides running? How did you train for it?

Jackie: Yes, the long jump. At first I practiced by jumping off my porch, but when Mr. Ward noticed how well I could jump, he helped me practice from then on. **(2)**

Name _____

Believe It or Not

Read the ads. Then complete the activity on page 277.

1.

Do you run out of steam before the clock strikes noon?
Are you too tired to get the job done, or even to have fun?
If so . . .

Jump-start your day with PowerCrunch Cereal!
Take the PowerCrunch Challenge. Eat PowerCrunch for
breakfast every morning for just one week. We guarantee
that you'll feel healthier and more alert all day, every day!

2.

Pump up your workouts with Muscle Bound sportswear!
Are you working out or wasting time? Top athletes agree: whether you're lifting
weights, running laps, or cross training, using the right clothing gives you a better
workout. Here's what two top athletes say about Muscle Bound sportswear:

A. J. Kamada, track star: "Nothing beats
Muscle Bound for fit, price, or
performance!"

Natasha Kosko, tennis pro: "Muscle
Bound is the only gear I ever wear, both
on the courts and off. It's the best! Try it
— you'll agree."

Name _____

Believe It or Not continued

Answer these questions about the ads on page 276.

1. What is the purpose of the first ad?

   To get people to buy PowerCrunch cereal. **(2 points)**

   _____

2. What does the ad promise will happen if you use the product?

   After one week, you will feel healthier and more alert all the time. **(2)**

   _____

3. Do you think readers should believe this statement? Why or why not?

   Sample answer: No, because it is an ad that's trying to sell the cereal. I also

   know that by itself, eating a certain brand of cereal is not likely to make a person

   feel healthier every day. **(2)**

4. What is the purpose of the second ad?

   To get people to buy a certain brand of sportswear. **(2)**

5. Think about how the ads on page 276 try to convince you to buy their products. Write the number of each ad next to the technique it uses.

   A. Testimonial (uses celebrities to endorse a product): 2 **(2)**

   B. Faulty cause and effect (claims that you will be better

   or happier by simply using the product): 1 **(2)**

Theme 5: **Doers and Dreamers**   277
Assessment Tip: Total **12** Points

Name _____

Word Part Match-Up

**Read each definition below. Then build words with the roots *ven* and
graph to fit the definitions, and write them on the correct lines. To
build a word, try adding letters before and after it from the chart.**

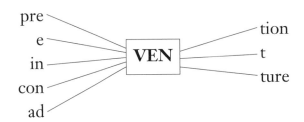

Example: an occurrence, incident, or experience: **event**

1. an opening through which vapor can escape vent **(1 point)** _____

2. a newly created device or process invention **(1)** _____

3. a memorable, exciting, or dangerous experience adventure **(1)** _____

4. a formal meeting of a group, often in a large city convention **(1)** _____

5. to stop something from happening prevent **(1)** _____

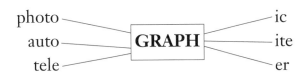

6. a signature, usually of a famous person autograph **(1)** _____

7. someone who takes pictures photographer **(1)** _____

8. an old-fashioned way to send messages using electrical impulses sent
   through wire telegraph **(1)** _____

9. having to do with written or drawn representations, such as picture
   symbols on a computer or in a book graphic **(1)** _____

10. a soft form of carbon used as the writing substance in pencils
    graphite **(1)** _____

Assessment Tip: Total **10** Points

Name _____

Final /īz/, /ĭv/, /ĭj/, /ĭk/, /chər/, and /əs/ Sounds

Each of the Spelling Words ends with the final /īz/, /ĭv/, /ĭj/, /ĭk/, /chər/, or /əs/ sound. When you hear these sounds, think of the following patterns:

final /īz/	*ize, ise*	advert**ise**, real**ize**
final /ĭv/	*ive*	act**ive**
final /ĭj/	*age*	us**age**
final /ĭk/	*ic*	scientif**ic**
final /chər/	*ture*	signa**ture**
final /əs/	*ous*	nerv**ous**

▶ The spelling of *college* differs from the usual spelling pattern. In this word, the final /ĭj/ sound is spelled *-ege*.

Write each Spelling Word under its final sound.
Order of answers for each category may vary.

Spelling Words

1. advertise
2. serious
3. scientific
4. active
5. usage
6. signature
7. realize
8. nervous
9. temperature
10. college*
11. tragic
12. positive
13. fantastic
14. exercise
15. jealous
16. organize
17. courage
18. curious
19. departure
20. storage

Final /īz/ Sound

advertise **(1 point)**

realize **(1)**

exercise **(1)**

organize **(1)**

Final /ĭv/ Sound

active **(1)**

positive **(1)**

Final /ĭj/ Sound

usage **(1)**

college **(1)**

courage **(1)**

storage **(1)**

Final /ĭk/ Sound

scientific **(1)**

tragic **(1)**

fantastic **(1)**

Final /chər/ Sound

signature **(1)**

temperature **(1)**

departure **(1)**

Final /əs/ Sound

serious **(1)**

nervous **(1)**

jealous **(1)**

curious **(1)**

Name _____

Spelling Spree

Word Root Hunt Write the Spelling Word that has the same root as each word below.

1. tragedy
2. temperate
3. useable
4. signify

5. department
6. science
7. fantasy

1. tragic **(1 point)**
2. temperature **(1)**
3. usage **(1)**
4. signature **(1)**

5. departure **(1)**
6. scientific **(1)**
7. fantastic **(1)**

Hidden Words Write the Spelling Word that is hidden in each row of letters. Don't let the other words fool you!

Example: p r e s e n s i t i v e g e   *sensitive*

8. h i s t o r a g e n t l e
9. d e p o s i t i v e r y
10. p a r t n e r v o u s i n g
11. l o a d v e r t i s e e k
12. b r o n c o l l e g e n d
13. m o r e a l i z e r o
14. o c c u r i o u s u a l
15. c o m i c o u r a g e d

Spelling Words

1. advertise
2. serious
3. scientific
4. active
5. usage
6. signature
7. realize
8. nervous
9. temperature
10. college*
11. tragic
12. positive
13. fantastic
14. exercise
15. jealous
16. organize
17. courage
18. curious
19. departure
20. storage

8. storage **(1)**
9. positive **(1)**
10. nervous **(1)**
11. advertise **(1)**

12. college **(1)**
13. realize **(1)**
14. curious **(1)**
15. courage **(1)**

Assessment Tip: Total **15** Points

Name _____

Proofreading and Writing

Proofreading Circle the five misspelled Spelling Words in this poster. Then write each word correctly.

Spelling Words

Join the team!

Are you interested in getting some (exercize?)
Are you (jealus) of friends who have their summer
activities all lined up already? We're trying to
(organise) a track team to compete over the
summer. If you're (serius) about running or just
curious about the team, come to our first
practice. It's this Wednesday after school at the
track. Now's your chance to stay (activ) this
summer instead of sitting in front of a TV!

Spelling Words

1. advertise
2. serious
3. scientific
4. active
5. usage
6. signature
7. realize
8. nervous
9. temperature
10. college*
11. tragic
12. positive
13. fantastic
14. exercise
15. jealous
16. organize
17. courage
18. curious
19. departure
20. storage

1. exercise **(1 point)**   4. serious **(1)**

2. jealous **(1)**   5. active **(1)**

3. organize **(1)**

 **Write a Play-by-Play Account** Suppose that you had been present
the first time that Jackie Joyner-Kersee did a long jump in front of
her coach. How would you have gone about describing the action for an
audience? What would you say about the jump itself? How would you
describe her coach's reaction?

**On a separate piece of paper, write a play-by-play account of Jackie
Joyner-Kersee's jump. Use Spelling Words from the list.** Responses will vary. **(5)**

Theme 5: **Doers and Dreamers**   281
Assessment Tip: Total **10** Points

Name _____

Antonym Journal

Read the following journal entry. In each blank, write an antonym of the clue word. Sample answers shown.

April 3, 1974

This ___summer **(1)**___ I get to join the East St. Louis Railers track
        (winter)

squad. I'm so excited! When I think ___back **(1)**___ to how I got into
                                        (ahead)

track, I can't believe I have come so far in just two years. I remember running

around the ___wide **(1)**___ track for the first time on a ___sunny **(1)**___
              (narrow)   (cloudy)

May afternoon when I was ten. I wasn't fast, but Mr. Ward told me that if I just

kept coming to practice, I would get ___better **(1)**___. So I did. I would
                                        (worse)

finish my homework ___quickly **(1)**___ after school and then go to practice. I
                      (slowly)

often had to run in the ___opposite **(1)**___ direction from the other girls as
                           (same)

punishment because I chatted too much, but I still loved running. I also began

___secretly **(1)**___ to practice long-jumping. Mr. Ward got excited when he
   (openly)

saw me long-jump one day, and began to coach me in that too. I don't know

where my running and jumping will ___lead **(1)**___ me, but I'm hoping it
                                     (follow)

will be to a world ___full **(1)**___ of adventure and a few ribbons!
                      (empty)

Assessment Tip: Total **10** Points

Name _____

The Subject Is Pronouns!

Subject and Object Pronouns A pronoun is a word that replaces one or more nouns. A **subject pronoun** replaces a noun used as a subject or after a linking verb. An **object pronoun** replaces a noun used as a direct object or after a word such as *to, of, in, for, at,* or *by.* This chart shows the singular and plural forms of subject pronouns and object pronouns.

Subject Pronouns		Object Pronouns	
Singular	**Plural**	**Singular**	**Plural**
I	we	me	us
you	you	you	you
he / she / it	they	him / her / it	them

Write the correct subject or object pronoun shown in parentheses ( ) for each sentence below.

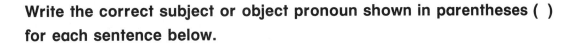

1. (We/Us) will have another race in our neighborhood this Saturday.
2. Liza will run with (we/us).
3. It is (she/her) who runs faster than anyone else in the neighborhood.
4. The prize is always awarded to (she/her).
5. When the people cheer, Liza waves at (they/them).
6. My brother Tim wants Zach to run with (he/him) this year.
7. (He/Him) thinks that maybe Zach will get the prize this year.
8. (They/Them) have been running every morning for practice.

1. We **(1 point)**

2. us **(1)**

3. she **(1)**

4. her **(1)**

5. them **(1)**

6. him **(1)**

7. He **(1)**

8. They **(1)**

Name _____

I Am Always Last!

Pronouns in Compound Subjects and Objects A **compound subject** is made up of two or more simple subjects joined by *and* or *or*. A **compound object** is made up of two or more objects of an action verb.

▶ Use a **subject pronoun** in a compound subject.
▶ Use an **object pronoun** in a compound object.
▶ If you include yourself as part of a compound subject or object, mention yourself last.

To check that the pronoun is correct in a compound subject or object, ask yourself which pronoun you would use alone. Here is an example.

    Incorrect: James and **me** went to the baseball game.

You would not use *me* alone as a subject pronoun. You would use *I*.

    Correct: James and **I** went to the baseball game.

Write the correct word or words from those in parentheses ( ) to complete the compound subject or compound object in each sentence. Then underline the compound subject or compound object in each sentence.

1. My friend Jenna and <u>I</u> dream of running in the Olympics. (I/me) **(2 points)**

2. The spirit of the Olympics motivates Jenna and <u>me</u> to do our best. (I/me) **(2)**

3. <u>She and I</u> go together to the outdoor track at our school. (She and I/Her and me) **(2)**

4. Our track coach encourages Jenna and <u>me</u> to run for the fun of it. (I/me) **(2)**

5. <u>He</u> and our teammates make every race fun. (He/Him) **(2)**

6. <u>Jenna and I</u> will hold on to our dream.
(I and Jenna/Jenna and I) **(2)**

284   Theme 5: **Doers and Dreamers**
Assessment Tip: Total **12** Points

Name _____

What's Right?

Using the Right Pronoun Be sure to use the correct forms of subject and
object pronouns in your writing.

**Austin has written a story for his school paper about his dream of
playing his violin in an orchestra. He has had some trouble choosing
the correct pronouns. Proofread his story, crossing out the six
incorrect pronouns and writing the correct ones above the errors.**

In Perfect Tune

I play the violin, and my older brother Gary plays the trumpet with

We **(1 point)**

the high school jazz band. Us brothers want to play in an orchestra

I **(1)**

together, but our school doesn't have one. My brother and me decided to

audition for the community orchestra. First, we each played a solo piece

and did pretty well. Then the orchestra members came in to start

her **(1)**

rehearsal. One player said I should sit next to she. At first, I couldn't

me **(1)**   she **(1)**

hear my own violin. The player next to I helped. It was her who told me

I **(1)**

to listen closely to the other violins. And now Gary and me are junior

members of the community orchestra!

Name _____

Clarification Composition

You write a **clarification composition** to clarify a quote, proverb, or statement, using examples and other details to support your explanation.

Use this clarification map to plan and organize a composition in which you clarify the meaning of the statement by Hall of Fame football coach Vince Lombardi. First, jot down what you think the statement means. Then list examples from Jackie Joyner-Kersee's story in *A Kind of Grace* **or from your own experience to support your ideas.**

Statement (3 points)

It's easy to have faith in yourself and have discipline when you're a winner. . . .What you've got to have is faith and discipline when you're not a winner. (Vince Lombardi)

Meaning (3)

Examples (3)

Examples (3)

Examples (3)

On a separate sheet of paper, write a composition at least three paragraphs long. The first sentence should include the Vince Lombardi statement. In the first paragraph, write what you think the statement means, restating it in your own words to expand or refine its meaning. In the following paragraphs, write reasons, details, and examples from *A Kind of Grace* **or from your own experience that support your opinion. Summarize with a concluding statement. (5)**

Assessment Tip: Total **20** Points

Name _____

Being Precise

When you write, use precise words and phrases to help your readers understand
your meaning and create clearer mental pictures. Follow these guidelines:

► Replace pronouns that are unclear with the nouns they stand for.

► Replace vague verbs with more exact verbs.

► Add precise adjectives and adverbs to nouns and verbs.

**Read this scouting report. Replace vague words with more precise words
from the chart. Add adjectives and adverbs from the chart. Then write
the revised report on the lines.** Responses may vary slightly. **(2 points each)**

> Two girls, Gwen and Jackie, on the Franklin-Freeman team threaten our
> own jumpers. One sprints down the runway but needs work on her landing.
> She places her foot solidly, though, and her form is superb. Jackie also runs
> down the lane. She pushes off and kicks her legs well. She soars through the
> air, and lands. They are in peak condition because of their training and will
> undoubtedly break many records.

Precise Words and Phrases

Nouns	Gwen	Gwen and Jackie	the girls
Verbs	plants	charges	shatter
Adjectives	powerful	track-and-field	rigorous
Adverbs	cleanly	squarely	

Two girls, Gwen and Jackie, on the Franklin-Freeman **track-and-field** team

threaten our own jumpers. **Gwen** sprints down the runway but needs work on her

landing. She **plants** her foot solidly, though, and her form is superb. Jackie also

charges down the lane. She pushes off **cleanly** and kicks her **powerful** legs well.

She soars through the air, and lands **squarely**. **Gwen and Jackie** are in peak

condition because of their **rigorous** training and will undoubtedly **shatter** many

records.

Name _____

Evaluating Your Personal Essay

Reread your personal essay. What do you need to make it better? Use this page to help you decide. Put a checkmark in the box for each sentence that describes your personal essay.

Loud and Clear!

☐ My essay has a strong beginning that will get my readers' attention.

☐ I keep to the focus of the topic.

☐ My voice comes through in the tone of the essay.

☐ I have an effective conclusion that sums up my point.

☐ There are almost no mistakes.

Sounding Stronger

☐ I could make the beginning more attention grabbing.

☐ I stray from the point in a couple of places.

☐ My voice isn't always clear in the writing.

☐ I need to add a stronger conclusion.

☐ There are a few mistakes, including some sentence fragments.

Turn Up the Volume

☐ I need a better beginning.

☐ There are a lot of things in here that aren't related to the topic.

☐ There is no conclusion.

☐ There are a lot of mistakes, including many sentence fragments.

Sentence Fragments

► A complete sentence expresses a complete thought. It has both a subject and a predicate.

► A fragment is an incomplete sentence. It lacks either a subject or a predicate.

Identify each group of words as a Complete Sentence or a Fragment. Change each fragment into a complete sentence on the lines provided. You may need to rearrange or add words.

1. Telephone calls from telemarketers every night during dinner.

   Fragment; I really hate getting telephone calls from telemarketers every

   night during dinner. **(2 points)**

2. What things irritate you?

   Complete Sentence **(2)**

3. Getting a recorded menu without a real person to talk to.

   Fragment; Getting a recorded menu without a real person to talk to also

   bothers me. **(2)**

4. Don't put me on hold!

   Complete Sentence **(2)**

5. On hold for one hour and fifty-seven minutes without speaking to anyone.

   Fragment; I was on hold for one hour and fifty-seven minutes

   without speaking to anyone. **(2)**

6. When I finally spoke to someone, I forgot what I was going to say.

   Complete Sentence **(2)**

Theme 5: **Doers and Dreamers**   289
Assessment Tip: Total **12** Points

Name _____

Spelling Words

Look for familiar spelling patterns to help you remember how to spell the Spelling Words on this page. Think carefully about the parts that you find hard to spell in each word.

Write the missing letters in the Spelling Words below.

1. <u>a</u>nyone (**1 point**)

2. cap <u>t</u> <u>a</u> <u>i</u> n (**1**)

3. <u>a</u> <u>l</u> <u>l</u> right (**1**)

4. b <u>e</u> <u>a</u> <u>u</u> t <u>i</u> ful (**1**)

5. en <u>o</u> <u>u</u> g <u>h</u> (**1**)

6. fam <u>i</u> ly (**1**)

7. som <u>e</u> one (**1**)

8. stre <u>t</u> <u>c</u> <u>h</u> (**1**)

9. favor <u>i</u> t <u>e</u> (**1**)

10. g <u>u</u> <u>y</u> (**1**)

11. <u>a</u> lot (**1**)

12. fr <u>i</u> <u>e</u> nd (**1**)

13. s <u>o</u> <u>m</u> <u>e</u> times (**1**)

14. <u>a</u> nyway (**1**)

15. <u>a</u> nything (**1**)

Spelling Words

1. anyone
2. captain
3. all right
4. beautiful
5. enough
6. family
7. someone
8. stretch
9. favorite
10. guy
11. a lot
12. friend
13. sometimes
14. anyway
15. anything

Study List On a separate piece of paper, write each Spelling Word. Check your spelling against the words on the list.

Order of words may vary. (**1**)

Assessment Tip: Total **16** Points

Name _____

Spelling Spree

Contrast Clues The second part of each clue contrasts with the first part. Write a Spelling Word to fit each clue.

1. not all the time, but _____
2. not a gal, but a _____
3. not fantastic, but _____
4. not to shrink, but to _____
5. not a little, but _____

1. sometimes **(1 point)**
2. guy **(1)**
3. all right **(1)**
4. stretch **(1)**
5. a lot **(1)**

1. anyone
2. captain
3. all right
4. beautiful
5. enough
6. family
7. someone
8. stretch
9. favorite
10. guy
11. a lot
12. friend
13. sometimes
14. anyway
15. anything

Word Maze Begin at the arrow and follow the Word Maze to find ten Spelling Words. Write the words in order.

6. anything **(1)**
7. family **(1)**
8. captain **(1)**
9. friend **(1)**
10. anyone **(1)**

11. someone **(1)**
12. favorite **(1)**
13. anyway **(1)**
14. beautiful **(1)**
15. enough **(1)**

Assessment Tip: Total **15** Points

Name _____

Proofreading and Writing

Proofreading Circle the five misspelled Spelling Words in this acceptance speech. Then write each word correctly.

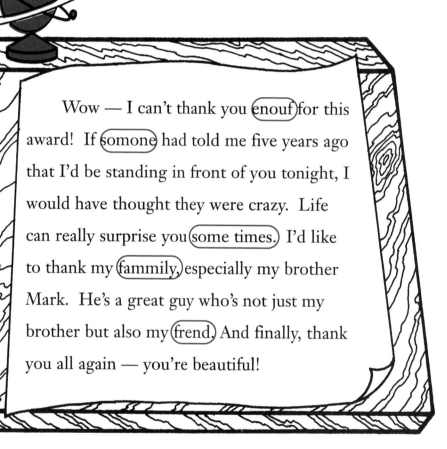

Wow — I can't thank you (enouf) for this award! If (somone) had told me five years ago that I'd be standing in front of you tonight, I would have thought they were crazy. Life can really surprise you (some times.) I'd like to thank my (fammily,) especially my brother Mark. He's a great guy who's not just my brother but also my (frend.) And finally, thank you all again — you're beautiful!

1. anyone
2. captain
3. all right
4. beautiful
5. enough
6. family
7. someone
8. stretch
9. favorite
10. guy
11. a lot
12. friend
13. sometimes
14. anyway
15. anything

1. enough **(1 point)**

2. someone **(1)**

3. sometimes **(1)**

4. family **(1)**

5. friend **(1)**

✏ **Write Inspirational Sentences** **Write five sentences that you could use to encourage someone to go out and achieve their dreams. Use Spelling Words from the list.** Responses will vary. **(5)**

Assessment Tip: Total **10** Points

Name _____

"Account" for These Sentences

Use the words in the box to complete the sentences below.

1. Tiny statues you might place on your bookshelf for decoration are called figurines **(1 point)** _____.

2. Something that is easy for people to get is accessible **(1)** _____.

3. Someone who is extremely careful and exact is meticulous **(1)** _____.

4. Books in which numbers are recorded are called ledgers **(1)** _____.

5. Someone trained to keep financial records for businesses is an accountant **(1)** _____.

6. Something used in place of something else is makeshift **(1)** _____.

7. If you don't try to act like you are rich or important, you are humble **(1)** _____.

8. If you are officially recognized as qualified to do something, you are certified **(1)** _____.

9. If you move your old books to make room for new ones on your bookshelf, you have relegated **(1)** _____ your old books to another shelf.

10. Small items of little value are called trinkets **(1)** _____.

Vocabulary

accountant
ledgers
meticulous
certified
trinkets
relegated
figurines
accessible
humble
makeshift

Theme 5: **Doers and Dreamers**   293
Assessment Tip: Total **10** Points

Name _____

Problem–Solution Chart

Fill in the solution the characters found to each problem stated on the chart.

Problem		Solution
The author's mother wanted to complete her education, but she had to take care of a new baby.	→	She completed her education by going to night school. **(2 points)**
The author's mother wanted to continue her accounting work while running her store.	→	She did her accounting work at the store counter in between helping customers. **(2)**
The author's mother had to watch her two daughters while working at the store.	→	She kept her baby in a makeshift playpen. The author did her homework at the store after school. **(2)**
The author's family didn't have enough money to keep up the big family house.	→	They bought a jewelry store to run, and lived in the store building. **(2)**
The author's family wanted to make the jewelry store a successful business.	→	Her father learned to fix watches. Her mother redecorated the store and expanded the merchandise. **(2)**
The author's family wanted to find affordable Nativity figurines to sell.	→	They figured out how to make inexpensive figurines from molds, and worked together to make them. **(2)**

Assessment Tip: Total **12** Points

Name _____

What's the Order?

First, read each sentence below. Circle *Mother* or *Father* to correctly complete each sentence. Then number the sentences to show the order in which the events occur in the selection. The first item has been numbered for you.

7 (1)   (Mother/Father) created molds for the figurines. **(1 point)**

3 (1)   (Mother/Father) convinced the family to take over a jewelry store in the city. **(1)**

5 (1)   (Mother/Father) searched for inexpensive figurines to sell. **(1)**

1   (Mother/Father) studied to become an accountant. **(1)**

4 (1)   (Mother/Father) learned how to fix watches. **(1)**

6 (1)   (Mother/Father) came up with a plan for the whole family to help make figurines. **(1)**

2 (1)   (Mother/Father) opened a small store selling buttons, thread, pencils, and paper. **(1)**

8 (1)   (Mother/Father) gave the figurines their first coat of paint. **(1)**

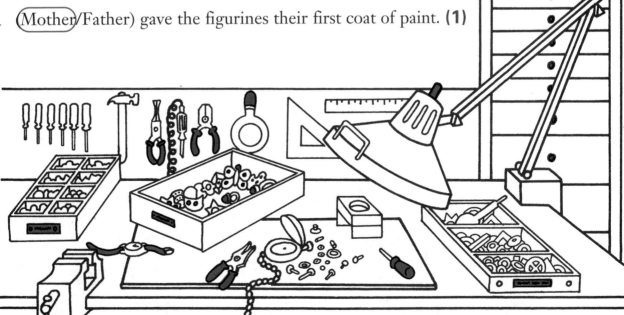

Name _____

Finding a Way

Read the passage below. Then complete the activity on page 297.

A Life of Art

Igor Koutsenko was born in the former Soviet Union. When he was six years old, his father brought him to a children's art school. It was there that he first saw a large box filled with what seemed like thousands of colored pencils. To him, that box shone with all the wonderful possibilities of art. Igor knew right then that he wanted to be an artist.

To become an artist, Igor decided to study in several art schools. After he graduated, he was required to serve in the Soviet Army for two years. Although he wanted to do his duty, he did not want to stop working as an artist. So he designed posters and slogans for the army. After leaving the army, he earned his living as an artist in Moscow.

Igor wanted to use his art to show people the difficulties in his country at that time. So he started drawing pen-and-ink miniatures with social or political themes. His drawings made people laugh, but they also made them look at the problems of society around them.

Eventually he started to explore different themes with his miniatures. He remembered the beautiful scenery of his childhood, which included grasslands, mountains, and the Black Sea. These images made him realize that harmony exists in the world. Through his work, he began to express his belief that the only way people can contribute to the survival of life on earth is to find peace and harmony in their own lives. Today Igor continues to work and lives in San Diego, California.

296   Theme 5: **Doers and Dreamers**

Finding a Way continued

Read the passage on page 296. Then complete the chart below.

Problem	Igor's Solution	Other Possible Solutions	My Judgment
Igor wanted to become an artist.	He went to art school to learn how. **(2 points)**	He could have tried to learn on his own. **(2)**	Sample answer: Going to art school was the best idea because he learned from good teachers. **(2)**
Igor had to join the army for two years but didn't want to stop doing art.	He combined the two by designing posters and slogans for the army. **(2)**	He could have tried to avoid joining the army. Or he could have not done any art while he was in the army. **(2)**	Sample answer: Combining the two was the best idea. It let him continue with art without getting into trouble with the army. **(2)**
Igor wanted to show the harsh realities of life under communism through his art.	He drew miniatures that made people laugh while also showing them the difficulties he saw. **(2)**	He could have made drawings that didn't make people laugh. **(2)**	Sample answer: He made a good choice. Often people don't like to see unpleasant things, but if they can laugh at something first, they might pay more attention to it. **(2)**

Theme 5: **Doers and Dreamers**   297
Assessment Tip: Total **18** Points

Name _____

Plural[s]

Read each sentence below and look at the underlined plural words. Write the singular form of each underlined word on the line provided.

1. Alma's mother used <u>ledgers</u> and <u>receipts</u> to do her accounting work.

   ledger **(1 point)** _____   receipt **(1)** _____

2. The <u>figurines</u> were just one of many <u>varieties</u> of <u>items</u> sold in the family store.

   figurine **(1)** _____   variety **(1)** _____   item **(1)** _____

3. The <u>men</u>, <u>women</u>, and <u>children</u> of the family all helped with the work.

   man **(1)** _____   woman **(1)** _____   child **(1)** _____

4. They painted colorful <u>costumes</u> on the tiny <u>people</u>.

   costume **(1)** _____   person **(1)** _____

Write the plural form of each word on the line provided.

Plural Form

5. variety   varieties **(1)** _____

6. half   halves **(1)** _____

7. receipt   receipts **(1)** _____

8. box   boxes **(1)** _____

9. man   men **(1)** _____

Assessment Tip: Total **15** Points

Name _____

Plurals

Remember the following patterns to form the plurals of nouns ending with *f* or *o*:

► For nouns ending with *ff*, add -*s*: sta**ff**/sta**ffs**.

► For nouns ending with *f*, add -*s* or change *f* to *v* and add -*es*: chie**f**/chie**fs**, hal**f**/hal**ves**.

► For nouns ending with a vowel + *o*, add -*s*: ster**eo**/ster**eos**.

► For nouns ending with a consonant + *o*, add -*s* or -*es* pi**ano**/pi**anos**, pota**to**/pota**toes**.

Write each Spelling Word under the heading that tells how its plural is formed. Order of responses for each category may vary.

Spelling Words

1. pianos
2. cellos
3. solos
4. altos
5. sopranos
6. staffs
7. stereos
8. potatoes
9. halves
10. chiefs
11. echoes
12. calves
13. studios
14. shelves
15. ratios
16. volcanoes
17. loaves
18. wolves
19. heroes
20. scarves

-*s* Added

pianos **(1 point)**

cellos **(1)**

solos **(1)**

altos **(1)**

sopranos **(1)**

staffs **(1)**

stereos **(1)**

chiefs **(1)**

studios **(1)**

ratios **(1)**

-*es* Added

potatoes **(1)**

echoes **(1)**

volcanoes **(1)**

heroes **(1)**

f Changed to *v*, -*es* Added

halves **(1)**

calves **(1)**

shelves **(1)**

loaves **(1)**

wolves **(1)**

scarves **(1)**

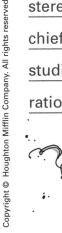

Theme 5: **Doers and Dreamers** 299
Assessment Tip: Total **20** Points

Name _____

Spelling Spree

Word Magic Write a Spelling Word to fit each clue.

1. Change a vowel in *soles* to write a word for one-person performances.
2. Replace a consonant in *herds* with two vowels to write a word for brave men.
3. Add a consonant to *caves* to write a word meaning "young cattle."
4. Replace one consonant in *loans* with two letters to write a word meaning more than one package of bread.
5. Insert one vowel into *chefs* to write a synonym for *leaders*.
6. Add a vowel to *cells* to write the plural form of a large string instrument.
7. Change the ending of *alter* to write a word meaning "low singing voices."

Spelling Words

1. pianos
2. cellos
3. solos
4. altos
5. sopranos
6. staffs
7. stereos
8. potatoes
9. halves
10. chiefs
11. echoes
12. calves
13. studios
14. shelves
15. ratios
16. volcanoes
17. loaves
18. wolves
19. heroes
20. scarves

1. solos **(1 point)**
2. heroes **(1)**
3. calves **(1)**
4. loaves **(1)**
5. chiefs **(1)**
6. cellos **(1)**
7. altos **(1)**

Alphabetizing Write the Spelling Word that fits alphabetically between the two words in each group.

8. vocabulary, volcanoes **(1)**, volume
9. stacks, staffs **(1)**, stagger
10. rating, ratios **(1)**, rattle
11. peanuts, pianos **(1)**, plants
12. scars, scarves **(1)**, scavenge
13. steers, stereos **(1)**, stores
14. eccentric, echoes **(1)**, ecology
15. sopping, sopranos **(1)**, sorrow

300   Theme 5: **Doers and Dreamers**
Assessment Tip: Total **15** Points

Proofreading and Writing

Proofreading Circle the five misspelled Spelling Words in this dialogue based on the selection. Then write each word correctly.

> Father: Well, the figurines aren't bad. Nothing like what
>
> artists can produce in their fancy (studioes,) but not bad
>
> — except for that shepherd. The two (halfs) of the mold
>
> didn't meet up right on that one.
>
> Manolo: They're better than not bad, I think. Besides,
>
> that's not the point, is it? Now our customers can have
>
> a Nativity scene and still afford their meat, (potatos,)
>
> and loaves of bread.
>
> Father: That's true. It wouldn't be much of a holiday if
>
> they were all hungry as (wolfes.)
>
> Manolo: So let's place these on the store (shelfs) tomorrow
>
> and see how they sell.

Spelling Words

1. pianos
2. cellos
3. solos
4. altos
5. sopranos
6. staffs
7. stereos
8. potatoes
9. halves
10. chiefs
11. echoes
12. calves
13. studios
14. shelves
15. ratios
16. volcanoes
17. loaves
18. wolves
19. heroes
20. scarves

1. studios **(1 point)**   4. wolves **(1)**

2. halves **(1)**   5. shelves **(1)**

3. potatoes **(1)**

✏️ **Write a Personal Narrative** Alma Flor Ada's family worked together to make their new store successful. Can you remember a time when you worked with others to get something accomplished? How did you feel about working as part of a team? Was your project a success?

On a separate piece of paper, write a personal narrative about a project that you did with a partner or a group. Use Spelling Words from the list. Responses will vary. **(5)**

Name _____

Mind These Meanings

Read each entry word and its definition. For each word write two sentences, using a different meaning of the word in each. Sample answers shown.

> **enlist** (ĕn **lĭst′**) *v.* **1.** To engage someone for service in the armed forces. **2.** To engage the support or cooperation of.
>
> **figure** (**fĭg′** yər) *n.* **1.** An amount represented in numbers. **2.** An indistinct object or shape.
>
> **live¹** (lĭv) *v.* To reside or dwell.
>
> **live²** (līv) *adj.* Alive; living.
>
> **miss** (mĭs) *v.* **1.** To fail to attend or be present for. **2.** To feel or regret the absence or loss of.
>
> **needle** (**nēd′** l) *n.* A small slender sewing implement, pointed at one end and having an eye at the other. —*v.* To goad, provoke, or tease.

1. My father enlisted in the army when he was a young man. Can I enlist your help to make decorations for the dance? **(2 points)**

2. The in-line skates were priced at a higher figure than I could pay. The boy trudging through the snowy field was a small figure in a large landscape. **(2)**

3. Have you seen the live animals at the zoo? They live there year-round. **(2)**

4. I missed my sister's orchestra concert, because I was sick. The girl missed her grandparents after they retired and moved away. **(2)**

5. I lost my mother's sewing needle. My mother needled me all day about it. **(2)**

Bonus Now try writing one sentence that uses two different meanings of one word.

Assessment Tip: Total **10** Points

Name _____

My or Mine?

Possessive and Indefinite Pronouns A **possessive pronoun** shows ownership. It takes the place of a possessive noun.

► *My, your, his, her, its, our,* and *their* are used before nouns: This is my bike.

► *Mine, yours, hers, his, its, ours, yours,* and *theirs* are used alone: It is mine.

► Notice that *his* and *its* can come before a noun or be used alone.

An **indefinite pronoun** does not have a definite antecedent. It does not refer to a specific person, place, or thing. Use a singular verb with a **singular indefinite pronoun**. Use a plural verb with a **plural indefinite pronoun**.

Indefinite Pronouns				
Singular			**Plural**	
any	everybody	nothing	all	others
anyone	everyone	somebody	both	several
anything	everything	someone	few	some
each	nobody	something	many	

Replace the possessive noun in each sentence with a possessive pronoun. Write the possessive pronoun after the sentence.

1. Rebecca's family owns a store on our block. _Her **(1 point)**_

2. The store was her grandparents' dream. _their **(1)**_

3. The store's goods come from all over the world. _Its **(1)**_

Complete each sentence by writing the correct form of the word in parentheses ( ).

4. Everyone _shops **(1)**_ at that little place. (shops/shop)

5. Many _are **(1)**_ telling their friends about the store. (is/are)

6. The advertisements in the newspaper are _yours **(1)**_. (your/yours)

7. Jessie bought _her **(1)**_ mom a present there. (her/hers)

8. I will shop for _mine **(1)**_ there too. (my/mine)

Theme 5: **Doers and Dreamers**   303
Assessment Tip: Total **8** Points

Name _____

Who Is It ?

Using *Who*, *Whom*, and *Whose* The words *who*, *whom*, and *whose* are forms of the pronoun *who*.

Use *who* as a **subject pronoun**, *whom* as an **object pronoun**, and *whose* as a **possessive pronoun**. The different forms of *who* are often used in questions. To check whether *whom* is correct, turn the question into a statement. Here is an example.

> *Whom* has Rita called? (Rita has called *whom*.)

Whom is correct because it is the **direct object** in the sentence.

Rita and her friends are hosting an international fair for charity. Everyone has lots of questions! Fill in the blank in each sentence with the correct form of the pronoun *who*.

1. Who **(1 point)** _____ wants to sell holiday decorations at the fair?

2. Whom **(1)** _____ will Rita invite to the fair?

3. Who **(1)** _____ brought the lemonade?

4. Whose **(1)** _____ decorations are these?

5. Whom **(1)** _____ will Carson ask for help?

6. Whose **(1)** _____ booth will do the most business?

7. Who **(1)** _____ is selling baked goods?

8. Whom **(1)** _____ should we thank for these posters?

9. Whose **(1)** _____ idea was it to play music?

10. Whom **(1)** _____ will Rita ask to deliver the money to the charity?

Assessment Tip: Total **10** Points

Who's Who

Whose or *Who's*?   A good writer is careful not to confuse the possessive
pronoun *whose* with *who's*, the contraction of the words *who is*. It helps to
remember that a possessive pronoun never has an apostrophe. Study
these examples.

Incorrect: **Whose** at the door?
Correct: **Who's** at the door? (Who is at the door?)
Incorrect: **Who's** house is that?
Correct: **Whose** house is that? (Who owns that house?)

**Ernesto's family is moving. He becomes curious about his family's
history from the interesting old family photos and belongings in the
attic. A list of Ernesto's questions is below. You can see that he has
been confused by the difference between *who's* and *whose*. Cross
out any error and write the correction above it. If a sentence has no
error, write *none* above the sentence.**

Whose **(1 point)**
1. Who's big old trunk is that?
   Who's **(1)**
2. Whose the man wearing a hat in the big portrait?
   none **(1)**
3. Whose military uniform hangs on the nail?
   Who's **(1)**
4. Whose the oldest member of our family?
   none **(1)**
5. Who's going to write down our family history?
   Whose **(1)**
6. Who's journal is on the shelf?
   Whose **(1)**
7. Who's maps are these?
   Who's **(1)**
8. Whose going to put all these photographs in order?

Name _____

How-To Paragraph

A **how-to paragraph** tells how to do something. It has clear, complete instructions.

Use this page to plan and organize a how-to paragraph. First, identify your topic. Next, list the materials that are needed. Then outline each step. Finally, jot down specialized terms and ideas for helpful diagrams.

How to **(2 points)** _____

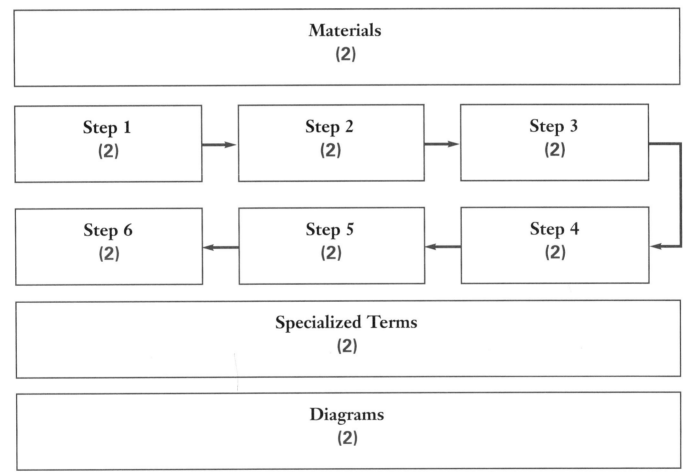

**Materials
(2)**

| Step 1 (2) | Step 2 (2) | Step 3 (2) |
| Step 6 (2) | Step 5 (2) | Step 4 (2) |

**Specialized Terms
(2)**

**Diagrams
(2)**

Now write your how-to paragraph on a separate sheet of paper. In the topic sentence, describe what skill will be taught. Then tell what materials are needed. Next, explain each step clearly and in order. Include a diagram and a glossary of specialized terms. (5)

Assessment Tip: Total **25** Points

Name _____

Writing Clearly with Pronouns

You often use **pronouns** such as *he*, *she*, *they*, or *it* in your writing. Using pronouns helps you replace nouns in sentences, streamline your language, and avoid unnecessary repetition. Careful writers, however, do not use pronouns with unclear **antecedents** — the nouns to which the pronouns refer.

Unclear:

Ann and Lia bake holiday cookies. **She** asks **her** to make the dough and shape it with a cookie cutter. (Who makes the dough and shapes it, Ann or Lia?)

Clear:

Ann and Lia bake holiday cookies. **Lia** asks **Ann** to make the dough and shape **it** with a cookie cutter. (The pronoun *it* clearly refers to the dough.)

Read the following paragraph about two sisters working together to make a plaster of paris figurine. Underline the pronouns. Then replace any pronouns with unclear antecedents with the nouns for which they stand. Write the nouns above the pronouns you underline.

The sisters
Flor and her sister Alma make figurines. They use these supplies: a

figurine mold, soft plaster of paris, grease, a kitchen knife, paints, and
these supplies
small brushes. You find them at an arts and crafts store. First, Alma

greases the inside of the mold before closing and locking the mold's
The sisters
hinges. They pour in a small amount of plaster of paris through a hole in
the mold
the bottom of the mold until it is filled. Once the plaster has completely
Flor or Alma Alma or Flor   the figurine
hardened, she helps her gently remove it from the mold.

Name ______________________

A Word Exhibition

Vocabulary

palette	painstaking	canvas	portrait
pixels	conceptual	hyperrealistic	exhibition
optically	obstacles	abstract	

Write each word from the box beneath the heading that tells about it.

Tools Used for Painting

palette **(1 point)**

canvas **(1)**

Three Styles of Art

hyperrealistic **(1)**

abstract **(1)**

conceptual **(1)**

Having to Do with Vision

optically **(1)**

Small Dots Used in Computer Art

pixels **(1)**

Painting of a Person

portrait **(1)**

Requiring Great Care and Effort

painstaking **(1)**

A Public Show of Artwork

exhibition **(1)**

A Word for *Difficulties*

obstacles **(1)**

Now use four words from the box to write a brief paragraph about what you might see in an artist's studio.

Accept well-written answers that use the words correctly. **(4)**

Assessment Tip: Total **15** Points

Name _____

Comparison Chart

Write the most important ideas you learn about Chuck Close in the chart below.

Pages 500–505	Pages 506–511
creates problems to solve **(1 point)**	suffered a major illness in 1988 and became paralyzed **(1)**
keeps changing his style **(1)**	through rehabilitation, regained partial movement in his arms and legs **(1)**
painted portraits from photographs **(1)**	started to paint again by strapping a brush to his arm **(1)**
found a new way to put color onto canvas by separating the colors in a photograph and then repainting them, one by one **(1)**	painting style continued to change and evolve; critics loved new work **(1)**
created portraits using fingerprints, and using tiny dots that mix optically inside the eye **(1)**	Museum of Modern Art showed his work **(1)**

After you read, compare Chuck Close's life before and after "the event." On a separate piece of paper make three lists: (10)

► Things that Chuck Close did before "the event"

► Things that Chuck Close did after "the event"

► Things Chuck did both before and after "the event"

Theme 5: **Doers and Dreamers**   309
Assessment Tip: Total **20** Points

Name _____

Fact Sheet

Write some facts about Chuck Close to complete the fact sheet below.

Name: Chuck Close **(1 point)** _____

Occupation: artist **(1)** _____

Best Known for: creating huge portraits of people using unusual painting techniques **(1)** _____

Place of Residence: New York **(1)** _____

Painting Methods:

 1. painted each color separately **(1)** _____

 2. used fingerprints **(1)** _____

 3. painted images with tiny colored dots **(1)** _____

Life's Greatest Challenge:

getting very sick and being paralyzed from the waist down **(1)** _____

How He Overcame His Challenge:

went to physical therapy for a long time; now paints with a brush strapped

to his arm **(2)** _____

Advice to Others:

Don't wait for inspiration. Just try as hard as you can, get into a rhythm,

and don't give up. Create problems to solve so you don't get too

comfortable. **(2)** _____

310   Theme 5: **Doers and Dreamers**
Assessment Tip: Total **12** Points

Name _____

Like or Unlike?

Read the passage. Then complete the activity on page 312.

Portrait of JoeSam.

Joseph Samuels, who uses the name *JoeSam.*, is a contemporary artist who lives and works in San Francisco. He has created works in a wide range of forms, including paintings, mixed-media pieces, and sculptures. He uses a variety of materials in his work: wood, metal, old photographs, paint, and even flannel shirts.

Although he has been creating art since he was young, he hasn't always been a full-time artist. In college he studied education and psychology. For many years he worked for organizations devoted to helping others, such as Headstart. Eventually he became a full-time artist, which he says is "fabulous." His interest in teaching continues in his art. He believes that his artwork needs to show "some awareness of what's happening in the world" and that it must teach people something. One of his most famous art projects, "Black West," focuses on teaching people little-known facts about the lives of African Americans who settled the American frontier.

JoeSam. loves being an artist. He volunteers at many schools to encourage a love of art in young people. His advice to them includes these words: "Just create your art. . . . Anyone can create art." He admits that art is not a likely way for a person to make a lot of money, but he believes it is still important. He says, "Art is something you do — it's just a part of what you love, that you want to create."

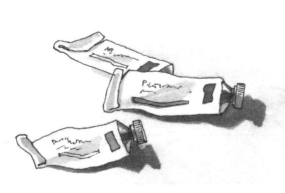

Name _____

Like or Unlike? continued

Complete the exercises below.

1. Compare and contrast the careers and art of JoeSam. and Chuck
   Close. Write your answers in the Venn diagram below. Sample answers shown.

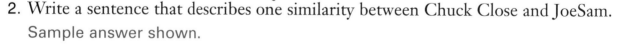

**JoeSam.'s Art
and Career**

His art includes
paintings, sculptures, and
mixed-media art using
unusual materials.
(2 points)
Before he became a full-
time artist, he worked at
places where he could
help people. Now he
creates art and
volunteers at
schools. **(2)**

Both
The artwork
of both
includes
paintings. **(2)**
Both made
adjustments
in their
careers. **(2)**

**Chuck Close's Art
and Career**

His art includes different
styles of portraits
painted with his fingers
or paintbrushes. **(2)**
He started an art career
at a young age. He
became paralyzed and
went through
rehabilitation. He
figured out a
way to continue
painting. **(2)**

2. Write a sentence that describes one similarity between Chuck Close and JoeSam.
   Sample answer shown.

   Both artists believe that art is very important in their lives and that it

   is something they need to create. **(3)**

3. Write a sentence that describes one difference between these two artists. Sample
   answer shown.

   Chuck Close creates mostly portraits while JoeSam. creates a variety

   of art forms. **(3)**

Chuck Close Up Close

Structural Analysis Suffixes
-ent/-ence, -ant/-ance,
-able/-ible, -ate

Name _____

Suffix Scramble

Read each sentence. In the letter spaces, write the word from the palette that best completes each sentence. Then unscramble the circled letters to answer the question at the bottom of the page.

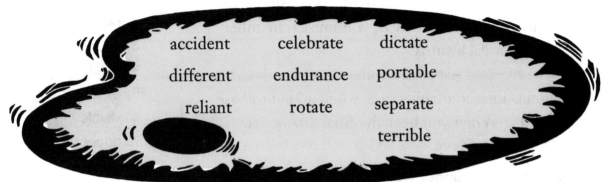

accident   celebrate   dictate

different   endurance   portable

reliant   rotate   separate

terrible

1. Chuck Close likes to try d i f f e (r) e n t
   painting styles. **(1 point)**

2. For some paintings, Chuck would (s) e (p) a r a t e
   a photograph into three colors. **(1)**

3. Chuck likes to c e l e b (r) a t e with music as
   he finishes a painting. **(1)**

4. While giving a speech, Chuck felt (t) e r r i b l e
   and went to the hospital. **(1)**

5. Chuck's injury can also happen to people who have been in an
   a c c (i) d e n t . **(1)**

6. "The event" will d i c (t) a t e how Chuck paints
   from now on. **(1)**

7. Chuck needs a lot of e n d u r (a) n c e to hold a
   paintbrush for many hours. **(1)**

8. After working through a whole painting, Chuck likes to
   r (o) t a t e the painting to a new position and go
   through it again. **(1)**

What kinds of paintings does Chuck Close most often create?

(p) (o) (r) (t) (r) (a) (i) (t) (s) **(2)**

Name _____

Suffixes: *-ant/-ance;*
-ent/-ence; -able/-ible; -ate

The suffixes *-ant*, *-ent*, *-able*, and *-ible* are sometimes added to base words or word roots to form adjectives. Because the spelling of the schwa sound is not clear, you must remember the spelling pattern for each suffix.

The suffixes *-ance* and *-ence* are similar to *-ant* and *-ent*, but they form nouns instead of adjectives when added to base words or word roots. When you hear the final /ĭt/ or /āt/ sounds, think of the pattern *ate*.

Write each Spelling Word under its suffix.
Order of responses for each category may vary.

-ant
brilliant **(1 point)**

fragrant **(1)**

-ance
appearance **(1)**

instance **(1)**

importance **(1)**

-ent
excellent **(1)**

client **(1)**

agent **(1)**

-ence
audience **(1)**

sentence **(1)**

difference **(1)**

-able
lovable **(1)**

noticeable **(1)**

workable **(1)**

-ible
visible **(1)**

responsible **(1)**

-ate
desperate **(1)**

celebrate **(1)**

fortunate **(1)**

separate **(1)**

Name _____

Spelling Spree

Word Detective Write a Spelling Word for each clue.

1. a particular case, or example
2. deserving of affection
3. an employee of the FBI
4. the way something looks
5. sweet-smelling, like a flower
6. a lawyer's customer
7. shining very brightly
8. kept apart

1. instance **(1 point)**
2. lovable **(1)**
3. agent **(1)**
4. appearance **(1)**

5. fragrant **(1)**
6. client **(1)**
7. brilliant **(1)**
8. separate **(1)**

Spelling Words

1. desperate
2. brilliant
3. audience
4. celebrate
5. excellent
6. visible
7. appearance
8. lovable
9. noticeable
10. sentence
11. difference
12. workable
13. instance
14. fragrant
15. fortunate
16. client
17. separate
18. agent
19. responsible
20. importance

Syllable Spot Write the Spelling Word that has one of the
syllables in each word below.

9. sponsor
10. person
11. audibly
12. portion
13. fortify
14. fertile
15. sentiment

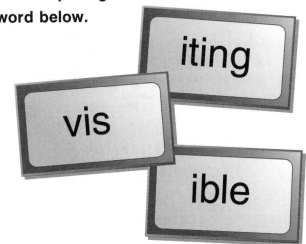

9. responsible **(1)**
10. desperate **(1)**
11. audience **(1)**
12. importance **(1)**

13. fortunate **(1)**
14. difference **(1)**
15. sentence **(1)**

Theme 5: **Doers and Dreamers**   315
Assessment Tip: Total **15** Points

Name _____

Proofreading and Writing

Proofreading Circle the five misspelled Spelling Words in
this newspaper column. Then write each word correctly.

Spelling Words

Eye on Art

NEW YORK– An (excelent) exhibit of Chuck Close's newest
paintings opened here yesterday. The artist has been
partially paralyzed from the neck down since December of
1988. With courage and determination, he has found a
(workible) way of continuing to paint, strapping brushes to his
hands and moving his arms across the canvas. There is a
(noticable) difference between his current paintings and his
earlier work. The canvas seems to contain many little
images when looked at closely. When the viewer steps back,
however, a larger figure becomes (visibel.) The paintings are
remarkable, and art lovers will (cellebrate) this fine
exhibition.

1. desperate
2. brilliant
3. audience
4. celebrate
5. excellent
6. visible
7. appearance
8. lovable
9. noticeable
10. sentence
11. difference
12. workable
13. instance
14. fragrant
15. fortunate
16. client
17. separate
18. agent
19. responsible
20. importance

1. excellent **(1 point)**   4. visible **(1)**

2. workable **(1)**   5. celebrate **(1)**

3. noticeable **(1)**

✏— **Write a Description** Chuck Close is very dedicated to his art. Is
there a favorite sport, hobby, or craft that you have a great interest in?
Why do you like it? How often do you participate in this activity?

**On a separate piece of paper, write a brief description of your
favorite sport, hobby, or craft. Be sure to tell what it means to you.
Use Spelling Words from the list.** Responses will vary. **(5)**

316   Theme 5: **Doers and Dreamers**
Assessment Tip: Total **10** Points

Name _____

Find That Origin!

Read the dictionary entries. Then read the sentences. For each underlined word, write the word origin and the meaning of the origin. Then use the word clues to write other common English words that have the same origin.

> **artist 1.** *n.* A person who produces works of art. **2.** *n.* A person who shows skill and creativity in a job or in his or her free time. [Latin *ars*, art.]
>
> **deposit 1.** *v.* To put or set down; place. [Latin, *dē* + *pōnere*, to put.]
>
> **person** *n.* A living human being; an individual. [Latin, *persōna*, mask used by actors.]

1. Chuck Close feels that the face of a <u>person</u> is a road map of her or his life.

   Origin: <u>persona **(1 point)**</u>   Meaning of origin: <u>mask used by an actor **(1)**</u>

   Word clue: to pretend to act and look like someone else   <u>impersonate **(1)**</u>

   Word clue: This makes one person different   <u>personality **(1)**</u>
   from another.

2. Chuck likes to feel how much ink he <u>deposits</u> on a painting.

   Origin: <u>ponere **(1)**</u>   Meaning of origin: <u>to put **(1)**</u>

   Word clue: to put off until later   <u>postpone **(1)**</u>

   Word clue: a person or group who opposes   <u>opponent **(1)**</u>
   another in a game

3. From a distance you can't tell how the <u>artist</u> created one of his paintings.

   Origin: <u>ars **(1)**</u>   Meaning of origin: <u>art **(1)**</u>

   Word clue: made by human beings, not by nature   <u>artificial **(1)**</u>

   Word clue: an object made by human beings, especially   <u>artifact **(1)**</u>
   an object from an ancient time

Name _____

Too Negative!

Avoiding Double Negatives A word that means "no" is called a **negative**.
A **negative** reverses the meaning of a sentence.

Do not use a **double negative**, or two negative words, in the same
sentence. Some common negatives are *no, none, not, nobody, nothing,
nowhere,* and *never.* Contractions using *not* are also negatives.
You will see that there is usually more than one way to correct
a **double negative**.

> **Incorrect**: I will not paint nothing.
>
> **Correct**: I will paint nothing. (Drop the negative *not.*)
>
> **Correct**: I will not paint anything. (Change *nothing* to *anything.*)

Most negative words have a matching positive word. Here are some
common negative-positive pairs.

hardly - almost   never - ever   no - any
neither - either   none - some

**Rewrite each sentence, correcting the double negatives. There may
be more than one way to correct a sentence. Choose the one you prefer.**

1. Art class was not never Pat's favorite.

   Art class was never Pat's favorite.; or Art class was not ever Pat's favorite. **(2)**

2. Pat thought he didn't have no talent.

   Pat thought he didn't have any talent.; or Pat thought he had no talent. **(2)**

3. Pat had not tried no kind of painting.

   Pat had tried no kind of painting.; or Pat had not tried any kind of painting. **(2)**

4. Once he tried oil painting, he didn't never want to stop!

   Once he tried oil painting, he never wanted to stop! ; or

   Once he tried oil painting, he didn't ever want to stop! **(2)**

5. There is not nobody in the class who likes to paint as much as Pat.

   There is nobody in the class who likes to paint as much as Pat.; or

   There is not anybody in the class who likes to paint as much as Pat. **(2)**

Assessment Tip: Total **12** Points

Name _____

Short and Sweet!

Contractions A **contraction** is formed by combining two words and shortening one of them. An apostrophe (') takes the place of the letter or letters left out. The word *not* can be combined with *is*, *are*, *was*, and *were* to form contractions. Pronouns and verbs can also be combined to form contractions. The two lists below contain some of the common contractions.

Contractions formed with *not*	Contractions formed with pronouns and verbs
isn't (is not)	I've (I have)
aren't (are not)	you're (you are)
won't (will not)	she'll (she will)
can't (cannot)	they're (they are)
hasn't (has not)	it's (it is)

Underline the contraction in each sentence below. Then write the words that make up the contraction.

1. I <u>hadn't</u> visited an art gallery before today. <u>had not **(2 points)**</u>

2. The artists <u>aren't</u> ones that I know. <u>are not **(2)**</u>

3. Mr. Watkins says <u>he'll</u> tell us about the paintings. <u>he will **(2)**</u>

4. He <u>doesn't</u> know all the artists either. <u>does not **(2)**</u>

5. <u>He's</u> pointed out a landscape. <u>He has **(2)**</u>

6. <u>It's</u> a painting of a lake and some deer. <u>It is **(2)**</u>

7. <u>Haven't</u> we gone swimming in that lake? <u>Have not **(2)**</u>

8. <u>Doesn't</u> the painting make you want to be there? <u>Does not **(2)**</u>

9. <u>I'd</u> like to try landscape painting. <u>I would **(2)**</u>

10. This <u>won't</u> be the last time I visit an art gallery. <u>will not **(2)**</u>

Name _____

Which One's Right?

Using *it's, its; there, their, they're* A good writer is careful not to confuse *it's* and *its* and *there, their,* and *they're.* These words sound alike, but they mean different things and are spelled differently.

it's	contraction of *it is*	**It's** opening day at the show!
its	possessive pronoun	I know **its** location.
there	adverb; can also be used to begin a sentence	Are you going **there**? **There** are many entries.
their	possessive pronoun	Joe and Meg have **their** drawings in it.
they're	contraction of *they are*	**They're** excited about the show.

Proofread Heather's review of the school art show. Cross out the errors she has made with the words in the list above, and write your correction above each error.

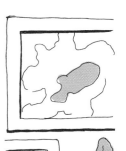

There **(1 point)**

The Student Art Show opened on Friday afternoon. Their are too

It's **(1)**

many wonderful works to be able to mention them all. Its an honor to be

able to tell you about a few of them. Shirley Jane G. entered a group of

they're **(1)**

drawings of her grandmother. Each one is beautiful, and together there

its **(1)**

very moving. Mark Z.'s entry is a small sculpture. "The Phoenix" is it's

title and Mark says it's his expression of hope. Students Cindy R. and

Their **(1)**

David M. worked together on a large mural. They're work is called

"Friends Forever." I recommend that everyone see the works of the

their **(1)**

students in the Student Art Show. You will be amazed at there talent!

Assessment Tip: Total **6** Points

Name _____

Writing a Summary

If you were asked to summarize *Chuck Close Up Close*, you would probably tell who Chuck Close is, how he paints, and what event changed his life. A **summary** is a brief account of a selection. Writing a summary is a good way to recall main ideas or events in a selection and to share what it is about.

Choose a selection you have read, such as *Under the Royal Palms* or *A Kind of Grace: The Autobiography of Jackie Joyner-Kersee*. Then fill in the graphic organizer below with the most important ideas or events in the selection.

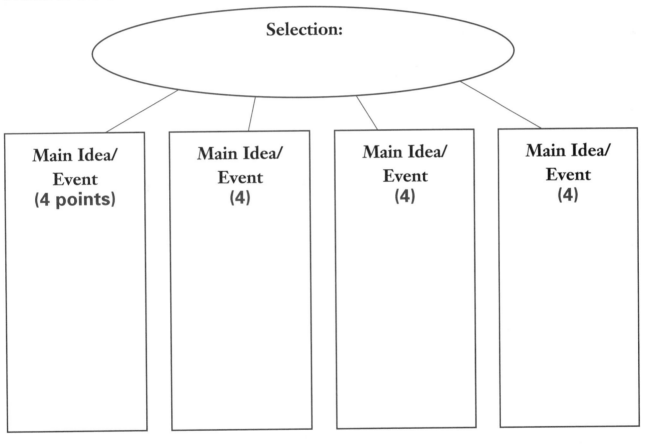

Selection: _____

Main Idea/ Event (4 points)	Main Idea/ Event (4)	Main Idea/ Event (4)	Main Idea/ Event (4)

Now write your summary of the selection on a separate sheet of paper. In the first sentence, tell who or what is being summarized. Briefly restate the main points or events in your own words. Remember to leave out details and minor events. End with a concluding sentence. (4)

Name _____

Paraphrasing

When you **paraphrase** a passage from a book, article, or story, you put it into your own words without changing the author's meaning. A careful writer paraphrases without copying word-for-word.

Read the following passage from *Chuck Close Up Close*.

He labored with weights, strengthening the muscles in his arms. Finally, after many long weeks of struggle, he developed a way to work. Seated in his wheelchair, with a brush strapped to his hand, he could put paint on a canvas. His arms took the place of his fingers.

Now read one sixth-grader's paraphrase of this passage.

Paraphrase

Chuck Close labored with weights to strengthen his arm muscles. Then he found a way to put paint on canvas with a brush strapped to his hand. He painted with his arms instead of his fingers.

Rewrite the paraphrase on the lines, using the checklist to help you improve the student's work. Responses will vary.

✔ Combines ideas from the original passage to produce fewer sentences.
✔ Presents details from the passage in a different order.
✔ Substitutes synonyms for some of the words and phrases.

Chuck Close adapted to a new way of painting. Now he works

from a seated position with a brush strapped to his hand and uses his

arms to paint.

Assessment Tip: Total **15** Points

Name _____

Writing an Answer to a Question

Use what you have learned about taking tests to help you write answers to questions about something you have read. This practice will help you when you take this kind of test.

Read these paragraphs from the selection *Chuck Close Up Close*.

The giant black-and-white paintings had been strikingly fresh in the late 1960s. Now he [Close] was ready to create another "problem" for himself — a new challenge. Around 1970 he invited some friends over to pose for a different set of "head shots," this time in color. He says there is a big advantage to using photographs. "If you paint from life, you have to do more than one sitting. The models gain weight, lose weight; their hair gets long; they cut it off. They're happy; they're sad. They're asleep or they're awake. But the camera provides the freshness and intimacy of one moment frozen in time."

To keep himself from making "the same old colors" on his palette, he found a way to mix the color directly on the canvas. Since color photo images are made up of three primary hues — red, blue, and yellow — he had the photographs separated into these three colors. Then he began to paint.

Now write your answer to each question.

1. How is using photographs different from using live models? *(compare and contrast)*

   Sample answer: Live models have to pose over long periods of

   time, during which they change in many ways. Photographs don't

   change over time, so they can be used for as long as needed. **(5 points)**

   _____

   _____

   _____

Name _____

Writing an Answer to a Question continued

2. How is using photographs the same as using live models? *(compare and contrast)*

   Sample answer: Both photographs and live models can be used as

   the subjects of paintings. **(5)**

   _____

   _____

   _____

   _____

3. Why did Close mix the color directly on the canvas? *(drawing conclusions)*

   Sample answer: He wanted to try something different, using the

   three primary colors of the color photographs. **(5)**

   _____

   _____

   _____

   _____

Theme 5: **Doers and Dreamers**   325
Assessment Tip: Total **15** Points

Name _____

Spelling Review

Write Spelling Words from the list to answer the questions.
Order of answers in each category may vary.

1–10. Which ten words have the final /īz/, /ĭv/, /ĭj/, /ĭk/, /chər/, or /əs/ sound?

1. scientific **(1 point)**
2. positive **(1)**
3. active **(1)**
4. courage **(1)**
5. realize **(1)**
6. temperature **(1)**
7. departure **(1)**
8. fantastic **(1)**
9. exercise **(1)**
10. curious **(1)**

11–20. Which ten words are plurals?

11. stereos **(1)**
12. chiefs **(1)**
13. staffs **(1)**
14. echoes **(1)**
15. studios **(1)**
16. shelves **(1)**
17. pianos **(1)**
18. halves **(1)**
19. loaves **(1)**
20. potatoes **(1)**

21–30. Which ten words have the suffix *-ant, -ance, -ent, -ence, -able, -ible,* or *-ate*?

21. visible **(1)**
22. noticeable **(1)**
23. separate **(1)**
24. workable **(1)**
25. fragrant **(1)**
26. difference **(1)**
27. importance **(1)**
28. excellent **(1)**
29. appearance **(1)**
30. celebrate **(1)**

Spelling Words

1. stereos
2. chiefs
3. scientific
4. visible
5. positive
6. noticeable
7. active
8. staffs
9. echoes
10. separate
11. workable
12. courage
13. realize
14. fragrant
15. studios
16. difference
17. shelves
18. temperature
19. importance
20. departure
21. excellent
22. pianos
23. fantastic
24. halves
25. exercise
26. curious
27. appearance
28. celebrate
29. loaves
30. potatoes

Assessment Tip: Total **30** Points

Name _____

Spelling Spree

Puzzle Play Write a Spelling Word to fit each clue. Then write
the word that you make from the letters in the boxes.

Spelling Words

1. courage
2. fantastic
3. halves
4. stereos
5. temperature
6. echoes
7. potatoes
8. noticeable
9. studios
10. difference
11. workable
12. separate
13. loaves
14. fragrant
15. excellent

1. places where artists work s t u d i o s **(1)**

2. having a pleasing odor f r a g r a n t **(1)**

3. two _____ of bread l o a v e s **(1)**

4. four quarters equal two _____ h a l v e s **(1)**

5. how hot or cold the air is
t e m p e r a t u r e **(1)**

6. of the highest quality, superb
e x c e l l e n t **(1)**

7. bravery c o u r a g e **(1)**

Special Word: d r e a m e r

The Next Word Write the Spelling Word that belongs in each group.

8. eye-catching, obvious, noticeable **(1)**

9. weird, bizarre, fantastic **(1)**

10. tape decks, CD players, stereos **(1)**

11. repeated sounds, reflections, echoes **(1)**

12. carrots, turnips, potatoes **(1)**

13. unlikeness, variation, difference **(1)**

14. doable, practical, workable **(1)**

15. distinct, individual, separate **(1)**

Name _____

Proofreading and Writing

Proofreading Circle the six misspelled Spelling Words in this speech. Then write each word correctly.

People who dream and make a difference in our world are
(curius) They go beyond the (visibel) (appearanse) of things to look
at their true (importans.) It is time we (realyze) how valuable their
(deparcher) from the ordinary really is.

1. curious **(1 point)**

2. visible **(1)**

3. appearance **(1)**

4. importance **(1)**

5. realize **(1)**

6. departure **(1)**

Brainstorming Write Spelling Words to complete each phrase.

7. take an active **(1)** part

8. either positive **(1)** or negative

9. shelves **(1)** of bookcases

10. items in a scientific **(1)** lab

11. lab workers on staffs **(1)** of science projects

12. chiefs **(1)** in charge

13. pianos **(1)** or other musical instruments

14. walking is good exercise **(1)**

15. celebrate **(1)** a success

✏️ **Write a Character Sketch** On a separate sheet of paper,
write a character sketch about a doer or a dreamer. Use the Spelling
Review Words. Responses will vary. **(5)**

Spelling Words

1. active
2. realize
3. departure
4. curious
5. scientific
6. positive
7. shelves
8. chiefs
9. staffs
10. celebrate
11. visible
12. appearance
13. exercise
14. importance
15. pianos

Assessment Tip: Total **15** Points

Name _____

Sound Bites

When a speech gets reported on television or in the newspaper, it is often not shown in its entirety. Instead, the most important or striking phrases are presented. These are called "sound bites." Choose some sound bites for the speeches below. Sample answers shown.

Speech	Sound Bites
The Gettysburg Address	"The world will little note nor long remember what we say here, but it can never forget what they did here." **(2 points)**
A Story of Courage, Bravery, Strength, and Heroism	"What I wear, what I eat, what I own does not define me. My situation does not define me. I define who I am." **(2)**
Spinelli Newbery Acceptance Speech	"You're the funny ones. You're the fascinating ones. You're the elusive and inspiring and promising and heroic and maddening ones. Don't you know that?" **(2)**
Ortega Speech	"If you are going to work for someone, give it the full eight hours plus. If you are going to do it at all, do it right." **(2)**
I Have a Dream	"I have a dream that my four little children will one day live in a nation where they will not be judged by the color of their skin but by the content of their character." **(2)**

Which speech did you like best? Why?

Answers will vary. _____

_____

Theme 5: **Doers and Dreamers**   329
Assessment Tip: Total **10** Points

Name ______________________________

Cover That Speech

You are a newspaper reporter assigned to the event at which one of these speeches was given. Write a news story about the speech.

Answers will vary. **(10 points)**

Assessment Tip: Total **10** Points

Name _____

New Frontiers: Oceans and Space

The selections in this theme will take you on journeys up into deep space and down into the deep sea. After reading each selection, add to this chart to show what you learned along the way.
(10 points per selection)

	Adventures of Sojourner	Franklin R. Chang-Díaz
What kind of writing is the selection an example of?	expository nonfiction	biography
What is the selection about?	It is about a roving robot named Sojourner that traveled over the surface of Mars and took pictures	It is about a young boy who studied hard and overcame many obstacles to become an astronaut.
In what way does the selection describe a frontier?	People did not know much about Mars at all before Sojourner's mission. Mars is like a frontier because we are just beginning to explore it.	Franklin R. Chang-Díaz is exploring a new frontier—space. His career has also been a new frontier for him.

Assessment Tip: Total **20** Points

Name _____

New Frontiers: Oceans and Space

(10 points per selection)

	Beneath Blue Waters	**Out There**
What kind of writing is the selection an example of?	expository nonfiction	fiction: short story
What is the selection about?	It is about a submersible named Alvin, which enables scientists to study life in the deep sea.	It is about a boy who encounters a sea creature and his struggle to get others to believe him.
In what way does the selection describe a frontier?	The sea bottom is like a frontier because we know so little about it, many of its creatures are mysterious, and very few people have visited it.	The creature that Danny sees is mysterious. When he researches other mysterious creatures like it, he is entering into unknown territory.

What important ideas have you learned about the oceans and about space?

Sample answers: Both are huge regions we have only begun to explore.

Both contain many mysteries. **(2)**

Assessment Tip: Total **22** Points

Name _____

Exploring a Distant World

Write words from the box to complete the sentences below.

Vocabulary

> monitoring
> engineers
> rover
> analysis
> stereoscopic
> sensors
> navigation
> interpreted
> maneuvers

1. If you are operating a vehicle designed to explore the surface of a planet, you are controlling a <u>rover</u> **(2 points)** .

2. If you use both your eyes to see something three-dimensionally, you are seeing a <u>stereoscopic</u> **(2)** image.

3. If you work with individuals who have special training that enables them to build and operate complex devices, you work with <u>engineers</u> **(2)** .

4. If you are checking something regularly, you are <u>monitoring</u> **(2)** it.

5. If a vehicle has sensitive devices that respond to light, sound, or movement, the vehicle has <u>sensors</u> **(2)** .

6. If you use instruments to figure out where you are and where you are going, you are using them for <u>navigation</u> **(2)** . If you use instruments to break a substance down into its parts for study, you are using them for <u>analysis</u> **(2)** .

7. If you have figured out the likely meaning of the data collected from a planet, you have <u>interpreted</u> **(2)** the data.

8. If you plan how a vehicle turns to avoid obstacles, you plan its <u>maneuvers</u> **(2)** .

Name _____

Cause and Effect Chart

Cause	Effect
Scientists had never tried to land a remote-control robot on Mars.	→ The scientists were tense about the descent and landing.
Pathfinder fired three small braking rockets.	→ The parachute and aeroshell were yanked away, and the lander slowed its descent. **(2 points)**
Pathfinder had a very smooth landing.	→ Golombek worried there were no rocks in the area. **(2)**
The lander's camera was stereoscopic.	The camera took pictures that appeared to be three-dimensional. **(2)**
The spirit of the mission was to let the public know the mission results as soon as possible. **(2)**	The science team almost immediately posted on the Internet the photos they were receiving.
As Sojourner approached Yogi, the alternate rover driver made a mistake in its estimate of where to turn.	Sojourner ran aground on the rock. **(2)**
Pathfinder's battery ran down. **(2)**	Sojourner could not communicate with the lander.
The Pathfinder Mission was considered a great success.	More missions to Mars were planned for the future. **(2)**

Assessment Tip: Total **14** Points

Name _____

Keep a Mission Log

Complete the mission log below to show the sequence of events in the Pathfinder mission.

Mission Log

Date	Events
Sol 1 (July 4, 1997)	Pathfinder sends radio signals back to Earth indicating that it has survived landing on Mars **(1 point)** . The lander sends back photos showing that an airbag is blocking Sojourner's path **(1)** and that the terrain of the landing site is rocky **(1)** .
Sol 2	Sojourner leaves the lander.
Sol 3	Sojourner travels to a rock named Barnacle Bill **(1)** to conduct an analysis of the rock's chemical content **(1)** .
Sol 4	Millions of people log onto the Internet to see the 3-D views of Mars **(1)** .
Sol 6	Sojourner travels to Yogi. During the trip the rover _____ accidentally runs aground on the shoulder of the rock **(1)** . Driver Brian Cooper is able to guide the rover off the rock.
Sol 83	Pathfinder sends its last transmission to Earth **(1)** .
Sol 93 (Oct. 7, 1997)	One final blip is heard from Pathfinder, and then nothing more.

Name _____

In Search of Causes and Effects

Read the passage. Then complete the activity on page 337.

The First Flying Machines

Some people must have thought that brothers Etienne and Joseph Montgolfier were full of hot air when they announced their plan to send a sheep, a duck, and a rooster into the sky. But in 1783, about 120 years before Orville and Wilbur Wright flew a self-propelled plane in the United States, the French paper-makers did exactly that.

The brothers had recognized a simple principle of aeronautics: hot air trapped inside a lightweight vessel causes the vessel to rise. Once the hot air cools, the vessel returns to the ground. The brothers made a series of huge round paper balloons with a firepot hung in a basket beneath each one to heat the air. The king of France, Louis XVI, decreed that no human being could ride in the Montgolfiers' balloon, so the first passengers were animals. The flight went perfectly.

It wasn't long, however, before humans were taking balloon flights. In 1785, the Montgolfiers discovered that because hydrogen is lighter than air, it is a better lifting agent for ballooning than heated air. Soon hydrogen-filled balloons were common in Europe and America. They were used for military purposes and for sport.

Early balloons had one huge disadvantage. It was impossible to control their direction, so a balloon's flight path was determined by the direction the wind was blowing. To solve this problem, motors powered by steam or by electric batteries were attached to the balloons. The motors turned small propellers, which gave pilots some ability to steer the balloon. However, the traditional round shape of a balloon did not work well for directional flight, so engineers next developed a huge craft called a dirigible, shaped like a stubby pencil. These new balloons could be steered, but they could operate safely only in nearly windless conditions. It wasn't until the invention of the internal-combustion gasoline engine that balloons could consistently be navigated.

Name _____

In Search of Causes and Effects continued

Complete the chart by writing the missing causes and effects. Use the information in the passage on page 336.

Cause		Effect
Air is heated and trapped inside a lightweight vessel.	→	The vessel rises up into the air. **(2 points)**
The air inside the vessel cools.	→	The vessel returns to the ground. **(2)**
King Louis XVI declared that no humans could ride in the Montgolfiers' balloon. **(2)**	→	The first passengers in a hot-air balloon were farm animals.
Hydrogen was discovered to be a better lifting agent than heated air.	→	Soon hydrogen-filled balloons were in use in Europe and America. **(2)**
Round balloons were not well suited for directional flight. **(2)**	→	Engineers created balloons called dirigibles that were shaped like stubby pencils.
The internal-combustion gasoline engine was invented.	→	Balloons could consistently be navigated for the first time. **(2)**

Assessment Tip: Total **12** Points

Name _____

Puzzling Out Prefixes

Read the diary page of an aerospace engineer. Underline each word with the prefix *de-, dis-, ex-, inter-, per-, pre-,* **or** *pro-.*

> The moment Sojourner <u>detached</u> herself from the lander and rolled onto Martian soil was so exciting! The next several weeks were busy ones as she gathered data from Martian rocks for us to <u>interpret</u>. When we <u>permitted</u> her to navigate herself, we would <u>disturb</u> her only when it was necessary to <u>prevent</u> her from running into <u>protruding</u> parts of rocks. Soon she <u>demonstrated</u> that she was very good at <u>extending</u> her APXS against the rocks to test them.

Now write the words you underlined. Use the word parts as well as sentence clues from the diary entry to write the meaning of each word. Write the word on the short line, and its meaning on the long line next to it.

1. detached **(1)** _____ separated **(1)** _____
2. interpret **(1)** _____ understand; explain **(1)** _____
3. permitted **(1)** _____ allowed **(1)** _____
4. disturb **(1)** _____ to bother; interrupt **(1)** _____
5. prevent **(1)** _____ to keep from happening **(1)** _____
6. protruding **(1)** _____ pushing onward **(1)** _____
7. demonstrated **(1)** _____ showed clearly **(1)** _____
8. extending **(1)** _____ stretching out to become longer **(1)** _____

338   Theme 6: **New Frontiers: Oceans and Space**
Assessment Tip: Total **16** Points

Name _____

Prefixes: *de-, dis-, ex-, inter-, per-, pre-, pro-*

The word parts *de-, dis-, ex-, inter-, per-, pre-,* and *pro-* are all prefixes. To spell a word with a prefix, find the prefix, the base word or the word root, and any ending. Then spell the word by parts.

decision   **dis**able   **ex**perience   **inter**national
permission   **pre**view   **pro**ceed

Write each Spelling Word under its prefix.

Order of responses for each category may vary. **(1 point each)**

1. disease
2. decision
3. proceed
4. international
5. permission
6. experience
7. disable
8. preview
9. describe
10. progress
11. product
12. exhaust
13. previous
14. demonstrate
15. extent
16. disturb
17. persuade
18. interview
19. determine
20. prepare

de-

decision

describe

demonstrate

determine

dis-

disease

disable

disturb

ex-

experience

exhaust

extent

inter-

international

interview

per-

permission

persuade

pre-

preview

previous

prepare

pro-

proceed

progress

product

Name _____

Spelling Spree

Changing Prefixes **Change the underlined prefix in each word to write a Spelling Word.**

1. <u>in</u>tent
2. <u>de</u>duct
3. <u>com</u>mission
4. <u>in</u>scribe
5. <u>ex</u>ceed
6. <u>un</u>able
7. <u>mult</u>inational

1. extent **(1 point)**
2. product **(1)**
3. permission **(1)**
4. describe **(1)**
5. proceed **(1)**
6. disable **(1)**
7. international **(1)**

Spelling Words

1. disease
2. decision
3. proceed
4. international
5. permission
6. experience
7. disable
8. preview
9. describe
10. progress
11. product
12. exhaust
13. previous
14. demonstrate
15. extent
16. disturb
17. persuade
18. interview
19. determine
20. prepare

Double Syllable Scramble **Rearrange the syllables in each item to write *two* Spelling Words. (There are no extra syllables.)** Order of answers for each question may vary.

8–9. suade pre per view
10–11. pare dis pre ease
12–13. ri ence dis pe turb ex
14–15. mine haust de ex ter

8–9. persuade preview **(2)**
10–11. prepare disease **(2)**
12–13. experience disturb **(2)**
14–15. determine exhaust **(2)**

Assessment Tip: Total **15** Points

Name _____

Proofreading and Writing

Proofreading **Circle the five misspelled Spelling Words in this television program description. Then write each word correctly.**

Spelling Words

1. disease
2. decision
3. proceed
4. international
5. permission
6. experience
7. disable
8. preview
9. describe
10. progress
11. product
12. exhaust
13. previous
14. demonstrate
15. extent
16. disturb
17. persuade
18. interview
19. determine
20. prepare

Mission to Mars! *(8 P.M. Wednesday)*

How did a team of scientists and engineers land a rover on Mars? This fascinating show is a preview of an upcoming documentary on the recent Pathfinder Mission. Beginning with NASA's (deccision) to make another mission to Mars possible, the program details each step of the project. The director was able to (innerview) many people who worked on the team. In one memorable scene, two scientists (demenstrate) how Pathfinder's complex parachute system allowed for a safe landing on Mars. As a result of Pathfinder, the (progres) made in our knowledge of Mars has increased greatly. The program also discusses (previus) attempts at exploration on Mars. ★★★★ 11 17 34

1. decision **(1 point)**   4. progress **(1)**
2. interview **(1)**   5. previous **(1)**
3. demonstrate **(1)**

✏️ **Write an Opinion** The Pathfinder Mission to Mars cost $266 million. Do you think it was worth it? What are some of the benefits of exploring other planets? What do we learn that we might not otherwise know? Are there other things that you think the money could be better spent on?

On a separate piece of paper, write a paragraph in which you state your opinion about the Pathfinder Mission. Use Spelling Words from the list.

Responses will vary. **(5)**

Assessment Tip: Total **10** Points

Name _____

The Adventures of Sojourner

Vocabulary Skill Analogies

Go Figure the Relationship!

Read each analogy. Then write the word that best completes each analogy. One has been done for you.

Example: Exploration is to explorer as invention is to <u>inventor</u>.

    laboratory   experiment   inventor   inconvenient

1. Sojourner is to rover as Pathfinder is to <u>lander **(1 point)**</u>.

    commands   lander   Mars   power

2. Applause is to clapping as laughter is to <u>laughing **(1)**</u>.

    laughing   anger   shouting   joy

3. Date is to calendar as time is to <u>clock **(1)**</u>.

    difficult   clock   dust   rough

4. Excited is to discouraged as kindly is to <u>cruel **(1)**</u>.

    cruel   helpful   clear   cruelty

5. Hazard is to danger as report is to <u>update **(1)**</u>.

    send   form   writing   update

6. Fail is to succeed as transmit is to <u>receive **(1)**</u>.

    computer   receive   satellite   send

Use some of the following words to write two incomplete analogies. Challenge a partner to complete each analogy with a remaining word.

Sample answers shown.

water	day	liquid	month
year	rock	week	solid

7. <u>Liquid is to water as solid is to rock.</u> **(2)**

8. <u>Year is to month as week is to day.</u> **(2)**

342   Theme 6: **New Frontiers: Oceans and Space**
Assessment Tip: Total **10** Points

Name _____

What's in a Phrase?

Prepositions and Prepositional Phrases A preposition shows the relationship between a noun or a pronoun and some other word in the sentence. A noun or pronoun that follows a preposition is the object of the preposition. A prepositional phrase is made up of a preposition, the object of the preposition and all the words between them. Here is a list of some common prepositions.

about	before	during	past
above	behind	for	through
across	below	from	throughout
after	beneath	in	to
against	beside	into	toward
along	between	near	under
around	beyond	of	until
as	by	on	up
at	down	over	with

Write the prepositional phrase in each sentence, and circle the object of the preposition.

1. The twentieth century saw machines and human beings blasted into space.
   into (space) **(2 point)** _____

2. Most of the NASA missions have been successful.
   of the NASA (missions) **(2)** _____

3. We have seen rocks brought back from the moon.
   from the (moon) **(2)** _____

4. Scientist astronauts have performed experiments during space missions.
   during space (missions) **(2)** _____

Theme 6: **New Frontiers: Oceans and Space**   343
Assessment Tip: Total **8** Points

Name _____

Ways to Describe

Prepositional Phrases as Adjectives and Adverbs A prepositional phrase can act as an adjective, modifying a noun or a pronoun. As an adjective, a prepositional phrase tells what kind or which one. A prepositional phrase can also act as an adverb, modifying a verb, an adjective or another adverb. As an adverb, a prepositional phrase tells how, where, or when.

Does the prepositional phrase in each sentence act as an adjective phrase or as an adverb phrase? Under each sentence write the prepositional phrase, label it *adjective* or *adverb*, and write the word the phrase modifies. Here is an example:

Example: Trina likes reading imaginative stories about outer space.

about outer space	adjective	stories

1. Every night she gazes at the stars.

at the stars	adverb	gazes **(3)**

2. The lights of the night sky stir her imagination.

of the night sky	adjective	lights **(3)**

3. Sometimes she points a telescope toward Mars.

toward Mars	adverb	points **(3)**

4. Trina has a book of science fiction stories.

of science fiction stories	adjective	book **(3)**

5. The stories take her imagination to distant planets.

to distant planets	adverb	take **(3)**

Assessment Tip: Total **15** Points

Name _____

Tell Me More!

Elaborating with Prepositional Phrases A good writer adds prepositional phrases to sentences to make them say more. Here is an example.

The space explorers landed on the distant planet.

Improved: The space explorers landed <u>with a great bounce</u> on the distant planet.

Here is the beginning of a science fiction story. Show the writer how the story might be improved by adding prepositional phrases that tell more about the event described. Add at least one new prepositional phrase to each sentence. Use your imagination! Write your paragraph on the lines below.

The lander's hatch opened. The brave explorers stepped out. They had never before visited this planet. All of a sudden, they noticed a strange creature peeking at them. The creature seemed to be pointing. The explorers looked. Sample answer shown. **(2 points for each sentence)**

The lander's hatch opened <u>with a creak.</u> The brave explorers <u>from Earth</u> stepped out <u>of their small ship.</u> They had never before visited this planet <u>in the distant galaxy of Snickers.</u> All of a sudden, they noticed a strange creature <u>with purple eyes</u> peeking at them <u>from behind a glowing rock.</u> The creature seemed to be pointing <u>with its long green fingers</u> <u>toward the pulsing light</u> <u>on the horizon.</u> The explorers looked <u>with curiosity</u> <u>at the strange sight.</u>

Assessment Tip: Total **12** Points

Name _____

Writing an Announcement

During the 1997 space mission you read about in *The Adventures of Sojourner*, members of the Mars Pathfinder Team made a number of announcements. An **announcement** is a short speech or notice that gives important information about an event. You might read an announcement on a bulletin board, on the Internet, or in a magazine, or you might hear one at school, in an airport, on the radio, or on TV.

Fill in the chart below with details for an announcement about an exhibition of Mars photographs that were taken by Pathfinder and Sojourner. Invent a date, time, and location where this event might take place in your community. Then draw on information in the selection to come up with details about how the photographs were taken, what they show, and why people should see them.

Date (1 point)
Time (1)
Place (1)
Cost (1)
Details about the program (2)

Now write your announcement on a separate sheet of paper. State the purpose of the announcement at the very beginning. Then provide information that answers these questions: *who? what? where? when? why? how?* and *how much?* Include the exact date, time, and location of the photography exhibit as well as other details about the program. Be sure to use clear, interesting, and friendly language that your audience will understand. (4)

Assessment Tip: Total **10** Points

Name _____

Ordering Important Information

Careful writers make sure that the information in an announcement is complete and presented in a clear order. The use of sequence words, such as *first*, *next*, and *last*, helps clarify the order of events.

Someone on the staff of the *Pleasantville Times* accidentally scrambled this announcement. Before the newspaper is printed, reorder the sentences so that the announcement begins clearly and follows a logical sequence of events. Pay attention to sequence words that give clues to the order of the sentences. Then write the revised announcement on the lines below.

Blast Off!

For any questions and further information, please call the library's Special Events Coordinator, Mr. Charles Luna, at 555-4321. After the film, there will be a brief question-and-answer period. The film will be shown on Sunday, February 13, from 2 P.M. to 4 P.M., in the Armstrong Conference Room on the lower level. This award-winning documentary details the ups and downs of the 1997 Mars landing of Pathfinder and Sojourner. Pleasantville native Jim Schuyler, an alternate rover driver, will be on hand to answer questions about his role during the historic Pathfinder mission. The Pleasantville Library is sponsoring a free screening of *Mars or Bust*.

The Pleasantville Library is sponsoring a free screening of *Mars or Bust*. This award-winning documentary details the ups and downs of the 1997 Mars landing of Pathfinder and Sojourner. The film will be shown on Sunday, February 13, from 2 P.M. to 4 P.M., in the Armstrong Conference Room on the lower level. After the film, there will be a brief question-and-answer period. Pleasantville native Jim Schuyler, an alternate rover driver, will be on hand to answer questions about his role during the historic Pathfinder mission. For any questions and further information, please call the library's Special Events Coordinator, Mr. Charles Luna, at 555-4321.

Assessment Tip: Total **12** Points

Evaluating Your Persuasive Essay

Reread your persuasive essay. What do you need to make it better?
Use this page to help you decide. Put a checkmark in the box for each
sentence that describes your persuasive essay.

Loud and Clear!

☐ My essay has a beginning that will capture my readers' attention.

☐ My goal is stated clearly at the beginning of the essay.

☐ I stated my reasons for my point of view and answered objections.

☐ I used facts and details to support my opinion.

☐ The essay is interesting to read and convincing.

Sounding Stronger

☐ I could make the beginning more attention grabbing.

☐ I could state my goal more clearly.

☐ I answered some objections people might raise, but I could deal with a few more.

☐ I need to add more facts and details to support my point of view.

☐ I didn't always use adverbs and adjectives correctly.

Turn Up the Volume

☐ I need a better beginning.

☐ I didn't state my goals or reasons for my opinion.

☐ I didn't answer any objections people might have.

☐ I need to add facts and details.

☐ This isn't very convincing.

Using Adverbs and Adjectives Correctly

► An adjective can modify a noun or a pronoun.
► An adverb can modify a verb or an adjective.

Underline the correct adjective or adverb. Write adverb or adjective in the space provided.

1. I (complete/completely) endorse the Channel Magic channel changer. adverb **(1 point)**

2. I give my (complete/completely) endorsement of the Channel Magic channel changer. adjective **(1)**

3. Channel Magic channel changer has a (clever/cleverly) design. adjective **(1)**

4. Channel Magic channel changer is designed (clever/cleverly). adverb **(1)**

5. Channel Magic (automatic/automatically) senses when a commercial comes on your TV screen. adverb **(1)**

6. Channel Magic has an (automatic/automatically) sensor that knows when a commercial comes on your TV screen. adjective **(1)**

7. The device then makes an (instant/instantly) switch to a different channel. adjective **(1)**

8. The device then (instant/instantly) switches to a different channel. adverb **(1)**

9. Channel Magic is an (effortless/effortlessly) way to avoid commercials. adjective **(1)**

10. Using Channel Magic, you can (effortless/effortlessly) avoid commercials. adverb **(1)**

Name _____

Spelling Words

Look for familiar spelling patterns to help you remember how to spell the Spelling Words on this page. Think carefully about the parts that you find hard to spell in each word.

Write the missing letters in the Spelling Words below.

1. w __e__ __i__ __r__ d **(1 point)**

2. th __o__ __u__ __g__ __h__ t **(1)**

3. thr __o__ __u__ __g__ __h__ **(1)**

4. c __a__ __u__ __g__ __h__ t **(1)**

5. br __o__ __u__ __g__ __h__ t **(1)**

6. fin __a__ __l__ __l__ __y__ **(1)**

7. su __p__ __p__ ose **(1)**

8. usua __l__ __l__ __y__ **(1)**

9. eig __h__ __t__ __h__ **(1)**

10. mi __l__ __l__ imeter **(1)**

11. hap __p__ __i__ __l__ ly **(1)**

12. g __u__ __e__ ss **(1)**

13. __S__ at __u__ __r__ day **(1)**

14. s __c__ __h__ ool **(1)**

15. bef __o__ __r__ __e__ **(1)**

Spelling Words

1. weird
2. thought
3. through
4. caught
5. brought
6. finally
7. suppose
8. usually
9. eighth
10. millimeter
11. happily
12. guess
13. Saturday
14. school
15. before

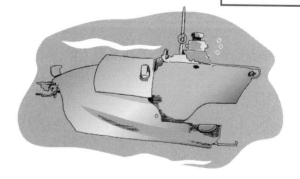

Study List On a separate piece of paper, write each Spelling Word. Check your spelling against the words on the list.

Order of words may vary. **(15)**

Assessment Tip: Total **30** Points

Name _____

Spelling Spree

Finding Words Each word below is hidden in a Spelling Word. Write the Spelling Word.

1. fin
2. lime
3. for
4. at
5. us
6. up
7. though

W E I R D

1. finally **(1 point)**
2. millimeter **(1)**
3. before **(1)**
4. Saturday **(1)**
5. usually **(1)**
6. suppose **(1)**
7. thought **(1)**

Spelling Words

1. weird
2. thought
3. through
4. caught
5. brought
6. finally
7. suppose
8. usually
9. eighth
10. millimeter
11. happily
12. guess
13. Saturday
14. school
15. before

Phrase Fillers Write the Spelling Word that best completes each phrase.

8. _____ in the act
9. to come in _____ place
10. a _____ whistling sound from the attic
11. to accept a gift _____
12. to make an educated _____
13. to attend summer _____
14. a trail _____ the woods
15. guests who _____ food to the party

8. caught **(1)**
9. eighth **(1)**
10. weird **(1)**
11. happily **(1)**
12. guess **(1)**
13. school **(1)**
14. through **(1)**
15. brought **(1)**

Theme 6: **New Frontiers: Oceans and Space**   351
Assessment Tip: Total **15** Points

Proofreading and Writing

Proofreading Circle the five misspelled Spelling Words on this computer game box. Then write each word correctly.

Spelling Words

1. weird
2. thought
3. through
4. caught
5. brought
6. finally
7. suppose
8. usually
9. eighth
10. millimeter
11. happily
12. guess
13. Saturday
14. school
15. before

≡NEW FRONTIERS≡

Are you ready to experience the feelings of hurtling (thru) the solar system? Do you want to come face-to-face with (wierd) deep-sea creatures? Then *New Frontiers* is the game for you! Now there's (finaly) a game that lets you go millions of miles into space or thousands of feet below the ocean's surface. Who would have (thot) that one game could combine two worlds so well? You'll get caught up in the action (befor) you even realize it!

1. through **(1 point)**
2. weird **(1)**
3. finally **(1)**
4. thought **(1)**
5. before **(1)**

Write Movie Titles If you were going to make movies about space or underwater exploration, what would you call them? What would they be about?

On a separate piece of paper, write four movie titles. Include a one-sentence description of each. Use Spelling Words from the list.
Responses will vary. **(5)**

Assessment Tip: Total **10** Points

Name _____

Journey into Space

Write each word from the box under the heading that best describes it.

fields of scientific study

aeronautics **(1 point)**

physics **(1)**

rocketry **(1)**

people who ask to be admitted to the space program

applicants **(1)**

what each of those people would like to become

astronaut **(1)**

skills and experiences those people need to have

qualifications **(1)**

place for doing experiments

laboratory **(1)**

how experiments should be done

methodically **(1)**

verb meaning "to imitate"

simulate **(1)**

verb meaning "showed clearly"

demonstrated **(1)**

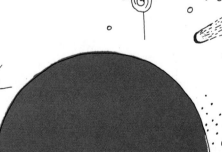

Name _____

Problem-Solution Chart

Problem		**Solution**
There were no astronauts as role models when Franklin was young.	→	He read science fiction and space stories. **(2 points)**
Franklin wanted to find out how to become an astronaut.	→	He wrote to Werner von Braun, who suggested he study science. **(2)**
Franklin wanted to earn money to move to the U. S.	→	He worked at a bank to earn money for the trip. **(2)**
Franklin needed to learn to speak English.	→	He enrolled at an American high school. **(2)**
Franklin was not learning English in the special class he was taking.	→	He persuaded his teachers to let him take regular classes. **(2)**
He was told he couldn't enroll at the University of Connecticut because he wasn't a U.S. citizen.	→	He got school officials to enlist the help of the state legislature in granting him an exception. **(2)**
Franklin was rejected in his first attempt to become an astronaut, possibly because his citizenship status was not complete.	→	While waiting for another chance to apply, he finalized his U.S. citizenship. Then he applied a second time, and was accepted. **(2)**

Assessment Tip: Total **16** Points

Name _____

Complete the Countdown

Complete the following sentences with information from the selection to show how Franklin Chang-Díaz became an astronaut.

1. Franklin Chang-Díaz was seven years old when <u>the Soviets launched</u> <u>Sputnik</u> **(1 point)** .

2. As a child, Franklin read <u>science fiction</u> **(1)** stories and played at <u>being an astronaut</u> **(1)** .

3. In 1967, Franklin wrote to <u>Werner von Braun</u> **(1)** at NASA to ask <u>how to become an astronaut</u> **(1)** .

4. Franklin decided he had to move to <u>the United States</u> **(1)** , so he worked <u>at a bank</u> **(1)** to earn the money.

5. In the United States, he enrolled in school in order to <u>learn English</u> **(1)** . He had to persuade his teachers to <u>let him</u> <u>take regular classes</u> **(1)** .

6. His efforts earned him a scholarship to <u>the University of Connecticut</u> **(1)** .

7. In college he earned degrees in <u>physics</u> **(1)** and <u>mechanical engineering</u> **(1)** . Then he went to graduate school at <u>the Massachusetts Institute of Technology</u> **(1)** .

8. In 1977 Franklin applied to NASA but <u>was rejected</u> **(1)** .

9. In 1979 he applied again, this time as <u>a U.S. citizen</u> **(1)** . He was accepted, and became one of the first <u>Hispanics in the space</u> <u>program</u> **(1)** .

10. Franklin became <u>an astronaut</u> **(1)** in 1981. In 1986 he was on board the <u>Shuttle *Columbia*</u> **(1)** during its nearly flawless launch.

Name _____

Kite in Space!

Read the directions. Answer the questions on page 357.

How to Make a Kite

Materials

► two pine or spruce sticks about 30" long, 3/8" wide, and 3/16" thick

► cotton string

► colored tissue paper, or a cotton sheet, or a sheet of plastic (such as from a trash bag)

► glue or rubber cement

► a short, thin nail

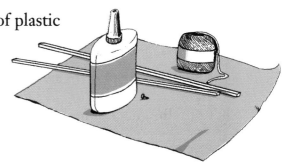

Assembly

1. Cut a notch at each end of both sticks.

2. Cross the sticks and nail them together where they cross.

3. Pass a string through one of the notches. Turn the string once around the stick, and pass it through the notch again. Rotate the frame 90 degrees. Repeat the stringing and rotating process until you are back where you started. Tie the end of the string at the starting notch.

4. Place the kite frame on the tissue paper, cloth, or plastic. Place a weight on the frame, and trim the paper, cloth, or plastic about 1/2" beyond the string outline. Apply a thin line of glue on the outermost part of the paper, cloth, or plastic. (Note: If you are using plastic instead of paper or cloth, use rubber cement instead of glue.) Do not put glue or rubber cement on the string.

5. Fold the paper, cloth, or plastic over the string and press down firmly. Allow to dry completely before handling kite.

Your kite is now ready for you to attach a string and a tail—and then to fly!

Name _____

Kite in Space! continued

Answer these questions about the directions on page 356.

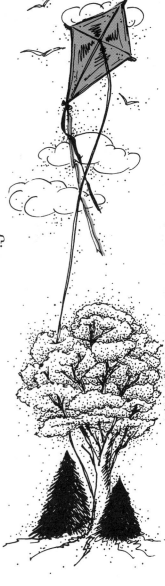

1. What is the first thing you should do in order to follow this set of directions?

   Read them carefully from beginning to end. **(2 points)**

2. What is the next thing you should do?

   Gather together all the materials. **(2)**

3. In what situation would you need to use rubber cement instead of glue?

   If I'm using plastic instead of paper or cloth **(2)**

4. What do you do after stringing the first notch?

   Rotate the frame 90 degrees. **(2)**

5. Why is it important to do steps 1 and 2 before doing step 3?

   If I don't first cut the notches in the wood and nail the two sticks

   together, I won't be able to run the string around the frame. **(2)**

6. What could you do if your kite did not come out right on the first try?

   Reread the directions, figure out which step I missed or did wrong,

   and then try again **(2)**

A Summary of Prefixes

Each description below is a description of a scene for a documentary film about Franklin Chang-Díaz. After each description, write the words that contain the prefixes *ad–* or *ob–* .

Summary of Film Sections

1. As a young boy, Franklin dreams of the opportunity to become an astronaut. He aims to work someday in the United States for the National Aeronautics and Space Administration (NASA). (Find 1 word.)

   Administration **(1 point)**

2. Franklin moves to the United States and attends an American high school. He objects to being placed in a Spanish-speaking class and moves to an English-speaking class. He adapts quickly to the new language and his grades improve rapidly. It is obvious that Franklin intends to reach his goals. (Find 3 words.)

   objects _____ adapts _____ obvious **(3)**

3. Franklin is admitted to college with a scholarship, but his progress is obstructed. Because of an obscure mix-up, he cannot use the scholarship until he becomes a U.S. citizen. However, the Connecticut state legislature makes an exception, and Franklin obtains the scholarship.

   (Find 4 words.) admitted

   obstructed _____ obscure _____ obtains **(4)**

4. After graduate school, Franklin begins work at a laboratory and tries to get a job at NASA. At first, he does not get in. On his second attempt, however, he advances to the interview stage. (Find 1 word.)

   advances **(1)**

5. In Houston, he meets many adventurers like himself, but he feels that his unique background and qualifications give him an obvious advantage. This time, NASA hires him. His next assignment: to fulfill his dream of becoming an astronaut! (Find 3 words.)

   adventurers _____ obvious _____ advantage **(3)**

Assessment Tip: Total **12** Points

Name _____

Prefixes: *ad-* and *ob-*

The prefix *ad-* can be spelled *ac*, *ap*, *as*, or *af* to match the first consonant or consonant sound of the base word or the word root.

advice   **ac**count   **ac**quire

approve   **as**sist   **af**fair

The prefix *ob-* is spelled *oc* when the base word or word root starts with *c*.

observe   **oc**cupy

Write each Spelling Word under the spelling of its prefix.
Order of answers for each category may vary.

1. account
2. observe
3. addition
4. accurate
5. occasion
6. approve
7. advice
8. occupy
9. assist
10. affair
11. occur
12. acquire
13. assume
14. adjust
15. assign
16. oblige
17. accomplish
18. approach
19. according
20. obtain

ad- Spelled *ad*

addition

advice

adjust

ad- Spelled *as*

assist

assume

assign

ad- Spelled *ac*

account

accurate

acquire

accomplish

according

ad- Spelled *af*

affair

ob- Spelled *ob*

observe

oblige

obtain

ad- Spelled *ap*

approve

approach

ob- Spelled *oc*

occasion

occupy

occur

Assessment Tip: Total **20** Points

Name _____

Spelling Spree

Finding Words Each word below is hidden in a Spelling Word. Write the Spelling Word.

Example: vent   *adventure*

1. cup
2. roach
3. rate
4. add
5. serve

1. account
2. observe
3. addition
4. accurate
5. occasion
6. approve
7. advice
8. occupy
9. assist
10. affair
11. occur
12. acquire
13. assume
14. adjust
15. assign
16. oblige
17. accomplish
18. approach
19. according
20. obtain

1. occupy **(1 point)** _____
2. approach **(1)** _____
3. accurate **(1)** _____
4. addition **(1)** _____
5. observe **(1)** _____

Code Breaker Some Spelling Words have been written in code. Use the code below to figure out each word. Then write the words correctly.

6. KVXNJH
7. BTTIKFH
8. BUALZW
9. BEDLNIH
10. BZZNZW
11. BEEKLQW
12. KVWBNQ
13. BUFNEH
14. BEEKCTXNZO
15. BPPBNI

6. oblige **(1)** _____
7. approve **(1)** _____
8. adjust **(1)** _____
9. acquire **(1)** _____
10. assist **(1)** _____
11. account **(1)** _____
12. obtain **(1)** _____
13. advice **(1)** _____
14. accomplish **(1)** _____
15. affair **(1)** _____

Code:	K	V	T	E	A	X	N	W	B	P	Z	H	C	U	F	J	L	I	Q	D	O
Letter:	o	b	p	c	j	l	i	t	a	f	s	e	m	d	v	g	u	r	n	q	h

Assessment Tip: Total 15 Points

Name _____

Proofreading and Writing

Proofreading Circle the five misspelled Spelling Words in this news bulletin. Then write each word correctly.

Spelling Words

It was a special (occashun) for NASA today, as the agency welcomed Franklin Chang-Díaz into the astronaut corps. Mr. Chang-Díaz, the first Hispanic American ever selected, impressed the selection board with his strong background in science and engineering. In addition, his performance during the required interviews and tests was outstanding, (acording) to an official at the agency. Don't (assuem) that his adventures in space will (occurr) anytime soon, though. Instead, NASA will (asign) him to a variety of projects here on Earth to prepare him for his time in orbit. We'll keep you posted on his progress.

Spelling Words

1. account
2. observe
3. addition
4. accurate
5. occasion
6. approve
7. advice
8. occupy
9. assist
10. affair
11. occur
12. acquire
13. assume
14. adjust
15. assign
16. oblige
17. accomplish
18. approach
19. according
20. obtain

1. occasion **(1 point)**
2. according **(1)**
3. assume **(1)**
4. occur **(1)**
5. assign **(1)**

✏ **Write a Biographical Sketch** Franklin Chang-Díaz worked hard to become an astronaut and was very dedicated to his profession. Do you know anyone with similar characteristics? What has that person done to achieve success? What do you admire about that person?

On a separate piece of paper, write a brief biographical sketch about someone you know who is similar to Franklin Chang-Díaz. Use Spelling Words from the list. Responses will vary. **(5)**

Name _____

Your Choice

Decide which word best completes each sentence. Then write the word in the blank.

unexpected	agency	emotion	science	laboratory
expectantly	agenda	mobile	conscience	labor
expectation	agility	motor	unscientific	collaborate

1. An astronaut must be able to move quickly and lightly, with great
   <u>agility **(1 point)**</u>.

2. NASA and other organizations sometimes join forces to <u>collaborate **(1)**</u>
   on space projects.

3. Franklin Chang-Díaz waited <u>expectantly **(1)**</u> for NASA to
   contact him after his interviews in Houston.

4. Experiments in the field of <u>science **(1)**</u> may lead to important
   advances in medicine and technology.

5. The space shuttle is carried to the launch pad by a "crawler" —
   a giant <u>mobile **(1)**</u> vehicle.

Now write a sentence using two words that you haven't used yet.
Sample answer shown.

<u>Franklin felt unexpected emotion when NASA accepted him. **(3)**</u>

_____

Assessment Tip: Total 8 Points

Name _____

Hey! It's an Interjection!

Interjections An **interjection** is a word or group of words that express feeling. Usually an interjection appears at the beginning of a sentence.

An **interjection** can be followed by either an **exclamation point** or a **comma**.

▶ If the interjection stands alone, use an **exclamation point**.

▶ If the interjection begins a sentence, set it off with a **comma**.

   Hey! Look over here!   Oh, I didn't see you.

Here are some common interjections.

Common Interjections

Oh	Hooray	Wow	Oh, dear	Hey
Well	Aha	Oh, no	Amazing	Oops

Here are some sentences with interjections. Write each sentence on the line. Add the punctuation that is needed.

1. Wow Can you imagine getting a phone call from NASA?

   Wow! Can you imagine getting a phone call from NASA? **(1 point)**

2. Well that will never happen to me. Well, that will never happen to me. **(1)**

3. Oh it might. Oh, it might. **(1)**

4. Hey Blasting off into space would be a great experience!

   Hey! Blasting off into space would be a great experience! **(1)**

5. Amazing The phone is ringing!

   Amazing! The phone is ringing! **(1)**

6. Aha Let me answer it!

   Aha! Let me answer it! **(1)**

Name _____

Keep It Short!

Abbreviations An **abbreviation** is a shortened form of a word. Most, but not all, **abbreviations** begin with a capital letter and end with a period. To find the correct form of an abbreviation, consult a dictionary.

Some Common Abbreviations

Place names:					
Apt.	Apartment	Mt.	Mount or Mountain	Rd.	Road
Ave.	Avenue	St.	Street	P. O.	Post Office

Businesses:					
Co.	Company	Inc.	Incorporated	Ltd.	Limited

Titles:					
Mr.	Mister	Ms.	(any woman)	Mrs.	(married woman)
Col.	Colonel	Dr.	doctor	Capt.	Captain

States:					
OH	Ohio	NY	New York	TX	Texas

Agencies and organizations:

NASA   National Aeronautics and Space Administration

FBI   Federal Bureau of Investigation

Write the following addresses, using abbreviations. Use your dictionary if necessary.

1. Doctor Constance Kline

   45 Elmo Street, Apartment 3

   Red Apple, Pennsylvania

2. Mister Buck Rogers

   Toy Rockets, Limited

   10 Countdown Avenue

   Kubrick, Indiana

1. Dr. Constance Kline **(1 point)**

   45 Elmo St., Apt. 3 **(2)**

   Red Apple, PA **(1)**

2. Mr. Buck Rogers **(1)**

   Toy Rockets, Ltd. **(1)**

   10 Countdown Ave. **(1)**

   Kubrick, IN **(1)**

Assessment Tip: Total **8** Points

Name _____

Suit the Occasion!

Abbreviations are suitable to use only in certain kinds of writing. For instance, it is usually not appropriate to use abbreviations in an essay or in the body of a letter.

In this draft of her essay, Lynette has used abbreviations to save time and space. Now she is ready to write another draft. Help her by writing out the words her abbreviations stand for. Cross out each abbreviation and write the word above it.

When I was only eight years old, I wanted to play music. I thought that it

would be easy and that soon I would be giving concerts in ~~NY~~ *(New York)* I was wrong.

My family lives in a small ~~apt~~ *(apartment)* on Kinsey ~~St~~ *(Street)* in Brooklyn. In the window of

a piano ~~co~~ *(company)* uptown there was a beautiful grand piano that I thought I needed. I

had not even had one lesson! When I told my sister about the piano, she asked

me if I knew how many ~~ft~~ *(feet)* long a grand piano was. She didn't really know how

big the piano was, but she said that our living room was too small by at

least a ~~yd~~ *(yard)*.

I thought about this problem all ~~Aug~~ *(August)* Then it came to me. A flute was

very small, and the school lent them to students in the band. I could learn to

play the flute instead! So that is what I did when we went back to school the

next ~~mo~~ *(month)* I have learned that it is not easy to be a good musician. I am not

ready to give a concert in Carnegie Hall, but next ~~Jan~~ *(January)* our band will travel

to ~~NJ~~ *(New Jersey)* to play in a music festival with ten other schools.

Name _____

Writing a Biography

In *Franklin R. Chang-Díaz*, you read about a boy who realizes his dream of becoming an astronaut in the NASA space program. A **biography** is a written account of important events and significant experiences in a person's life and may highlight reasons why a famous person is remembered. Before you write a biography of your own, follow these steps:

▶ **Choose a real person whom you admire or someone you have read about.**

▶ **Research important facts, dates, places, events, and accomplishments in this person's life. To gather information, use the Internet, reference or history books in your library, or, if possible, conduct a telephone or in-person interview.**

▶ **Record and organize major dates, locations, and events in this person's life on the timeline below.**

The Life of **(1 point)** _____

DATE	EVENT
_____	(2)
_____	(2)
_____	(2)
_____	(2)

Now write your biography on a separate sheet of paper. Start with an anecdote or a famous quotation from this person's life. Then work from your timeline. Write about important events and experiences, using chronological order, time-clue words, and key dates. Highlight the events that you think best reveal this person's character or lifetime achievements. Finally, conclude by summarizing why this person is remembered. (6)

Assessment Tip: Total **15** Points

Combining Sentences with Prepositional Phrases

One way to streamline your writing is to combine short sentences that have a repeated subject but differing prepositional phrases into a single sentence with consecutive prepositional phrases.

Dr. Chang-Díaz is a native **of Costa Rica.** He dreamed **of becoming an astronaut.** He wanted to be an astronaut with **NASA.** NASA is **in the United States.**

Dr. Chang-Díaz, a native **of Costa Rica,** dreamed **of becoming an astronaut with NASA in the United States.**

Imagine you are the editor of a new reference book, *Who's Who in Space.* Revise these sentences from a biographical sketch about Dr. Franklin R. Chang-Díaz that will appear in the book. Combine short sentences that have a repeated subject into a single sentence.

1. Franklin R. Chang-Díaz was fascinated by space exploration as a child. He read about flying in space in newspapers. He read articles in magazines. He found thrilling tales in science fiction stories.

   Fascinated by space exploration as a child, Franklin R. Chang-Díaz read about

   flying in space in newspapers, in magazines, and in science fiction stories. **(2)**

2. When he was a young boy, he played in a make-believe spaceship. The spaceship was made from old TV and radio parts. He put the parts inside a large cardboard box.

   When he was a young boy, he played in a make-believe spaceship made from

   old TV and radio parts inside a large cardboard box. **(2)**

3. He studied science in school. He attended school in the United States. He went to school until he landed a job at a well-known lab. He got the job in 1977.

   He studied science in school in the United States until he landed a job at a

   well-known lab in 1977. **(2)**

Name _____

Marvels of the Deep

Write a word from the box to answer each riddle.

Vocabulary

submersible
oceanographers
menagerie
unfathomable
tentacles
crustacean
gelatinous
undulates

1. We are scientists who study the sea. Who are we?
   oceanographers **(1)**

2. We will grab or sting any prey that floats near us. What are we? tentacles **(1)**

3. I am a creature with a body that is almost like jelly. How would you describe me? gelatinous **(1)**

4. I am a vehicle that travels underwater. What am I?
   submersible **(1)**

5. I am something too deep to measure. How would you describe me?
   unfathomable **(1)**

6. We are a collection of animals. What are we?
   menagerie **(1)**

7. As this creature swims, it moves slowly up and down with the currents. How does it move? It undulates **(1)** .

8. I am a hard-shelled animal with jointed parts, and I live mostly in water. What am I? crustacean **(1)**

Assessment Tip: Total **8** Points

Name _____

Ocean Diagram

Ocean's Surface

Mother Ship

Atlantis **(1 point)** _____

Alvin

portholes **(1)** _____

chilly inside **(1)** _____

has camera inside and out **(1)** _____

12 lights **(1)** _____

operating since 1964 **(1)** _____

Other Submersibles

Shinkai 6500 **(1)**   Jason **(1)**

Hydrothermal Vent

650°F **(1)** _____   huge tubeworms **(1)** _____   giant clams **(1)** _____

Benthopelagic Zone

Benthocodon _____   sediment **(1)** _____   Deepstaria enigmatica,

 pedunculata, a jellyfish **(1)**   ctenophore **(1)**   a jellyfish **(1)**

siphonophore **(1)** _____   squid **(1)** _____   deep-sea cucumber **(1)**

crustacean **(1)** _____   little octopus **(1)**

Seafloor

Name _____

Profile of a Submersible

Answer each question below to describe Alvin for a person who knows nothing about it.

What is *Alvin?*

a submersible that

can go deep under

the ocean's surface

(2 points)

_____

Who travels aboard *Alvin?* Why?

Scientists travel on

Alvin to do research

and locate sunken

objects. **(2)**

What special equipment does *Alvin* have?

lights, different kinds

of cameras, and video

monitors **(2)**

_____

What surprising things have people learned as a result of *Alvin's* exploration?

They have learned

that creatures thrive

around hydrothermal

vents. They have

seen creatures never

seen before. **(2)**

What is a traveler aboard *Alvin* likely to see on the journey?

a menagerie of rare

deep-sea jellyfish,

giant clams, and

octopuses **(2)**

_____

_____

Why can't people travel to the seafloor without a vessel like *Alvin?*

The water is too cold

and the water pres-

sure is too great. **(2)**

_____

_____

_____

Assessment Tip: Total **12** Points

Name _____

Classified Information!

Read the passage. Then complete the activity on page 372.

Miniature Menageries at the Shore

The dark depths of the ocean are full of fascinating life forms, but interesting pockets of sea life are also visible in places much closer to us. When the tide goes out on a rocky shore, small pools of water called tide pools are left behind. A menagerie of small creatures remains in the tide pools until the tide returns.

A careful look into a tide pool can reveal an astonishing array of creatures. You might first see brightly colored starfish clinging to the tide pool's rocky walls. Starfish move across the surface of the rocks more slowly than the eye can detect, propelled by rows of tiny tube feet that act like suction cups. Their hard bodies feel spiny to the touch. Barnacles, shellfish that fasten themselves to fixed objects, cling in piles atop rocky ledges. Barnacles feed by opening their hinged centers and waving their leaf-like legs through the water. Their legs act as a filter that draws food into the soft body inside the shell, where it is digested. Barnacles are usually dull gray, blue, or black in color, and can be mistaken for rocks.

You're also likely to see several sea anemones in the pool. These soft and beautiful creatures look like flowers and might surprise you with their range of color. Sea anemones in the same tide pool might be dark red, lime green, and bright orange. Sea anemones also attach themselves to rocks. They feed by catching tiny fish with their sticky, sponge-like tentacles.

Small fish are often trapped in tide pools, forced to dart back and forth until high tide releases them. Look fast! A small brown crab skitters over the rocks and plunges into the tide pool. It grasps an unfortunate fish in it claws.

Tide pools are brimming with activity. If you have a chance to visit a rocky shore where these miniature pockets of marine life are found, be sure to take a look!

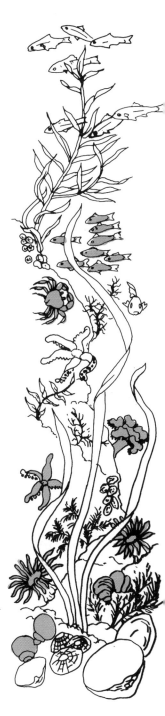

Name _____

Classified Information! continued

Read the category headings in each chart. Then classify the tide pool creatures described in the passage on page 371 by writing their names in the correct columns. Refer to the information in the passage.

Brightly colored creatures	Dully colored creatures
starfish (**1 point**)	barnacles (**1**)
sea anemones (**1**)	crabs (**1**)

Creatures that attach themselves to rocks	Creatures that move freely
barnacles (**1**)	crabs (**1**)
starfish (**1**)	fish (**1**)
sea anemones (**1**)	

Think of two categories that haven't been named yet. Use the chart below to classify tide pool creatures into those categories.
Sample answers shown. (**1 point for each heading; 2 for each list**)

Creatures without shells	Creatures with shells
fish	crabs
sea anemones	barnacles
starfish	

Assessment Tip: Total **15** Points

Name _____

The *ie*/*ei* Shuffle

Read each sentence below. For each underlined word, decide whether
***ie* or *ei* sounds like the long *e* sound in *key*, or the long *a* sound in *aim*.**
Then write the word in the correct column of the chart.

1. Around deep-sea vents on the ocean floor, a <u>menagerie</u> of animals thrives.

2. At first, the harsh environment <u>deceived</u> scientists into thinking that
   nothing could live in such a place.

3. Some of the deep-sea animals appear almost <u>weightless</u>.

4. Scientists must stay constantly alert because they can only stay on the
   sea floor <u>briefly</u>.

5. The bottom of the sea is like a dark, slow-moving <u>neighborhood</u>.

6. In the future, humans will <u>receive</u> data from remotely operated submersibles.

Like *key*	Like *aim*
menagerie **(1 point)**	weightless **(1)**
deceived **(1)**	neighborhood **(1)**
briefly **(1)**	
receive **(1)**	

Now, choose four words from the chart and use them correctly in
sentences of your own. Answers will vary.

7. **(1)** _____

8. **(1)** _____

9. **(1)** _____

10. **(1)** _____

Name _____

Words with *ie* or *ei*

Use *i* before *e* except after *c* or in words with the /ā/ sound, as in *freight*. You must memorize exceptions to this generalization.

yi**e**ld   rec**ei**pt   fr**ei**ght

► The *ei* vowel pairs in *neither, foreign, seize,* and *leisure* do not follow this generalization. Be sure to remember the spellings of these words.

Write each Spelling Word under its spelling pattern.

Order of responses for each category may vary.

Spelling Words

1. freight
2. receipt
3. yield
4. review
5. belief
6. eighty
7. brief
8. ceiling
9. neither*
10. foreign*
11. shield
12. diesel
13. reign
14. fiery
15. conceit
16. veil
17. grief
18. relieve
19. seize*
20. leisure*

i Comes Before e

yield **(1 point)**

review **(1)**

belief **(1)**

brief **(1)**

shield **(1)**

diesel **(1)**

fiery **(1)**

grief **(1)**

relieve **(1)**

ei Follows c

receipt **(1)**

ceiling **(1)**

conceit **(1)**

ei Spells /ā/

freight **(1)**

eighty **(1)**

reign **(1)**

veil **(1)**

Other Spelling Patterns

neither **(1)**

foreign **(1)**

seize **(1)**

leisure **(1)**

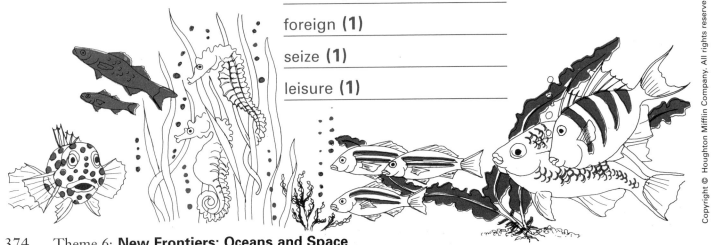

374   Theme 6: **New Frontiers: Oceans and Space**
Assessment Tip: Total **20** Points

Name _____

Spelling Spree

Word Addition Write a Spelling Word by adding the beginning of the first word to the end of the second word.

1. yip + held
2. rent + sign
3. neigh + father
4. fine + ornery
5. vent + nail
6. grime + reef
7. died + weasel

1. yield **(1 point)**
2. reign **(1)**
3. neither **(1)**
4. fiery **(1)**
5. veil **(1)**
6. grief **(1)**
7. diesel **(1)**

Word Squid Begin at the arrow and follow the letters to find eight Spelling Words. Write the words in order. Don't let the other words fool you!

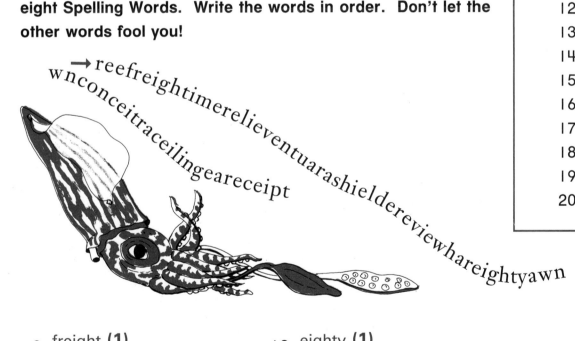

→ reefreightimerelieventuarashieldereviewhareightyawn
wnconceitraceilingeareceipt

8. freight **(1)**
9. relieve **(1)**
10. shield **(1)**
11. review **(1)**

12. eighty **(1)**
13. conceit **(1)**
14. ceiling **(1)**
15. receipt **(1)**

Assessment Tip: Total **15** Points

Name _____

Proofreading and Writing

Proofreading Circle the five misspelled Spelling Words in this advertisement. Then write each word correctly.

Spelling Words

1. freight
2. receipt
3. yield
4. review
5. belief
6. eighty
7. brief
8. ceiling
9. neither*
10. foreign*
11. shield
12. diesel
13. reign
14. fiery
15. conceit
16. veil
17. grief
18. relieve
19. seize*
20. leisure*

> ## Come to an Underwater Paradise!
>
> Want to spend your vacation in a different place without traveling to a (forign) country? Then (sieze) this opportunity to come spend it under the sea! The Grand Neptune Hotel, with eighty rooms located two thousand feet below sea level, is now open for business. You can make your stay as (breif) as one night, or as long as two weeks. Our expert staff will fill your (leizure) time with a variety of activities, including rides in deep-sea submersibles. We think you'll agree that the Grand Neptune is an experience beyond (beleif!)

1. foreign **(1 point)**
2. seize **(1)**
3. brief **(1)**
4. leisure **(1)**
5. belief **(1)**

✏️ **Write a Prediction** Scientists continue to make new discoveries under the ocean's surface, yet vast areas remain unexplored. What do you think the future holds for underwater exploration? What sorts of creatures might scientists find in coming years? Will deep-sea submersibles make longer and deeper voyages possible?

On a separate piece of paper, write your prediction for the future of underwater exploration. Use Spelling Words from the list. Responses will vary. **(5)**

Assessment Tip: Total **10** Points

Name _____

Idiom and Run-on Entry Challenge

Read the sentences. If the underlined part of the sentence is a run-on entry, write its part of speech and the main dictionary entry word. If the underlined part is an idiom, write the meaning of the idiom.

> **black** *n.* Without light. —**blackly** *adv.* —**blackness** *n.*
>
> **eventual** adj. Occurring at an unspecified future time. —**eventually** *adv.*
>
> **look** *v.* To turn one's gaze or attention. —*idioms.* **look after.** To take care of. **look forward to.** To think of a future event with pleasure and excitement.
>
> **successful** *adj.* Having gained something desired or intended. —**successfully** *adv.*
>
> **take** *v.* To acquire possession of something. — *idioms.* **take care.** To be careful. **take on.** To oppose in competition.
>
> **world** *n.* 1. The earth. 2. The universe. — *idioms.* **for all the world.** In all respects; precisely.

1. Maria Jackson, the reigning tennis champion, offered to <u>take on</u> her competitors <u>oppose in competition **(2 points)**</u>

2. The creatures came into view out of the <u>blackness</u>.
   <u>noun; black **(2)**</u>

3. <u>Eventually</u>, deep-sea creatures drift by some food.
   <u>adverb; eventual **(2)**</u>

4. The little octopus looked <u>for all the world</u> like Dumbo.
   <u>in all respects; precisely **(2)**</u>

5. The crew <u>successfully</u> filmed a number of creatures.
   <u>adverb; successful **(2)**</u>

6. The crew members <u>look forward to</u> their next chance to ride in *Alvin*.
   <u>think of with pleasure and excitement **(2)**</u>

Name _____

One, Two, Three, or More

Commas in a Series A list of three or more items is called a **series**. Use a **comma** to separate all the items in a series, except the last. Usually, a **conjunction** such as *and* or *or* appears before the last item in the series and connects the items.

> Dogs, cats, birds, **and** fish are popular pets.

Insert commas where they belong in the following sentences.

1. Mark, David, and Shirley like tropical fish. **(3 points)**

2. They buy gravel, filters, and plants for their aquariums.

3. Mark has goldfish, angelfish, guppies, and snails. **(3)**

4. A plaster castle, a plastic diver, and brightly colored gravel decorate David's aquarium. **(3)**

5. Shirley named her goldfish George, Paul, John, and Theresa. **(3)**

Now write this sentence, adding a series. Insert commas and a conjunction where they belong.

6. Three sea creatures are
   Answers will vary. **(3)** _____

   _____

Assessment Tip: Total **18** Points

Name _____

Consider the Useful Comma

More Uses for Commas Besides separating items in a series, commas
have several other uses.

> ► Use commas to set off an **appositive** from the rest of the sentence. An
>   appositive is a word or a group of words that identify or explain the noun that
>   they follow.
>
>   Robert Ballard, an undersea explorer, found the wreckage of the *Titanic*.
>
> ► Set off an **introductory word** like *yes*, *no*, or *well* at the beginning of a
>   sentence from the rest of the sentence with a comma.
>
>   Yes, people were amazed by the discovery.
>
> ► Use a comma or commas to set off a noun used in **direct address**.
>
>   Sarah, did you see the documentary?

Add commas where they belong in the sentences below.

1. Jim, let's walk along the seashore today. **(1 point)**

2. Tess, my cousin, goes deep sea diving with her father. **(2)**

3. I'd like to dive in Alvin, a special deep-diving submarine, to see a big
   jellyfish. **(2)**

4. Well, maybe someday you'll have the chance. **(1)**

5. Here is a small jellyfish near the water, Moesha. **(1)**

6. This animal is round, soft, and clear. **(2)**

7. Yes, Jim, it is an unusual creature. **(2)**

8. I'd like to be an oceanographer, a scientist who studies the sea. **(1)**

9. Well, you will need to study biology. **(1)**

10. Look, Jim, at this crab! **(2)**

Name _____

Commas for Good Reason

Proofreading for Commas A good writer proofreads carefully to be sure that commas are correctly used. This requires close attention because commas are so small!

Julio is getting ready to turn in a paper to his teacher. He knows that he needs to proofread carefully for comma errors. Help him by proofreading the portion of his draft below. Add six commas where they are needed. Use the proofreading marks on page 434.

My Career as an Oceanographer

I read the story about the chemist, biologist, and pilot with great interest. They dived in *Alvin*, a special submarine, to study the ocean's depths. What they found there surprised me! Yes, they found a very strange world. I thought I'd have to go to outer space to see such an exotic place. That is why I had wanted to be an astronaut. Now, Ms. Kovacs and Ms. Kate, because of your story I want to explore the oceans. I want to dive in the Atlantic Ocean, the Pacific Ocean, the Mediterranean Sea, and even the Arctic Ocean. **(1 point each)**

Assessment Tip: Total **6** Points

Name _____

Writing a Compare/ Contrast Essay

In *Beneath Blue Waters*, you read about similarities and differences between sea creatures in the deepest zone and those in other parts of the ocean. One way to explain similarities and differences is by writing a **compare/contrast essay.** A good essay describes both the ways things are alike and the ways they are different.

Choose two of the following deep-sea creatures from the article to compare and contrast:

▶ "fried egg" siphonphore, Stephalia corona

▶ Benthocodon pedunculata

▶ the jellyfish, Deepstaria enigmatica

▶ unnamed ctenophore

Write the names of the creatures on the lines below. Then use the Venn diagram to gather and organize details that compare and contrast the creatures' diet, size, shape, color, and so on. (4 points)

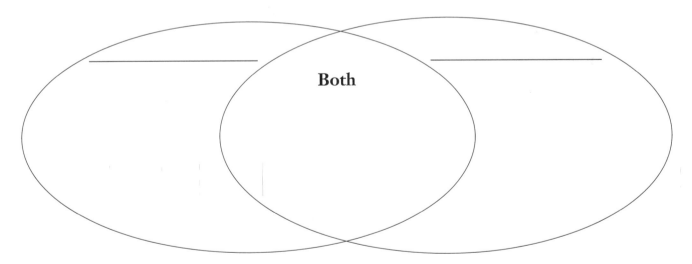

On a separate sheet of paper, write a compare/contrast essay about the two deep-sea creatures you chose. In the opening paragraph, clearly state the subject being compared and contrasted. In the following paragraphs, present details from your Venn diagram. Group details that compare and details that contrast in a clear manner. Use clue words such as *similarly* or *likewise* to help readers identify likenesses and *however* or *unlike* to help them identify differences. (6)

Assessment Tip: Total **10** Points

Name _____

Using Commas to Combine Sentences

Good writers strive to avoid using dull, choppy sentences. One way to improve the flow of your writing is to combine sentences using commas. You can combine two short, choppy sentences into either a compound or a complex sentence, depending on how the two ideas you are combining are related.

A biologist aboard the submersible Alvin tape-recorded some observations about deep-sea creatures. Revise the transcript of the biologist's notes by using commas to combine sentences as follows: **(2 points** for each combined sentence)

▶ Use a comma and a coordinating conjunction like *and*, *or*, or *but* to join two simple sentences into a compound sentence.

   The chemist analyzed data. The biologist videotaped unusual creatures.

   The chemist analyzed data, **and** the biologist videotaped unusual creatures.

▶ Use a comma and a subordinating conjunction like *when*, *because*, *although*, or *while* to join two simple sentences into a complex sentence.

   While the chemist analyzed data, the biologist videotaped unusual creatures.

Monday, 11:23 A.M.

The submersible has landed at the dive site. I look out of the Plexiglas window. I observe the sandy seafloor. A ctenophore catches my eye. Most deep-sea creatures eat rarely. This football-sized animal feeds on a small crustacean. A siphonophore swims into view. I have never seen this kind before. I decide not to collect this creature. It is too fragile to survive the long trip up to the surface.

The submersible has landed at the dive site, **and** I look out of the Plexiglas window.

When I observe the sandy seafloor, a ctenophore catches my eye. **Although** most deep-sea creatures eat rarely, this football-sized animal feeds on a small crustacean.

A siphonophore swims into view, **but** I have never seen this kind before. **Because** it is too fragile to survive the long trip up to the surface, I decide not to collect this creature.

Assessment Tip: Total **10** Points

Name _____

Mystery at Sea

Read the story below. Write words from the box to complete the story.

visibility
buoy
inquiries
discount
afterdeck
bulkhead
derelict
port side

Stephanie boarded the boat, went all the way to the rear, and began setting up her camera on the afterdeck **(2 points)** . She could barely contain her excitement. She was about to begin making her first movie. It was going to be a mystery involving the sea. The setting was to include an old, abandoned fishing boat – a derelict **(2)** . She had made many inquiries **(2)** before finding a boat she could use. Most owners seemed to discount **(2)** her promises that she would not harm the boat. Finally she had found an owner willing to allow her aboard—Earl Cuthbert, a friend of her uncle. His battered old boat was now carrying Stephanie toward a buoy **(2)** that marked the mouth of the harbor. It was very foggy, and Stephanie hoped the visibility **(2)** would improve. If the weather stayed foggy, she would not be able to get good shots of the harbor or the shore. While she waited, she decided to film Earl at work on the left, or port side **(2)** , of the boat. Just then a wave rocked the boat, and she heard a thud from below the deck. A frown crossed Earl's face. "Sounds like something bumped against a bulkhead **(2)** in my sleeping cabin," he said. "I think we have someone else aboard."

Name _____

Conclusions Chart

Story Clues   **Conclusions**

pages 620–621

| Danny Aldo drops anchor and fishes near the buoy to wait for the fog to lift. | + | He has fished for a long time and knows what kind of fish he might catch. | = | Danny is an experienced boater who doesn't take unnecessary risks. **(2 points)** |

pages 621–622

| Danny is more amazed than afraid after he sees a huge eel swim by. | + | He boards the abandoned boat to explore. | = | Danny is level-headed and brave, and he doesn't frighten easily. **(2)** |

pages 623–627

| Danny tells Sergeant Lamont everything that happened even though he thinks he'll be laughed at. **(2)** | + | Danny sticks to his account even after the sergeant and sheriff's deputies doubt him. **(2)** | = | Danny is responsible and honest and not afraid of being laughed at. |

pages 627–628, 633

| Because of the blood, Danny thinks the eel ties in with Jack Stokes's disappearance. | + | The medical examiner says the blood wasn't human blood. | = | Something strange did happen to Jack Stokes. **(2)** |

pages 628–632

| On the Internet, Danny finds reports of strange serpent-like sea creatures. **(2)** | + | Captain Carroll shows Danny his photo of a serpent-like creature. **(2)** | = | Danny is assured that strange sea creatures do exist, despite most people's skepticism. |

384   Theme 6: **New Frontiers: Oceans and Space**

Assessment Tip: Total **14** Points

Name _____

Recording Reactions

Complete each sentence below to tell about important events that
happen in *Out There* and how Danny reacts to each one. Sample answers shown.

Event	How Danny Reacts to the Event
1. When Danny sees the huge eel-like creature,	he is amazed, but he isn't afraid.**(2 points)**
2 When he first sees the *Lotta Fun*,	he worries that something is wrong and goes aboard to see what has happened. **(2)**
3. After seeing <u>the pool of blood **(2)**</u> aboard the *Lotta Fun*,	Danny begins to feel frightened.
4. When the sheriff's deputies at the Harbor Patrol <u>doubt him and make fun of his story, **(2)**</u>,	Danny is frustrated and angry.
5. When Danny reads stories on the Internet about <u>other sightings</u> of strange creatures at sea, **(2)**	he is convinced that what he saw is real.
6. After hearing Captain Carroll's story,	Danny is so encouraged that he sets out to prove that huge sea creatures exist. **(2)**

Theme 6: **New Frontiers: Oceans and Space**   385
Assessment Tip: Total **12** Points

Name _____

What Do You Conclude?

Read the passage. Then complete the activity on page 387.

Stargazing

I was perched on top of our roof with my telescope and a plastic bottle full of lemonade, ready for a long night of stargazing. I had finished all my homework and done the dishes. Mom had watched over my shoulder to make sure I got it all done. My two brothers were watching a TV show about UFOs, and Mom was on the phone. I was all alone, thinking how I would love to see a real UFO.

It was a perfectly clear night. I could pick out the Big Dipper and Orion's belt. I thought I noticed a star with a red glow that could have been the planet Mars. A plane passed by, its red lights flashing. Then I saw something that made me drop my lemonade. Emerging from the black sky was a crisp blue light shaped like a saucer. It looked as if it was headed straight for me.

I quickly ran downstairs, shouting, "Mom! Come here, you've got to see this!"

"Billy, I'm on the phone," she said.

When I told her this was serious, she ended her phone conversation in a hurry and followed me. I stood on the roof, my chest heaving, and pointed at the sky. The blue light was gone. The constellations twinkled in the darkness. Mom put her hands on her hips. "What was it you wanted me to see?" she asked.

I stuttered and pointed. "I saw . . . there was a . . . a blue light. . . ."
She was staring at me with a skeptical expression. "Never mind," I said.
"It was probably a shooting star."

Mom told me to come inside. When we joined my brothers, a special announcement came on TV. A reporter was standing in the middle of a field in front of an unusual-looking airplane with blue lights glowing steadily on its wings. The reporter said, "We have discovered the source of the mysterious blue lights tonight. New planes are being tested in the vicinity for a special flight show planned for October."

Name _____

What Do You Conclude?

continued

Answer these questions about the passage on page 386.

1. How does Billy feel about the stars and stargazing? How do you know?
   He is fascinated with stars and loves to look at them. He owns his own
   telescope and has a full bottle of lemonade, ready for a long night. **(2 points)**

2. Has Billy spent time studying the stars? How can you tell?
   Yes. He knows how to recognize some constellations and planets. **(2)**

3. What does Billy think he sees in the sky? How can you tell?
   He thinks he sees a UFO. He has said he would love to see a real UFO. Then he
   says the object in the sky looks like a saucer; and he runs to get his mom. **(2)**

4. How does Billy's mom feel when he tells her that the situation is serious?
   How do you know? She seems to be concerned, because she ends her phone
   conversation immediately and goes with Billy up to the roof. **(2)**

5. What was it that Billy saw? How do you know? Billy saw a new plane being
   tested for a flight show. The description of the plane in the TV announcement
   matches the description of the object Billy saw in the sky. **(2)**

Name _____

Word Relatives

Read each group of words below. Decide what word part the words have in common. Choose a word from the tackle box with the same word part, and write it in the blank.

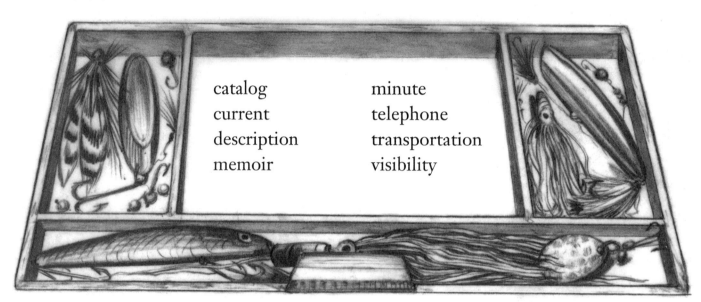

catalog   minute
current   telephone
description   transportation
memoir   visibility

1. scribe, transcribe, script   description **(1 point)**

2. important, reported, portable   transportation **(1)**

3. telescope, televise, telegraph   telephone **(1)**

4. revise, vision, invisible   visibility **(1)**

5. recur, cursive, occurrence   current **(1)**

6. logical, dialogue, analogy   catalog **(1)**

7. remember, memorize, commemorate   memoir **(1)**

8. miniature, minimize, minor   minute **(1)**

Assessment Tip: Total **8** Points

Name _____

Word Parts

Many words are made up of a prefix, a base word or a word root, and a suffix. Find these parts in each word, and then spell the word by the parts.

<u>un</u>belie**vable**   **in**vent**ion**

<u>ad</u>vance**ment**   **con**centr**ation**

Write each Spelling Word. Underline its prefix and circle its suffix or suffixes. Order of answers may vary.

develop(ment) **(1 point)**

inform(ation) **(1)**

prepar(ation) **(1)**

improve(ment) **(1)**

invent(ion) **(1)**

<u>ad</u>vance(ment) **(1)**

<u>ac</u>cident(ally) **(1)**

<u>un</u>kind(ness) **(1)**

<u>con</u>centr(ation) **(1)**

<u>un</u>skill(ful) **(1)**

respect(ful) **(1)**

<u>pre</u>vent(ion) **(1)**

<u>re</u>gard(less) **(1)**

<u>re</u>petit(ion) **(1)**

<u>dis</u>grace(ful) **(1)**

<u>un</u>believ(able) **(1)**

<u>dis</u>agree(ment) **(1)**

<u>im</u>prison(ment) **(1)**

<u>en</u>courage(ment) **(1)**

<u>inter</u>miss(ion) **(1)**

Spelling Words

1. development
2. information
3. preparation
4. improvement
5. invention
6. advancement
7. accidentally
8. unkindness
9. concentration
10. unskillful
11. respectful
12. prevention
13. regardless
14. repetition
15. disgraceful
16. unbelievable
17. disagreement
18. imprisonment
19. encouragement
20. intermission

Theme 6: **New Frontiers: Oceans and Space** 389
Assessment Tip: Total **20** Points

Name _____

Spelling Spree

Base Word/Word Root Blanks Write a Spelling Word by placing the correct base word or word root in the blank between each item's prefix and suffix.

Example: de_____ful   delightful

1. con_____ation
2. de_____ment
3. re_____less
4. re_____ful
5. ad_____ment
6. re_____ion
7. pre_____ation
8. un_____ful

1. development
2. information
3. preparation
4. improvement
5. invention
6. advancement
7. accidentally
8. unkindness
9. concentration
10. unskillful
11. respectful
12. prevention
13. regardless
14. repetition
15. disgraceful
16. unbelievable
17. disagreement
18. imprisonment
19. encouragement
20. intermission

1. concentration **(1 point)**
2. development **(1)**
3. regardless **(1)**
4. respectful **(1)**
5. advancement **(1)**
6. repetition **(1)**
7. preparation **(1)**
8. unskillful **(1)**

Meaning Match Combine each meaning below with its prefix or suffix(es) to write a Spelling Word.

9. dis + moving elegantly and beautifully
10. to create something new + ion
11. to make better + ment
12. to keep from occurring + ion
13. inter + a special task
14. to put in jail + ment
15. something not planned + ally

9. disgraceful **(1)**
10. invention **(1)**
11. improvement **(1)**
12. prevention **(1)**
13. intermission **(1)**
14. imprisonment **(1)**
15. accidentally **(1)**

Assessment Tip: Total **15** Points

Name _____

Proofreading and Writing

Proofreading **Circle the five misspelled Spelling Words in this wanted poster. Then write each word correctly.**

Spelling Words

WANTED

Do you have any (infermation) about a large, eel-like creature that lives in the waters outside Dana Harbor? It may seem (unbelievabel) to you, but there have been several recent sightings by local fishermen. These people have stuck to their stories, regardless of the (unkindnes) with which the authorities have treated them. There is some (disagreemint) about the exact length of the creature, but most reports put it at over twenty feet. If you have a story to tell, we want to offer you every (encouragement) to step forward. Please contact the Dana Harbor Sighting Board at 555-8232.

Spelling Words

1. development
2. information
3. preparation
4. improvement
5. invention
6. advancement
7. accidentally
8. unkindness
9. concentration
10. unskillful
11. respectful
12. prevention
13. regardless
14. repetition
15. disgraceful
16. unbelievable
17. disagreement
18. imprisonment
19. encouragement
20. intermission

1. information **(1 point)**
2. unbelievable **(1)**
3. unkindness **(1)**
4. disagreement **(1)**
5. encouragement **(1)**

Write a Comparison and Contrast Like the scientists in *Beneath Blue Waters*, Danny finds an unknown sea creature in *Out There*. But unlike them, Danny's report isn't taken seriously. Why do you think that might be? What makes the scientists' accounts so believable? What are some things about Danny's encounter that might make it hard to believe?

On a separate piece of paper, write a paragraph in which you compare and contrast Danny's encounter with those of the scientists. Use Spelling Words from the list. Responses will vary. **(5)**

Which Spelling? Which Pronunciation?

**Read the dictionary entries, paying special attention to the spellings
and pronunciations. Then answer the questions.**

anchovy (ăn′ chō vē *or* ăn **chō′** vē) *n.* A small sea fish related to the herring.
burn (bûrn) *v.* **burned** *or* **burnt** (bûrnt). To set on fire.
diesel (dē′ zəl *or* **dē′** səl) *n.* A type of internal-combustion engine.
toward (tôrd *or* tə **wôrd′**) also **towards** (tôrdz or tə **wôrdz′**) *prep.*
    In the direction of.
water (wô′ tər *or* wŏt′ ər) *n.* A compound of hydrogen and oxygen
    occurring as a liquid.

1. What is the other way to spell *toward*? towards **(2 points)**

2. In what single way are the two pronunciations of *anchovy* different?
   only in the stressed syllable **(1)** _____ Is the second

   pronunciation more like *recognize* or like (remember?) (Circle the correct

   answer.) **(1)**

3 Is the first pronunciation of *diesel* more like (weasel) or like *creases*?

   (Circle the correct answer.) **(2)**

4. If you are using the first pronunciation of *water*, are you saying

   WAHT ur or (WAW tur)? (Circle the correct answer.) **(2)**

5. What are the two ways to spell the past tense of *burn*?
   burned and burnt **(2)**

Assessment Tip: Total **10** Points

Name _____

Please, Quote Me!

Punctuating Dialogue There are a number of rules for punctuating dialogue.
Study the list below.

Rules for Punctuating Dialogue

▶ Use **quotation marks** to set off dialogue from the rest of the sentence.

▶ Begin the first word of a quotation with a capital letter.

▶ Place punctuation marks inside the closing quotation marks.

▶ Use commas to separate most quotations from the rest of the sentence.

▶ When a quotation is interrupted in the middle, end the first part of the
   quotation with quotation marks. Begin the second part with quotation marks.
   Use commas to separate the quotation from the speaker.

▶ Begin a new paragraph with each change of speaker.

Write each sentence, using correct punctuation and capitalization.

1. Tom said Sea adventure stories are exciting Tom said, "Sea adventure stories are
   exciting." **(4 points)**

2. I took a trip said Miranda on a whale watching boat "I took a trip," said Miranda,
   "on a whale watching boat." **(4)**

3. Three whales came very close to our boat she said "Three whales came very
   close to our boat," she said. **(4)**

4. Have you ever visited the New England Aquarium asked Tom "Have you ever
   visited the New England Aquarium? " asked Tom.**(4)**

5. Tom said it's fun to watch the seals Tom said, "It's fun to watch the seals." **(4)**
   _____

Theme 6: **New Frontiers: Oceans and Space**   393
Assessment Tip: Total **20** Points

Name _____

Put It in Print!

Capitalization in Titles When you write the titles of books, magazines, newspapers, songs, movies, and other works, you must treat them in special ways. Here are some rules to study.

Titles in Writing or in Print

► Capitalize the first, the last, and each important word.

► Capitalize forms of the verb *be*, including *is*, *are*, and *am*.

► Capitalize words like *and*, *in*, *of*, *to*, *a*, and *the* only when they are the first or last word in a title.

► When you use a word processor, put titles of books, movies, magazines, and newspapers in italic type.

► When you write with a pen or pencil, underline titles of books, movies, magazines, and newspapers.

► When you write the title of a song, poem, article, or short story, put the title in quotation marks. Punctuation that follows a title usually goes inside the quotation marks.

Write the following sentences, correcting the capitalization and punctuation of each title.

1. I took a book called deep sea fishing out of the library.

   I took a book called Deep Sea Fishing out of the library. **(1 point)**

2. Sarah can recite Edgar Allan Poe's poem the raven.

   Sarah can recite Edger Allan Poe's poem "The Raven." **(1)**

3. Will you do a book report on ghost ship?

   Will you do a book report on Ghost Ship? **(1)**

4. Read the article called back to basics.

   Read the article called "Back to Basics." **(1)**

5. Circle game is my favorite song. "Circle Game" is my favorite song. **(1)**

Assessment Tip: Total **5** Points

Name _____

Finishing Touches

Proofreading for Capitalization and Punctuation A good writer proofreads work before turning it in, to make sure that all words that should be capitalized are capitalized and that all sentences, quotations, and titles are properly punctuated.

Proofread this portion of Laurie's account of her trip to the library with her friend Zack. Use the proofreader's marks on page 434. Find and correct ten errors in capitalization and punctuation. (2 points each)

> Zack and I went to the kenner Memorial Library the public library in our town last Saturday. It is only two blocks away from our apartment building on High Street. The librarian, Ms Conway, knows Zack and me, and she knows what we like to read.
>
> Last Saturday, Ms. Conway said "Laurie I want to show you a book called The houseboat Mystery. "Thanks, Ms. Conway" I said.

Name _____

Writing an Answer to an Essay Question

An **essay question** is a test question that asks for a written answer of one or more paragraphs. An essay question may ask you to write about an experience, give a personal opinion about an issue and back it up with reasons and examples, explain a process, or persuade readers to do or think something.

Think about Danny's experiences on the day he saw the giant eel. Then prepare to answer this essay question:

If you see something unbelievable, how would you know whether to trust your eyes? Should you tell others about what you saw? Why or why not?

Organize your answer by filling in the planning chart. First, read the essay question carefully, identifying key words that tell you what kind of answer is needed. Next, jot down main ideas and details you might include. Finally, number your ideas, beginning with *1*, to arrange the order in which you will present them. (5 points)

Key Words/ Their Meaning	how (give evidence); should (give reasons why or why not)
Main Ideas	
Details	

On a separate sheet of paper, write your answer to the essay question. Begin by restating the question. Then write your main ideas and details in a logical order. When you finish, check to make sure that your response answers the question. (5)

396   Theme 6: **New Frontiers: Oceans and Space**
Assessment Tip: Total **10** Points

Name _____

Keeping to the Point

Good writers stay on the subject they are writing about. Whether you are writing to respond to an essay question or for another purpose, make sure that you include only information about the topic at hand without repeating ideas or straying from the topic.

Proofread the following passage from a web site about unusual ocean sightings like the one Danny Aldo experienced in *Out There*. Draw a line through any sentences that give unnecessary information or stray from the point. (2 points for each sentence)

In December 1938 Captain Goosen and his crew caught a bizarre fish in a shark gill net near the Comoros Islands off the east coast of South Africa. ~~Nelson Mandela became president of South Africa in 1994. His election marked the end of apartheid in that country.~~ The fishermen brought their mysterious fish to a local museum. ~~Our local museum currently has an exhibit about the mill industry in the 1800s.~~ Eventually, a well-known biologist identified this fish as a living fossil, the Coelacanth. Until this remarkable discovery, scientists believed that the Coelacanth was extinct because no live specimens or fossil remains had been seen for about 80 million years! ~~Last year I read an interesting book about collecting fossils.~~ More recently, American and Indonesian scientists found a new species of Coelacanths near Sulawesi, Indonesia, in July 1998. Like their Comoros cousins, these elusive modern Coelacanths also live about 600 feet deep in dark underwater caves in the Indian Ocean.

Name _____

Writing a Persuasive Essay

Use what you have learned about taking tests to help you write an essay to persuade someone to agree with your opinion. This practice will help you when you take this kind of test.

Curiosity drives humans to explore space. In *The Adventures of Sojourner: The Mission to Mars That Thrilled the World*, you read about the unmanned exploration of Mars. Some people think that humans should go to Mars, and some think only unmanned spacecraft should go there. Write an essay to persuade a general audience that humans should explore Mars.

Answers will vary. **(15 points)**

_____

_____

_____

_____

_____

_____

_____

_____

_____

_____

_____

_____

_____

_____

Name _____

Writing a Persuasive Essay

continued

Read your essay. Check to be sure that
- the introduction states your goal clearly
- you have at least three strong reasons to support your goal
- you have facts and examples to back up each reason
- your voice is confident and persuasive
- your conclusion sums up the important points
- there are few mistakes in capitalization, punctuation, grammar, or spelling

Now pick one way to improve your essay. Make your changes below.

Answers will vary. **(5)**

_____

_____

_____

_____

_____

_____

_____

_____

_____

_____

_____

_____

Spelling Review

Write each Spelling Word. Then underline the seven words that begin with the prefix *en-, re-, un-, inter-, ac-,* **or** *dis-,* **and that also end with a suffix.**

1. encouragement **(1 point)**
2. relieve **(1)**
3. observe **(1)**
4. extent **(1)**
5. freight **(1)**
6. decision **(1)**
7. regardless **(1)**
8. review **(1)**
9. assist **(1)**
10. preview **(1)**
11. unbelievable **(1)**
12. reign **(1)**
13. acquire **(1)**
14. disable **(1)**
15. intermission **(1)**
16. ceiling **(1)**
17. occur **(1)**
18. demonstrate **(1)**
19. addition **(1)**
20. accidentally **(1)**
21. brief **(1)**
22. interview **(1)**
23. disgraceful **(1)**
24. disagreement **(1)**
25. belief **(1)**
26. obtain **(1)**
27. approve **(1)**
28. affair **(1)**
29. persuade **(1)**
30. product **(1)**

Spelling Words

1. encouragement
2. relieve
3. observe
4. extent
5. freight
6. decision
7. regardless
8. review
9. assist
10. preview
11. unbelievable
12. reign
13. acquire
14. disable
15. intermission
16. ceiling
17. occur
18. demonstrate
19. addition
20. accidentally
21. brief
22. interview
23. disgraceful
24. disagreement
25. belief
26. obtain
27. approve
28. affair
29. persuade
30. product

Assessment Tip: Total **30** Points

Name _____

Spelling Spree

Alphabet Puzzler Write the Spelling Word that fits alphabetically between the two words shown.

1. assign, _assist **(1 point)**_, assort
2. dirt, _disable **(1)**_, disadvantage
3. rehearse, _reign **(1)**_, reindeer
4. interlude, _intermission **(1)**_, intermix
5. achieve, _affair **(1)**_, agent
6. interrupt, _interview **(1)**_, introduce
7. refuse, _regardless **(1)**_, register
8. debate, _decision **(1)**_, defeat

Analogies Write a Spelling Word that completes each analogy.

9. *Conflict* is to *harmony* as _disagreement **(1)**_ is to *agreement*.
10. *Review* is to *repay* as _preview **(1)**_ is to *prepay*.
11. *Truth* is to *fact* as *opinion* is to _belief **(1)**_.
12. *Final* is to *finally* as *accident* is to _accidentally **(1)**_.
13. *Show* is to *tell* as _demonstrate **(1)**_ is to *explain*.
14. *Help* is to *assist* as *ease* is to _relieve **(1)**_.
15. *Persuasion* is to _persuade **(1)**_ as *decision* is to *decide*.

Spelling Words

1. disable
2. relieve
3. belief
4. regardless
5. decision
6. interview
7. intermission
8. assist
9. accidentally
10. disagreement
11. demonstrate
12. preview
13. affair
14. persuade
15. reign

Assessment Tip: Total **15** Points

Name _____

Proofreading and Writing

Proofreading Circle the six misspelled Spelling Words from this website. Then write the words correctly.

Our goal is to (acuire) information about space. Perhaps we will discover the full (exstent) of the universe. Maybe we will find new ways to ship (frieght) from Earth to other planets. In (adition,) we would like to (obzerve) Earth's weather from the moon, and to develop at least one new (praduct) to help predict the weather.

1. acquire **(1 point)**
2. extent **(1)**
3. freight **(1)**
4. addition **(1)**
5. observe **(1)**
6. product **(1)**

Computer Glitch! **This e-mail message is missing some words. Write Spelling Words to complete the message.**

I'm coming home as soon as I 7. _____ a plane ticket. It's 8. _____ to me how quickly time passes! I miss you and don't need much 9. _____ to visit. What I hope will 10. _____ while I'm home is that the school will 11. _____ my project idea. The committee still has to 12. _____ and vote on my proposal. My proposal was 13. _____, only five pages; I hope I wrote enough. My project is about small oil spills and sealife. I think it's 14. _____ that people are so careless about the ocean.

By the way, the seashell mobile you gave me is hanging from my dorm room 15. _____. I love it!

7. obtain **(1)**
8. unbelievable **(1)**
9. encouragement **(1)**
10. occur **(1)**
11. approve **(1)**
12. review **(1)**
13. brief **(1)**
14. disgraceful **(1)**
15. ceiling **(1)**

✏️➡ **Write a Web Page** **On a separate sheet of paper, write a paragraph about the ocean for your website. Use the Spelling Review Words.** Responses will vary. **(5)**

Spelling Words

1. approve
2. encouragement
3. addition
4. brief
5. extent
6. observe
7. product
8. obtain
9. occur
10. review
11. freight
12. acquire
13. ceiling
14. unbelievable
15. disgraceful

Theme 6: **New Frontiers: Oceans and Space** 403
Assessment Tip: Total **20** Points

Student Handbook

Contents

How to Study a Word

1. LOOK at the word.
► What does the word mean?
► What letters are in the word?
► Name and touch each letter.

2. SAY the word.
► Listen for the consonant sounds.
► Listen for the vowel sounds.

3. THINK about the word.
► How is each sound spelled?
► Close your eyes and picture the word.
► What familiar spelling patterns do you see?
► Did you see any prefixes, suffixes, or other word parts?

4. WRITE the word.
► Think about the sounds and the letters.
► Form the letters correctly.

5. CHECK the spelling.
► Did you spell the word the same way it is spelled in your word list?
► If you did not spell the word correctly, write the word again.

affectionate
again
all right
a lot
always
another
anyone
anything
anyway
applicable

beautiful
because
before
believe
brought
bureau

cannot
can't
captain
catastrophe
caught
clothes
coming
cousin

didn't
different
don't

eighth
embarrass
enough
essential
everybody
everything
everywhere

family
fatigue
favorite
field
finally
forfeit
friend

getting
going
guess
guy

happened
happily
haven't
heard
height
here

illustrator
indictment
instead
interpret
irreplaceable
its
it's

knew
know

might
millimeter
morning

o'clock
once

pennant
people
perceive
perspiration
pneumonia
pretty
probably

questionnaire

really
received
reversible
right

Saturday
school
someone
sometimes
stopped
stretch
sufficient
suppose
suppress
swimming

that's
their
there
there's
they're
thought
through
to
tonight
too
two

usually

weird
we're

whole
would
wouldn't
write
writing

your
you're

Words Often Confused

affect
effect

alley
ally

ascent
assent

bauble
bubble

bellow
below

bisect
dissect

bazaar
bizarre

bland
blend

confidant
confident

decent
descent

desert
dessert

eclipse
ellipse

hurdle
hurtle

illegible
ineligible

eminent
imminent

moral
mortal

pastor
pasture

sleek
slick

Take-Home Word List

Passage to Freedom

Long Vowels

/ā/ → g**a**ze, tr**ai**t
/ē/ → th**e**me, pr**ea**ch, sl**ee**ve
/ī/ → str**i**ve
/ō/ → qu**o**te, r**oa**m
/yōō/ → m**u**te

Spelling Words

1. theme
2. quote
3. gaze
4. pace
5. preach
6. strive
7. trait
8. mute
9. sleeve
10. roam
11. strain
12. fade
13. league
14. soak
15. grease
16. throne
17. fume
18. file
19. toast
20. brake

Challenge Words

1. microphone
2. emphasize
3. refugee
4. pertain
5. coax

My Study List
Add your own spelling words on the back. ➡

Take-Home Word List

Courage
Reading-Writing Workshop

Look for familiar spelling patterns in these words to help you remember their spellings.

Spelling Words

1. your
2. you're
3. their
4. they're
5. its
6. it's
7. wouldn't
8. we're
9. to
10. too
11. that's
12. knew
13. know

Challenge Words

1. pennant
2. bureau
3. interpret
4. forfeit
5. perspiration

My Study List
Add your own spelling words on the back. ➡

Take-Home Word List

Hatchet

Short Vowels

/ă/ → cr**a**ft
/ĕ/ → d**e**pth
/ĭ/ → f**i**lm
/ŏ/ → b**o**mb
/ŭ/ → pl**u**nge

Spelling Words

1. depth
2. craft
3. plunge
4. wreck
5. sunk
6. film
7. wince
8. bomb
9. switch
10. length
11. prompt
12. pitch
13. else
14. cliff
15. pledge
16. scrub
17. brass
18. grill
19. stung
20. bulk

Challenge Words

1. habitat
2. cobweb
3. tepid
4. magnetic
5. deft

My Study List
Add your own spelling words on the back. ➡

Name _____

 My Study List

1. _____
2. _____
3. _____
4. _____
5. _____
6. _____
7. _____
8. _____
9. _____
10. _____

Review Words

1. swift
2. tense
3. bunch
4. grasp
5. ditch

How to Study a Word

Look at the word.
Say the word.
Think about the word.
Write the word.
Check the spelling.

Name _____

 My Study List

1. _____
2. _____
3. _____
4. _____
5. _____
6. _____
7. _____
8. _____
9. _____
10. _____

How to Study a Word

Look at the word.
Say the word.
Think about the word.
Write the word.
Check the spelling.

Name _____

My Study List

1. _____
2. _____
3. _____
4. _____
5. _____
6. _____
7. _____
8. _____
9. _____
10. _____

Review Words

1. greet
2. boast
3. brain
4. code
5. squeak

How to Study a Word

Look at the word.
Say the word.
Think about the word.
Write the word.
Check the spelling.

Courage
Spelling Review

Spelling Words

1. wince	16. craft
2. league	17. throne
3. strive	18. rhythm
4. routine	19. vault
5. prompt	20. avoid
6. strain	21. depth
7. meant	22. roam
8. foul	23. reply
9. hoist	24. stout
10. naughty	25. squawk
11. bulk	26. gaze
12. theme	27. sleeve
13. mute	28. ravine
14. sponge	29. sought
15. bloom	30. annoy

See the back for Challenge Words.

The True Confessions of Charlotte Doyle

The /ou/, /o͞o/, /ô/, and /oi/ Sounds

/ou/ ➡ st**ou**t

/o͞o/ ➡ bl**oo**m

/ô/ ➡ v**au**lt, squ**aw**k, s**ough**t, n**augh**ty

/oi/ ➡ av**oi**d, ann**oy**

Spelling Words

1. bloom	11. mound
2. stout	12. groove
3. droop	13. foul
4. crouch	14. hoist
5. annoy	15. gloom
6. vault	16. trout
7. squawk	17. noun
8. avoid	18. roost
9. sought	19. clause
10. naughty	20. appoint

Challenge Words

1. bountiful
2. adjoin
3. nauseous
4. turquoise
5. heirloom

Climb or Die

More Vowel Spellings

/ē/ ➡ rout**ine**

/ĕ/ ➡ sw**ea**t

/ī/ ➡ c**y**cle

/ĭ/ ➡ rh**y**thm

/ŭ/ ➡ sh**ove**
    (*o consonant e*)

Spelling Words

1. cycle	11. sponge
2. sweat	12. apply
3. rhythm	13. threat
4. rely	14. myth
5. pleasant	15. deny
6. routine	16. leather
7. cleanse	17. rhyme
8. shove	18. thread
9. reply	19. meadow
10. meant	20. ravine

Challenge Words

1. endeavor
2. oxygen
3. nylon
4. realm
5. trampoline

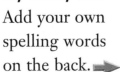

My Study List
Add your own spelling words on the back. ➡

My Study List
Add your own spelling words on the back. ➡

My Study List
Add your own spelling words on the back. ➡

My Study List

1. _____
2. _____
3. _____
4. _____
5. _____
6. _____
7. _____
8. _____
9. _____
10. _____

Review Words

1. breath
2. measure
3. typical
4. deaf
5. crystal

How to Study a Word

Look at the word.
Say the word.
Think about the word.
Write the word.
Check the spelling.

412

 My Study List

1. _____
2. _____
3. _____
4. _____
5. _____
6. _____
7. _____
8. _____
9. _____
10. _____

Review Words

1. scoop
2. moist
3. haul
4. loose
5. hawk

How to Study a Word

Look at the word.
Say the word.
Think about the word.
Write the word.
Check the spelling.

412

 My Study List

1. _____
2. _____
3. _____
4. _____
5. _____
6. _____
7. _____
8. _____
9. _____
10. _____

Challenge Words

1. cobweb   6. endeavor
2. tepid   7. oxygen
3. refugee   8. nauseous
4. coax   9. bountiful
5. nylon   10. heirloom

How to Study a Word

Look at the word.
Say the word.
Think about the word.
Write the word.
Check the spelling.

412

The Girl Who Married the Moon

Homophones
Homophones are words that sound alike but have different spellings and meanings.

Spelling Words

1. fir
2. fur
3. scent
4. sent
5. scene
6. seen
7. vain
8. vein
9. principal
10. principle
11. manor
12. manner
13. who's
14. whose
15. tacks
16. tax
17. hangar
18. hanger
19. died
20. dyed

Challenge Words

1. phase
2. faze
3. burrow
4. burro
5. borough

My Study List
Add your own spelling words on the back. ➡

What Really Happened? Reading-Writing Workshop

Look for familiar spelling patterns in these words to help you remember their spellings.

Spelling Words

1. tonight
2. everywhere
3. everybody
4. another
5. because
6. whole
7. people
8. cousin
9. clothes
10. height
11. always
12. right
13. might
14. really
15. everything

Challenge Words

1. essential
2. questionnaire
3. affectionate
4. illustrator
5. embarrass

My Study List
Add your own spelling words on the back. ➡

Amelia Earhart: First Lady of Flight

Vowel + /r/ Sounds
/ûr/ ➡ sk**ir**t, **ur**ge, **ear**th
/ôr/ ➡ th**or**n, c**our**t
/är/ ➡ ch**ar**t
/îr/ ➡ f**ier**ce

Spelling Words

1. fierce
2. sword
3. court
4. snarl
5. thorn
6. earth
7. skirt
8. chart
9. urge
10. yarn
11. whirl
12. mourn
13. rehearse
14. curb
15. earnest
16. starch
17. purse
18. birch
19. pierce
20. scorn

Challenge Words

1. circumstances
2. turmoil
3. absurd
4. territory
5. sparse

My Study List
Add your own spelling words on the back. ➡

Take-Home Word List

Name _____

 My Study List

1. _____
2. _____
3. _____
4. _____
5. _____
6. _____
7. _____
8. _____
9. _____
10. _____

Review Words

1. pearl
2. stir
3. inform
4. pour
5. scar

How to Study a Word

Look at the word.
Say the word.
Think about the word.
Write the word.
Check the spelling.

Take-Home Word List

Name _____

 **My Study List**

1. _____
2. _____
3. _____
4. _____
5. _____
6. _____
7. _____
8. _____
9. _____
10. _____

How to Study a Word

Look at the word.
Say the word.
Think about the word.
Write the word.
Check the spelling.

Take-Home Word List

Name _____

 My Study List

1. _____
2. _____
3. _____
4. _____
5. _____
6. _____
7. _____
8. _____
9. _____
10. _____

Review Words

1. berry
2. bury
3. soar
4. sore

How to Study a Word

Look at the word.
Say the word.
Think about the word.
Write the word.
Check the spelling.

Where the Red Fern Grows

VCV, VCCV, and VCCCV Patterns	
VC|V:	bal | ance
V|CV:	mi | nus
VC|CV:	law | yer
V|CCV:	au | thor
VCC|V:	meth | od
VC|CCV:	sup | ply

Spelling Words

1. balance
2. lawyer
3. sheriff
4. author
5. minus
6. method
7. item
8. require
9. supply
10. whisper
11. spirit
12. tennis
13. adopt
14. instant
15. poison
16. deserve
17. rescue
18. journey
19. relief
20. laundry

Challenge Words

1. enhance
2. delete
3. precious
4. structure
5. decade

My Study List
Add your own spelling words on the back. ➡

What Really Happened?
Spelling Review

Spelling Words

1. chart
2. starch
3. hangar
4. manner
5. gallon
6. whirl
7. curb
8. vein
9. similar
10. rural
11. sword
12. purse
13. hanger
14. manor
15. direction
16. mourn
17. who's
18. scent
19. channel
20. passenger
21. pierce
22. thorn
23. vain
24. struggle
25. frighten
26. rehearse
27. whose
28. sent
29. familiar
30. calendar

See the back for Challenge Words.

My Study List
Add your own spelling words on the back. ➡

Dinosaur Ghosts

Final /ər/, /ən/, and /əl/	
/ər/ ➡	messenger, director, similar
/ən/ ➡	weapon, frighten
/əl/ ➡	struggle, channel, mental

Spelling Words

1. struggle
2. director
3. weapon
4. similar
5. mental
6. frighten
7. channel
8. messenger
9. familiar
10. acre
11. error
12. gallon
13. rural
14. calendar
15. elevator
16. stumble
17. youngster
18. kitchen
19. passenger
20. quarrel

Challenge Words

1. agricultural
2. colonel
3. predator
4. corridor
5. maneuver

My Study List
Add your own spelling words on the back. ➡

Name _____

 My Study List

1. _____
2. _____
3. _____
4. _____
5. _____
6. _____
7. _____
8. _____
9. _____
10. _____

Review Words

1. matter
2. novel
3. mayor
4. consider
5. dozen

How to Study a Word

Look at the word.
Say the word.
Think about the word.
Write the word.
Check the spelling.

Name _____

 My Study List

1. _____
2. _____
3. _____
4. _____
5. _____
6. _____
7. _____
8. _____
9. _____
10. _____

Challenge Words

1. territory	6. predator
2. absurd	7. colonel
3. turmoil	8. faze
4. phase	9. burro
5. burrow	10. corridor

How to Study a Word

Look at the word.
Say the word.
Think about the word.
Write the word.
Check the spelling.

Name _____

 My Study List

1. _____
2. _____
3. _____
4. _____
5. _____
6. _____
7. _____
8. _____
9. _____
10. _____

Review Words

1. protect
2. effort
3. actor
4. credit
5. merchant

How to Study a Word

Look at the word.
Say the word.
Think about the word.
Write the word.
Check the spelling.

The Challenge

Endings and Suffixes
divide + ed = divid**ed**
grace + ful = grace**ful**

Spelling Words

1. graceful
2. divided
3. advanced
4. privately
5. replacement
6. excitement
7. adorable
8. heaving
9. forgiveness
10. mileage
11. barely
12. forceful
13. scarcely
14. blaming
15. entirely
16. usable
17. sincerely
18. amusement
19. lifeless
20. manageable

Challenge Words

1. deflated
2. disciplined
3. consecutively
4. silhouetted
5. refinement

My Study List
Add your own spelling words on the back. ➡

Last Summer with Maizon

Words with -ed or -ing
map**ped**   pilot**ing**
fit**ting**   begin**ning**

Spelling Words

1. mapped
2. piloting
3. permitting
4. beginning
5. bothered
6. limited
7. forgetting
8. reasoning
9. preferred
10. equaled
11. wondering
12. slipped
13. listening
14. fitting
15. pardoned
16. shoveling
17. favored
18. knitting
19. answered
20. modeling

Challenge Words

1. propelling
2. equipped
3. transmitted
4. recurring
5. beckoned

My Study List
Add your own spelling words on the back. ➡

Growing Up
Reading-Writing Workshop

Look for familiar spelling patterns in these words to help you remember their spellings.

Spelling Words

1. bland
2. blend
3. below
4. bellow
5. pastor
6. pasture
7. moral
8. mortal
9. bauble
10. bubble
11. bisect
12. dissect
13. assent
14. ascent

Challenge Words

1. imminent
2. eminent
3. illegible
4. ineligible

My Study List
Add your own spelling words on the back. ➡

Name _____

 My Study List

1. _____
2. _____
3. _____
4. _____
5. _____
6. _____
7. _____
8. _____
9. _____
10. _____

How to Study a Word

Look at the word.
Say the word.
Think about the word.
Write the word.
Check the spelling.

Name _____

 My Study List

1. _____
2. _____
3. _____
4. _____
5. _____
6. _____
7. _____
8. _____
9. _____
10. _____

Review Words

1. ordered
2. planned
3. spotted
4. winning
5. gathering

How to Study a Word

Look at the word.
Say the word.
Think about the word.
Write the word.
Check the spelling.

Name _____

My Study List

1. _____
2. _____
3. _____
4. _____
5. _____
6. _____
7. _____
8. _____
9. _____
10. _____

Review Words

1. breathless
2. collapsed
3. valuable
4. retirement
5. government

How to Study a Word

Look at the word.
Say the word.
Think about the word.
Write the word.
Check the spelling.

Lost Temple of the Aztecs

The /sh/ Sound
/sh/ → poli**sh**, mo**ti**on
offi**ci**al, mi**ss**ion

Spelling Words

1. glacier	11. official
2. motion	12. edition
3. pressure	13. musician
4. direction	14. mention
5. caution	15. mission
6. partial	16. portion
7. ancient	17. session
8. polish	18. selfish
9. station	19. establish
10. shallow	20. cushion

Challenge Words

1. expedition	4. beneficial
2. diminish	5. technician
3. recession	

My Study List
Add your own spelling words on the back. ➡

Growing Up
Spelling Review

Spelling Words

1. method	16. balance
2. author	17. slipped
3. answered	18. advanced
4. forgiveness	19. control
5. complicate	20. impolite
6. supply	21. minus
7. beginning	22. listening
8. heaving	23. adorable
9. scarcely	24. immediate
10. include	25. involve
11. relief	26. lawyer
12. forgetting	27. preferred
13. amusement	28. graceful
14. excitement	29. conversation
15. consumer	30. community

See the back for
Challenge Words.

My Study List
Add your own spelling words on the back. ➡

The View from Saturday

Prefixes: in- and con-
in + active = **in**active
in + volve = **in**volve
in + polite = **im**polite
in + mense = **im**mense
con + trol = **con**trol
con + test = **con**test
con + ment = **com**ment
con + pete = **com**pete

Spelling Words

1. computer	11. infection
2. impolite	12. concert
3. control	13. import
4. include	14. conversation
5. immigrant	15. community
6. compete	16. incomplete
7. consumer	17. immense
8. involve	18. contest
9. immediate	19. inactive
10. comment	20. complicate

Challenge Words

1. imply	4. inadequate
2. consequence	5. communicate
3. comprehensive	

My Study List
Add your own spelling words on the back. ➡

Name _____

 My Study List

1. _____
2. _____
3. _____
4. _____
5. _____
6. _____
7. _____
8. _____
9. _____
10. _____

Review Words

1. concern
2. insist
3. compare
4. improve
5. convince

How to Study a Word

Look at the word.
Say the word.
Think about the word.
Write the word.
Check the spelling.

Name _____

 My Study List

1. _____
2. _____
3. _____
4. _____
5. _____
6. _____
7. _____
8. _____
9. _____
10. _____

Challenge Words

1. precious
2. enhance
3. beckoned
4. propelling
5. deflated
6. consecutively
7. refinement
8. communicate
9. imply
10. consequence

How to Study a Word

Look at the word.
Say the word.
Think about the word.
Write the word.
Check the spelling.

Name _____

 My Study List

1. _____
2. _____
3. _____
4. _____
5. _____
6. _____
7. _____
8. _____
9. _____
10. _____

Review Words

1. vanish
2. nation
3. condition
4. migration
5. confession

How to Study a Word

Look at the word.
Say the word.
Think about the word.
Write the word.
Check the spelling.

The Royal Kingdoms of Ghana, Mali, and Songhay

Unstressed Syllables
prob | lem ➡
   /**prŏb´** ləm/
ex | am | ple ➡
   /ĭg **zăm´** pəl/

Spelling Words

1. company
2. success
3. position
4. problem
5. policy
6. difficult
7. document
8. quality
9. surprise
10. physical
11. crisis
12. awake
13. example
14. ignore
15. accept
16. parallel
17. admiral
18. desire
19. garage
20. ambulance

Challenge Words

1. efficient
2. utensil
3. morale
4. ethical
5. potential

My Study List
Add your own spelling words on the back. ➡

The Great Wall

Adding -ion or -ation
connect, connect**ion**
situate, situat**ion**
admire, admir**ation**

Spelling Words

1. construct
2. construction
3. connect
4. connection
5. combine
6. combination
7. cooperate
8. cooperation
9. attract
10. attraction
11. admire
12. admiration
13. situate
14. situation
15. examine
16. examination
17. contribute
18. contribution
19. explore
20. exploration

Challenge Words

1. negotiate
2. negotiation
3. insulate
4. insulation

My Study List
Add your own spelling words on the back. ➡

Discovering Ancient Cultures

Reading-Writing Workshop

Look for familiar spelling patterns in these words to help you remember their spellings.

Spelling Words

1. decent
2. descent
3. affect
4. effect
5. desert
6. dessert
7. slick
8. sleek
9. alley
10. ally
11. confident
12. confidant
13. hurdle
14. hurtle

Challenge Words

1. bizarre
2. bazaar
3. ellipse
4. eclipse

My Study List
Add your own spelling words on the back. ➡

My Study List

1. _____
2. _____
3. _____
4. _____
5. _____
6. _____
7. _____
8. _____
9. _____
10. _____

How to Study a Word

Look at the word.
Say the word.
Think about the word.
Write the word.
Check the spelling.

My Study List

1. _____
2. _____
3. _____
4. _____
5. _____
6. _____
7. _____
8. _____
9. _____
10. _____

Review Words

1. inspect
2. inspection
3. create
4. creation

How to Study a Word

Look at the word.
Say the word.
Think about the word.
Write the word.
Check the spelling.

My Study List

1. _____
2. _____
3. _____
4. _____
5. _____
6. _____
7. _____
8. _____
9. _____
10. _____

Review Words

1. industry
2. orphan
3. president
4. absent
5. attention

How to Study a Word

Look at the word.
Say the word.
Think about the word.
Write the word.
Check the spelling.

Doers and Dreamers

Reading-Writing Workshop

Look for familiar spelling patterns in these words to help you remember their spellings.

Spelling Words

1. anyone
2. captain
3. all right
4. beautiful
5. enough
6. family
7. someone
8. stretch
9. favorite
10. guy
11. a lot
12. friend
13. sometimes
14. anyway
15. anything

Challenge Words

1. irreplaceable
2. suppress
3. sufficient
4. catastrophe
5. perceive

My Study List
Add your own spelling words on the back. ➡

A Kind of Grace

Final /īz/, /ĭv/, /ĭj/, /ĭk/, /chər/, and /əs/

/īz/	➡	advert**ise**, organ**ize**
/ĭv/	➡	act**ive**
/ĭj/	➡	us**age**
/ĭk/	➡	trag**ic**
/chər/	➡	signa**ture**
/əs/	➡	nerv**ous**

Spelling Words

1. advertise
2. serious
3. scientific
4. active
5. usage
6. signature
7. realize
8. nervous
9. temperature
10. college
11. tragic
12. positive
13. fantastic
14. exercise
15. jealous
16. organize
17. courage
18. curious
19. departure
20. storage

Challenge Words

1. chronic
2. merchandise
3. unanimous
4. legislature
5. visualize

My Study List
Add your own spelling words on the back. ➡

Discovering Ancient Cultures

Spelling Review

Spelling Words

1. ancient
2. pressure
3. connect
4. cooperate
5. problem
6. shallow
7. partial
8. connection
9. cooperation
10. ambulance
11. official
12. cushion
13. combine
14. success
15. example
16. edition
17. mission
18. combination
19. position
20. physical
21. musician
22. construct
23. admire
24. difficult
25. surprise
26. establish
27. construction
28. admiration
29. accept
30. crisis

See the back for Challenge Words.

My Study List
Add your own spelling words on the back. ➡

Name _____

 My Study List

1. _____
2. _____
3. _____
4. _____
5. _____
6. _____
7. _____
8. _____
9. _____
10. _____

Challenge Words

1. expedition	6. negotiate
2. diminish	7. morale
3. beneficial	8. insulation
4. insulate	9. potential
5. utensil	10. negotiation

How to Study a Word

Look at the word.
Say the word.
Think about the word.
Write the word.
Check the spelling.

424

Take-Home Word List

Name _____

 My Study List

1. _____
2. _____
3. _____
4. _____
5. _____
6. _____
7. _____
8. _____
9. _____
10. _____

Review Words

1. message
2. public
3. future
4. sensitive
5. dangerous

How to Study a Word

Look at the word.
Say the word.
Think about the word.
Write the word.
Check the spelling.

424

Take-Home Word List

Name _____

My Study List

1. _____
2. _____
3. _____
4. _____
5. _____
6. _____
7. _____
8. _____
9. _____
10. _____

How to Study a Word

Look at the word.
Say the word.
Think about the word.
Write the word.
Check the spelling.

424

Doers and Dreamers
Spelling Review

Spelling Words

1. active
2. curious
3. stereos
4. potatoes
5. difference
6. realize
7. scientific
8. echoes
9. workable
10. studios
11. exercise
12. temperature
13. chiefs
14. separate
15. noticeable
16. courage
17. positive
18. staffs
19. celebrate
20. importance
21. fantastic
22. halves
23. visible
24. fragrant
25. loaves
26. departure
27. shelves
28. pianos
29. appearance
30. excellent

See the back for Challenge Words.

My Study List
Add your own spelling words on the back. ➡

Chuck Close, Up Close

Suffixes: *-ant/-ance; -ent/-ence; -able/-ible; -ate*

/ənt/ ➡ brilli**ant**, excell**ent**

/əns/ ➡ import**ance**, sent**ence**

/əbəl/ ➡ lov**able**, vis**ible**

/ĭt/ ➡ desper**ate**

/āt/ ➡ separ**ate**

Spelling Words

1. desperate
2. brilliant
3. audience
4. celebrate
5. excellent
6. visible
7. appearance
8. lovable
9. noticeable
10. sentence
11. difference
12. workable
13. instance
14. fragrant
15. fortunate
16. client
17. separate
18. agent
19. responsible
20. importance

Challenge Words

1. portable
2. irresistible
3. resemblance
4. magnificent
5. elaborate

My Study List
Add your own spelling words on the back. ➡

Under the Royal Palms

Plurals

staff	chief	half
staf**fs**	chief**s**	hal**ves**

ster**eo**	pia**no**	pota**to**
ster**eos**	pia**nos**	pota**toes**

Spelling Words

1. pianos
2. cellos
3. solos
4. altos
5. sopranos
6. staffs
7. stereos
8. potatoes
9. halves
10. chiefs
11. echoes
12. calves
13. studios
14. shelves
15. ratios
16. volcanoes
17. loaves
18. wolves
19. heroes
20. scarves

Challenge Words

1. patios
2. maestros
3. tuxedos
4. vetoes
5. mementos

My Study List
Add your own spelling words on the back. ➡

Name _____

 My Study List

1. _____
2. _____
3. _____
4. _____
5. _____
6. _____
7. _____
8. _____
9. _____
10. _____

Review Words

1. abilities
2. countries
3. duties
4. enemies
5. lilies

How to Study a Word

Look at the word.
Say the word.
Think about the word.
Write the word.
Check the spelling.

Name _____

 My Study List

1. _____
2. _____
3. _____
4. _____
5. _____
6. _____
7. _____
8. _____
9. _____
10. _____

Review Words

1. terrible
2. science
3. distance
4. remarkable
5. constant

How to Study a Word

Look at the word.
Say the word.
Think about the word.
Write the word.
Check the spelling.

Name _____

 My Study List

1. _____
2. _____
3. _____
4. _____
5. _____
6. _____
7. _____
8. _____
9. _____
10. _____

Challenge Words

1. legislature	6. tuxedos
2. visualize	7. portable
3. unanimous	8. irresistible
4. patios	9. resemblance
5. vetoes	10. magnificent

How to Study a Word

Look at the word.
Say the word.
Think about the word.
Write the word.
Check the spelling.

Franklin R. Chang-Díaz

Prefixes: *ad-* and *ob-*

advice   **ac**count
acquire   **ap**prove
assist   **aff**air
observe   **oc**cupy

Spelling Words

1. account	11. occur
2. observe	12. acquire
3. addition	13. assume
4. accurate	14. adjust
5. occasion	15. assign
6. approve	16. oblige
7. advice	17. accomplish
8. occupy	18. approach
9. assist	19. according
10. affair	20. obtain

Challenge Words

1. applicant
2. accumulate
3. obscure
4. affiliated
5. obstinate

My Study List
Add your own
spelling words
on the back. ➡

New Frontiers: Oceans and Space
Reading-Writing Workshop

Look for familiar spelling patterns in these words to help you remember their spellings.

Spelling Words

1. weird	9. eighth
2. thought	10. millimeter
3. through	11. happily
4. caught	12. guess
5. brought	13. Saturday
6. finally	14. school
7. suppose	15. before
8. usually	

Challenge Words

1. fatigue
2. pneumonia
3. applicable
4. indictment
5. reversible

My Study List
Add your own
spelling words
on the back. ➡

The Adventures of Sojourner

Prefixes: *de-, dis-, ex-, inter-, per-, pre-, pro-*

describe   **inter**national
determine   **per**mission
disable   **pre**view
exhaust   **pro**ceed

Spelling Words

1. disease	11. product
2. decision	12. exhaust
3. proceed	13. previous
4. international	14. demonstrate
5. permission	15. extent
6. experience	16. disturb
7. disable	17. persuade
8. preview	18. interview
9. describe	19. determine
10. progress	20. prepare

Challenge Words

1. deliberate
2. perception
3. expertise
4. interdependent
5. procure

My Study List
Add your own
spelling words
on the back. ➡

Name _____

 My Study List

1. _____
2. _____
3. _____
4. _____
5. _____
6. _____
7. _____
8. _____
9. _____
10. _____

Review Words

1. providing
2. disagree
3. explain
4. detail
5. program

How to Study a Word

Look at the word.
Say the word.
Think about the word.
Write the word.
Check the spelling.

Name _____

 My Study List

1. _____
2. _____
3. _____
4. _____
5. _____
6. _____
7. _____
8. _____
9. _____
10. _____

How to Study a Word

Look at the word.
Say the word.
Think about the word.
Write the word.
Check the spelling.

Name _____

 My Study List

1. _____
2. _____
3. _____
4. _____
5. _____
6. _____
7. _____
8. _____
9. _____
10. _____

Review Words

1. address
2. object
3. accident
4. adventure
5. arrive

How to Study a Word

Look at the word.
Say the word.
Think about the word.
Write the word.
Check the spelling.

New Frontiers: Oceans and Space
Spelling Review
Spelling Words

1. decision	16. product
2. interview	17. addition
3. obtain	18. approve
4. brief	19. relieve
5. unbelievable	20. regardless
6. disable	21. demonstrate
7. persuade	22. assist
8. occur	23. review
9. freight	24. ceiling
10. disagreement	25. intermission
11. preview	26. extent
12. observe	27. affair
13. acquire	28. belief
14. reign	29. accidentally
15. encourage-ment	30. disgraceful

See the back for Challenge Words.

My Study List
Add your own spelling words on the back. ➡

Out There

Word Parts
unbelie**vable**
advanc**ement**
invent**ion**
concent**ration**

Spelling Words

1. development	12. prevention
2. information	13. regardless
3. preparation	14. repetition
4. improvement	15. disgraceful
5. invention	16. unbelievable
6. advancement	17. disagreement
7. accidentally	18. imprisonment
8. unkindness	19. encourage-ment
9. concentration	
10. unskillful	20. intermission
11. respectful	

Challenge Words

1. precision
2. reputation
3. distinction
4. immeasurable
5. inevitable

My Study List
Add your own spelling words on the back. ➡

Beneath Blue Waters

Words with *ie* or *ei*
y**ie**ld
rec**ei**pt
fr**ei**ght

Spelling Words

1. freight	11. shield
2. receipt	12. diesel
3. yield	13. reign
4. review	14. fiery
5. belief	15. conceit
6. eighty	16. veil
7. brief	17. grief
8. ceiling	18. relieve
9. neither	19. seize
10. foreign	20. leisure

Challenge Words

1. retrieve
2. deceit
3. wield
4. eerie
5. hygiene

My Study List
Add your own spelling words on the back. ➡

My Study List

1. _____
2. _____
3. _____
4. _____
5. _____
6. _____
7. _____
8. _____
9. _____
10. _____

Review Words

1. piece
2. view
3. niece
4. pier
5. mischief

How to Study a Word

Look at the word.
Say the word.
Think about the word.
Write the word.
Check the spelling.

 My Study List

1. _____
2. _____
3. _____
4. _____
5. _____
6. _____
7. _____
8. _____
9. _____
10. _____

Review Words

1. enjoyment
2. delightful
3. reaction
4. comfortable
5. conviction

How to Study a Word

Look at the word.
Say the word.
Think about the word.
Write the word.
Check the spelling.

 My Study List

1. _____
2. _____
3. _____
4. _____
5. _____
6. _____
7. _____
8. _____
9. _____
10. _____

Challenge Words

1. interdependent
2. expertise
3. applicant
4. obstinate
5. retrieve
6. immeasurable
7. inevitable
8. deceit
9. precision
10. reputation

How to Study a Word

Look at the word.
Say the word.
Think about the word.
Write the word.
Check the spelling.

Problem Words

Words	Rules	Examples
bad badly	*Bad* is an adjective. It can be used after linking verbs like *look* and *feel*. *Badly* is an adverb.	This was a <u>bad</u> day. I feel <u>bad</u>. I play <u>badly</u>.
borrow lend	*Borrow* means "to take." *Lend* means "to give."	You may <u>borrow</u> my pen. I will <u>lend</u> it to you for the day.
can may	*Can* means "to be able to do something." *May* means "to be allowed or permitted."	Nellie <u>can</u> read quickly. <u>May</u> I borrow your book?
good well	*Good* is an adjective. *Well* is usually an adverb. It is an adjective only when it refers to health.	The weather looks <u>good</u>. She sings <u>well</u>. Do you feel <u>well</u>?
in into	*In* means "located within." *Into* means "movement from the outside to the inside."	Your lunch is <u>in</u> that bag. He jumped <u>into</u> the pool.
its it's	*Its* is a possessive pronoun. *It's* is a contraction of *it is*.	The dog wagged <u>its</u> tail. <u>It's</u> cold today.
let leave	*Let* means "to permit or allow." *Leave* means "to go away from" or "to let remain in place."	Please <u>let</u> me go swimming. I will <u>leave</u> soon. <u>Leave</u> it on my desk.
lie lay	*Lie* means "to rest or recline." *Lay* means "to put or place something."	The dog <u>lies</u> in its bed. Please <u>lay</u> the books there.

Problem Words continued

Words	Rules	Examples
sit set	*Sit* means "to rest in one place." *Set* means "to place or put."	Please <u>sit</u> in this chair. <u>Set</u> the vase on the table.
teach learn	*Teach* means "to give instruction." *Learn* means "to receive instruction."	He <u>teaches</u> us how to dance. I <u>learned</u> about history.
their there they're	*Their* is a possessive pronoun. *There* is an adverb. It may also begin a sentence. *They're* is a contraction of *they are.*	<u>Their</u> coats are on the bed. Is Carlos <u>there</u>? <u>There</u> is my book. <u>They're</u> going to the store.
two to too	*Two* is a number. *To* means "in the direction of." *Too* means "more than enough" and "also."	I bought <u>two</u> shirts. A squirrel ran <u>to</u> the tree. May we go <u>too</u>?
whose who's	*Whose* is a possessive pronoun. *Who's* is a contraction for *who is.*	<u>Whose</u> tickets are these? <u>Who's</u> that woman?
your you're	*Your* is a possessive pronoun. *You're* is a contraction for *you are.*	Are these <u>your</u> glasses? <u>You're</u> late again!

Read each question below. Then check your paper. Correct any mistakes you find. After you have corrected them, put a check mark in the box next to the question.

☐   1. Did I spell all words correctly?

☐   2. Did I indent each paragraph?

☐   3. Does each sentence state a complete thought?

☐   4. Are there any run-on sentences or fragments?

☐   5. Did I begin each sentence with a capital letter?

☐   6. Did I capitalize all proper nouns?

☐   7. Did I end each sentence with the correct end mark?

☐   8. Did I use commas, apostrophes, and quotation marks correctly?

Are there other problem areas you should watch for? Make your own proofreading checklist.

☐ _____

☐ _____

☐ _____

☐ _____

☐ _____

☐ _____

☐ _____

Mark	Explanation	Examples
¶	Begin a new paragraph. Indent the paragraph.	¶The space shuttle landed safely after its five-day voyage. It glided to a smooth, perfect halt.
∧	Add letters, words, or sentences.	My ^best^ friend eats lunch with me ev^e^ry day.
∧ (with comma)	Add a comma.	Carlton‸ my Siamese cat‸ has a mind of his own.
⁄⁄	Add quotation marks.	˅Where do you want us to put the piano?˅ asked the gasping movers.
⊙	Add a period.	Don't forget to put a period at the end of every statement⊙
✗	Take out words, sentences, and punctuation marks. Correct spelling.	We ~~looked at and~~ admired the model air⁄planes.
⁄	Change a capital letter to a small letter.	We are studying about the Louisiana Purchase in ⁄History class.
≡	Change a small letter to a capital letter.	The Nile ⎯river in ⎯africa is the longest river in the world.
∼	Reverse letters or words.	To complet͡e the task successfully, you must follow ⌢carefully⌢ the steps⁄

My Notes